INTRODUCTION
TO
ELECTRONICS

FOR STUDENTS OF PHYSICS

AND ENGINEERING SCIENCE

INTRODUCTION

TO

ELECTRONICS

FOR STUDENTS OF PHYSICS

AND ENGINEERING SCIENCE

Donald M. Hunten
University of Saskatchewan

HOLT, RINEHART AND WINSTON
New York, Chicago, San Francisco, Toronto, London

Copyright © 1964 by Holt, Rinehart and Winston, Inc.
All Rights Reserved
Library of Congress Catalog Card Number: 64-10122
23820-0114
Printed in the United States of America

PREFACE

With the invasion of electronic techniques into almost every kind of measurement, it is necessary for most students of physics and engineering science to have at least some acquaintance with the subject of electronics. Even if the student does not design his own instruments, he is much better able to set up specifications if he knows the kinds of things that can be done. This text is based on a course that has attempted to impart the required knowledge to a class of third-year physics and engineering-physics students. The course has attracted a number of graduate students in physics, and also in chemistry. A student with interest and aptitude in the subject finishes with enough competence to be able to design and operate many kinds of electronic circuits, and the rest of the class is at least able to understand existing instruments. This objective would be difficult to attain without the help of the weekly laboratory. Moreover, the electronics laboratory must in many courses replace the traditional one in electrical measurements. A list, and a brief discussion, of the experiments used in the author's laboratory is given in Appendix 2, and Appendix 1 discusses some of the more frequently used instruments for the benefit of students who find them unfamiliar.

The course assumes a knowledge of elementary electricity and magnetism, and familiarity with Kirchhoff's laws, although the latter are briefly reviewed. Use is made of differential equations from time to time, but it is possible for a student to manage without a formal course in this subject if he has some prior knowledge of electronics. All the required knowledge of circuit analysis is treated in the first two chapters, and the last chapter gives a brief treatment of transmission lines.

Parts of this book bear a resemblance to a number of excellent textbooks of engineering electronics. The author has not found any of the latter satisfactory because they do not cover all the topics required by a class of physics students. Electrical engineering students may spend one year studying circuit analysis, another on the physics of tubes and transistors, and a third on electronic circuits. Although the last is the main business of this book, it also gives a sufficient coverage of the other two, because there is no room in a physics course for three classes on these topics. The types of circuit treated differ somewhat from the usual, being chosen for their importance in physical measurement. Very little attention is paid to circuits and techniques used in radio communication and broadcasting. Extended treatment is given to negative feedback and to direct-current amplifiers—topics of great importance in measurement. The limitation of sensitivity by noise is discussed in Chapter 16, and the filtering of signals to reduce noise is considered. These treatments are at an elementary level, but are as thorough as possible within this limitation.

The text is designed for students of both physics and engineering physics. It may be found suitable for other branches of engineering science as well. Like physicists, many engineers require some familiarity with electronic measuring techniques, but may not have time to take the series of specialized courses offered to students of electrical engineering.

Third-year students will probably not be able to absorb all the material in this book in a one-year course. The material omitted will probably be equivalent to three or four chapters, and the choice will depend on the preferences of the instructor. All the chapters have been taught by the author at one time or another, but the increasing emphasis on transistor circuits has crowded out some of the others. It will be noted that no serious mention is made of solid-state circuits until Chapter 8. This is deliberate. The equivalent circuit of a tube is much simpler to analyze than that of a transistor. Both equivalent circuits and circuit analysis are new to most of the students, and there is no point in making the circuits any more complicated than absolutely necessary. After the transistor equivalent circuit is introduced and applied in Chapter 9, the rest of the chapters use tubes and transistors interchangeably, giving preference to one or the other as seems appropriate. For example, trigger circuits are normally made with transistors and this is recognized in Chapter 10. Although tubes may be disappearing from many commercial applications of electronics, they will survive much longer in measurement applications, and they must still be studied in their own right, quite aside from their value in introductory material.

A small but adequate number of problems is included. It is expected that the students will do nearly all of them, and as a reminder they are placed in the text at the points where they should be done. Many texts include more problems, but it is then necessary to choose a few to be worked out, and ignore the rest.

It is possible that some students or physicists may wish to study the subject from this book, independent of a lecture course. Because the book is based on lectures, this should be perfectly practical. It should be remembered, however, that the course ordinarily includes a laboratory, and that it would be advisable to give extra attention to the topics mentioned in Appendix 2.

I should like to record my thanks to the twelve successive classes of students at the University of Saskatchewan on whom this material was polished into its present form. Dr. G. W. Farnell, in reviewing the manuscript, made a large number of valuable suggestions; the comments of Dr. H. E. Duckworth were also useful. The drawings are the work of Mr. R. L. Hilliard.

Saskatoon, Canada   D.M.H.
November, 1963

CONTENTS

ix

INTRODUCTION
TO
ELECTRONICS

FOR STUDENTS OF PHYSICS

AND ENGINEERING SCIENCE

CHAPTER I

Direct- current
Circuit Analysis

1.1 INTRODUCTION

Electronic circuits are electric circuits, and a quantitative understanding of their operation requires that they be analyzed quantitatively.
We therefore begin our study by developing the technique known as
"linear circuit analysis"; to simplify the introduction, we begin with
d-c circuits and later generalize to the a-c case. For the d-c case,
a linear circuit is one containing elements that obey Ohm's law, such
as metallic conductors. Many of the devices used in electronics do not
obey Ohm's law and are therefore "nonlinear." Although simple
circuits can be analyzed by graphical methods, many must be studied
by approximations that reduce them to linear circuits. Thus, linear
circuit analysis will be a basic tool throughout the course.

Let us begin with a brief review of Ohm's law, $V = IR$, in which
V is the potential difference, I the current, and R the constant resistance.
(The symbol E is often used instead of V, but we shall have occasion
to use E for field strength.) With the law written in this form, it is
reasonable to regard I as the independent variable, or cause, and V as
the dependent variable, or effect. That is, if a current I is forced through
the resistor, a potential difference V is developed across it. Fig. 1.1(a)
shows a resistor connected to a *constant-current generator*, as suggested
by this interpretation. Such a generator is a bit difficult to visualize,

1

because it is not commonly encountered in the laboratory, but an approximation to it can be produced, as shown in Fig. 1.1(b), by connecting a very large resistor in series with a very high voltage. ("Voltage" is a colloquial term that will be used as synonymous with the rather clumsy "potential difference"; however, there is no such excuse for using "amperage" for "current".)

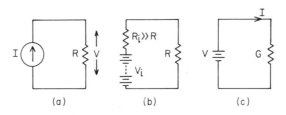

(a)   (b)   (c)

Fig. 1.1 Different ways of looking at Ohm's law: (a) with a constant-current generator; (b) a practical realization of the same thing; (c) with a potential source.

If we wish to regard Ohm's law as giving the current that will flow when a battery is connected to a resistor, it is reasonable to write it in the transposed form $I = GV$, where G, the *conductance*, is equal to $1/R$ and is measured in *mhos*; thus, a 10-ohm resistor has a conductance of 0.1 mho. The corresponding circuit is shown in Fig. 1.1(c). Clearly, in this simple example the difference between the two forms of Ohm's law is trivial, but in complex circuits this is not so and a suitable choice of representation can greatly simplify the algebra.

1.2 POWER SOURCES

Fig. 1.1 shows two kinds of "ideal" power source: a constant-current source and a constant-voltage source or source of constant electromotive force (emf). No actual power source conforms to either of these ideals, although most are much closer to the latter. When current is drawn from a real source, the terminal voltage usually falls; in many cases this effect can be represented to a satisfactory approximation by including an *internal resistance* in series with the ideal constant-voltage source as in Fig. 1.2(a). When a current I is drawn from the *equivalent circuit*, a potential drop IR_i is produced across the internal resistance, and the terminal voltage is $V - IR_i$. For example, the common No. 6 dry cell can deliver about 35 amp to a short circuit; its internal resistance is then V/I or 0.043 ohm.

For some purposes, the representation shown in Fig. 1.2(b) is more useful. Here, the power comes from a constant-current generator, and it is shunted by a conductance G_i which is equal to $1/R_i$ (that is, it represents the same resistance). The constant current from the source is the short-circuit current, or V/R_i in Fig. 1.2(a). As far as measure-

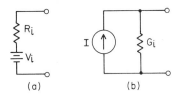

(a)   (b)

Fig. 1.2   Representations of power sources.

ments made at the terminals are concerned, Figs. 1.2(a) and 1.2(b) are identical. The open-circuit emf of Fig. 1.2(b) is determined by the fact that all the current I flows through G_i, producing a potential drop I/G_i; since $I = V/R_i$, this is equal to V/R_iG_i or V. If current I_o is drawn by a load connected to the terminals, only $(I - I_o)$ is available to flow through G_i; therefore, the terminal voltage falls to $(I - I_o)/G_i$, which is equal to $V - I_oR_i$ as before. The equivalence of the two circuits is thus demonstrated. It must be admitted that the current-generator circuit is not a good physical representation of an ordinary power source, such as a battery, because it is continuously dissipating power within itself to maintain the terminal voltage, even if it is not driving a load. However, this fact does not detract from its mathematical usefulness, and it is essential in "nodal analysis," which will be introduced soon.

The current-generator equivalent circuit of the No. 6 dry cell contains a generator of 35 amp shunted by a conductance of 23.2 mhos, or a resistance of 0.043 ohm as before. With no load, all this current flows through the internal conductance to develop the emf of 1.5 volts. Though the cell does not actually work this way, the representation is still a useful one.

1.3 KIRCHHOFF'S LAWS

Many simple circuits can be solved by the application of Ohm's law along with the rules for combining resistances in series and parallel. An example is shown in Fig. 1.3. First, we combine R_2 and R_3 into a single resistance by adding their conductances: $G = G_2 + G_3$ or $R = R_2R_3/(R_2 + R_3)$. Then the total circuit resistance is $R_1 + R$ and the current from the battery is $V/(R_1 + R)$. This is also the current through

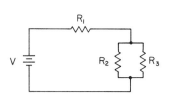

Fig. 1.3 A circuit that can be solved by elementary methods.

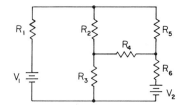

Fig. 1.4 A circuit that cannot be solved by elementary methods; Kirchhoff's laws or the equivalent are required.

R_1, and it splits into R_2 and R_3 in proportion to their conductances. For this circuit, any more sophisticated method would be a waste of time; but now consider Fig. 1.4. It may not be impossible to solve this circuit by the same method just used, but it would certainly be difficult and the chances of error would be large. Instead, we have recourse to Kirchhoff's laws or the methods derived from them. The first law states that there is a quantity which behaves as a potential: in traversing any complete loop, the potential drops encountered must add to zero. One assumes a current through each resistance; the potential drop across it is then given by Ohm's law. Power sources are represented by an emf, or fixed potential rise, in series with an internal resistance, as in Fig. 1.2(a). The second law states that charge cannot pile up nor be depleted at any junction or *node*; thus, the algebraic sum of all the currents entering each junction must be zero. Application of these laws will always give enough independent equations to allow the calculation of all the assumed currents. In fact, the first law can give several extra equations, and the second law one extra, but they are not independent of the others. This matter will be considered later.

As an example, the first law gives the following equation for the loop including R_1, R_2, and R_3, in Fig. 1.4:

$$I_1 R_1 + I_2 R_2 + I_3 R_3 - V_1 = 0$$

At the upper node, the second law gives

$$I_1 - I_2 - I_5 = 0$$

Altogether, the first law yields three independent equations, and the second also yields three; these are then enough to determine the six currents, one through each resistance. The methods to be described next reduce the number of equations to three for this example, greatly reducing the amount of algebra required. Moreover, the equations are easier to find and are in a form that is useful for symbolic analysis and for solution by means of determinants.

1.4 MESH METHOD

In the mesh method, we assume a set of currents called *mesh currents*, or sometimes *Maxwell's cyclic currents*. They are chosen so as to traverse a complete loop, or mesh, as in Fig. 1.5, which shows the same

Fig. 1.5 The same circuit as Fig. 4, set up for solution by the mesh method.

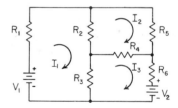

circuit as Fig. 1.4. The *branch currents* used in the Kirchhoff method are found by adding all the mesh currents which traverse the branch in question. For example, the current in R_2 is $(I_1 - I_2)$ in the downward direction; as in the Kirchhoff method, if this is negative the current is actually flowing upwards. Use of the mesh currents replaces the use of Kirchhoff's second law by this simple operation. It is clear that the mesh currents automatically satisfy the second law, since each current passes right through every junction it encounters.

The number of mesh currents required is the same as the number of independent first-law equations, and may be found as follows. Each current must traverse a complete loop; each new current must traverse a branch that has not already been used. It is possible to choose the three meshes in Fig. 1.5 in several ways, but there will never be more than three independent ones. It can also be shown that the number of mesh equations is $B - J + 1$, where B is the number of branches and J the number of junctions; in Fig. 1.5, $B = 6$ and $J = 4$, so that $B - J + 1 = 3$, as before.

The mesh equations may be written down in the same way as those of Kirchhoff's first law, remembering the way in which the branch currents are formed:

$$I_1 R_1 + (I_1 - I_2) R_2 + (I_1 - I_3) R_3 = V_1$$
$$(I_2 - I_1) R_2 + I_2 R_5 + (I_2 - I_3) R_4 = 0$$
$$(I_3 - I_1) R_3 + (I_3 - I_2) R_4 + I_3 R_6 = -V_2$$

for the circuit in Fig. 1.5. Let us now collect the terms for each I, since they are the unknowns, and rewrite the equations in the following form:

$$(R_1 + R_2 + R_3) I_1 - R_2 I_2 - R_3 I_3 = V_1$$
$$-R_2 I_1 + (R_2 + R_5 + R_4) I_2 - R_4 I_3 = 0$$
$$-R_3 I_1 - R_4 I_2 + (R_3 + R_4 + R_6) I_3 = -V_2$$

Comparing these equations with Fig. 1.5, we note that the terms have a simple interpretation: for example, in the first, the coefficient of I_1 is the total resistance around the first mesh, or *self-resistance of mesh I*, R_{11}; the coefficient of I_2 is the *mutual resistance*, R_{12}, the resistance common to meshes 1 and 2, taken negative when currents 1 and 2 flow in opposite directions through it; and similarly for I_3. The potential on the right is the algebraic sum of all the emf's encountered around the loop, each one taken positive if it will drive the mesh current in the way it is taken to go, as with V_1, and negative if it will drive it the opposite way, as with V_2. The mesh equations can and should be written down directly from the circuit in this way rather than in the first way, which is suitable with Kirchhoff's laws in their original form. The rules for writing down mesh equations may be summarized as follows:

(1) Choose a suitable set of mesh currents such that all branches are traversed. Each new current must traverse at least one new branch. If only one particular branch current is required in the final answer,

have only one mesh current traversing that branch, to avoid unnecessary algebra.

(2) Write down one equation for each mesh. The coefficient of the mesh's own current is the total resistance all around the mesh and is always positive; the coefficient of each other current is the resistance common to the two meshes, positive if the two currents traverse it in the same direction and negative if in the opposite direction.

(3) The right-hand side of each equation is the algebraic sum of all the emf's traversed by the mesh current, with signs taken according to the direction in which they are traversed.

The resulting equations can be symbolically written as follows:

$$R_{11}I_1 + R_{12}I_2 + \cdots + R_{1n}I_n = V_1$$
$$R_{21}I_1 + R_{22}I_2 + \cdots + R_{2n}I_n = V_2$$
$$\cdot \qquad \cdot \qquad \cdot$$
$$\cdot \qquad \cdot \qquad \cdot$$
$$\cdot \qquad \cdot \qquad \cdot$$
$$R_{n1}I_1 + R_{n2}I_2 + \cdots + R_{nn}I_n = V_n$$

This is a set of linear equations in n unknowns; a consequence is that circuits obeying Ohm's law are called *linear* and so is the corresponding circuit analysis. The solution may be written down in determinant notation with the help of the definitions that follow. Let D be the determinant of the coefficients, and D_{ij} the cofactor of R_{ij} including the sign; thus

$$D = \begin{vmatrix} R_{11} & R_{12} & \cdots & R_{1n} \\ R_{21} & R_{22} & \cdots & R_{2n} \\ \cdot & \cdot & & \cdot \\ \cdot & \cdot & & \cdot \\ \cdot & \cdot & & \cdot \\ R_{n1} & R_{n2} & \cdots & R_{nn} \end{vmatrix}$$

and

$$D_{12} = - \begin{vmatrix} R_{21} & R_{23} & \cdots & R_{2n} \\ R_{31} & R_{33} & \cdots & R_{3n} \\ \cdot & \cdot & & \cdot \\ R_{n1} & R_{n3} & \cdots & R_{nn} \end{vmatrix}.$$

The solution is

$$I_j = \frac{1}{D} \sum_{i=1}^{n} V_i D_{ij}$$

This may look unfamiliar at first sight, but it is merely a symbolic representation of the usual rule: to find I_j, substitute the column of Vs from the right-hand side for the jth column of D, and divide the substituted determinant by D. The summation is the expansion of the substituted determinant about that column. It is well to remember that a determinant can often be reduced by subtracting one column from another or one row from another. Examples of this will be seen later.

1.5 CIRCUIT THEOREMS

There are two important theorems applying to all linear circuits; they are of great use in simplifying analysis. It is far more important to understand them and be able to use them than to be able to derive them, but the derivations are not difficult and will now be carried out.

The *superposition theorem* is familiar in many fields of physics, because it applies to all systems obeying linear differential or algebraic equations. Here it may be stated in this way: each source of emf produces its own set of currents, which do not depend on the presence or absence of other sources. When the current attributable to one source is to be found, all other sources are omitted; however, it must be remembered that if a source is removed its internal resistance must be left in the circuit or replaced. If there is no more than one source in each mesh, the superposition theorem is immediately obvious from the form of the solution just given, in which I_j is a sum of terms each depending on one mesh voltage. The extension to a mesh containing two or more sources is simple and need not be spelled out here.

With the aid of the superposition theorem, circuits containing two or more sources can often be solved by inspection. In this way, the trouble of writing and solving the mesh equations is avoided, and often the result is a better insight into the reason for a particular type of solution. Examples will be found in later chapters.

Thévenin's theorem is not so easy to prove, but it is even more useful than the superposition theorem. It has already been used implicitly in the discussion of power sources in Section 1.2; in Fig. 1.2(a) the result is illustrated. The theorem states that *any* linear d-c circuit having two terminals can be represented by the series combination of an emf in series with a resistance. The values of these two parameters can be calculated from a knowledge of the circuit, or by operations carried out at the terminals. The latter method was used in the discussion of the No. 6 dry cell in Section 1.2.

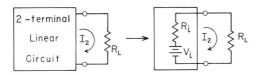

Fig. 1.6 Thévenin's theorem.

To prove the theorem, take any two-terminal linear circuit, no matter how complicated, and connect a *load resistance* R_L to the terminals as in Fig. 1.6. Set up a system of mesh currents in such a way that only I_2 traverses the external branch R_L. If the total number of meshes is n, then we have already seen that I_2 is given by

$$I_2 D = V_1 D_{12} + V_2 D_{22} + V_3 D_{32} + \cdots + V_n D_{n2}$$

Now divide both sides by the cofactor D_{22} and consider the right-hand side. Each term is a potential multiplied by the ratio of two cofactors of the same order, and thus has dimensions of potential. No term contains the load resistance R_L, since R_L is contained only in mesh 2, and therefore the only term in D containing it is R_{22}, the self-resistance of this mesh. But column 2 of D has been removed in forming all these cofactors, and therefore R_{22} does not appear in any of them. Thus, the right-hand side is a potential whose value does not depend on R_L; we call it V, and will later identify it with V_i in Fig. 1.6. The equation can thus be written

$$\frac{I_2 D}{D_{22}} = V$$

Now expand D about the second column:

$$I_2 \left(\frac{R_{12} D_{12}}{D_{22}} + R_{22} + \frac{R_{32} D_{32}}{D_{22}} + \cdots + \frac{R_{n2} D_{n2}}{D_{22}} \right) = V$$

By the same argument, only the second term on the left contains R_L; all the rest of the terms in the parentheses may be lumped into a single resistance R characteristic of the network. Then

$$I_2(R + R_{22}) = V$$

Now R_{22} consists of one part contributed by the network, and R_L. We may lump the former part in with R, calling the sum R_i, and get

$$I_2(R_i + R_L) = V.$$

Now apply Ohm's law to the equivalent circuit on the right in Fig. 1.6, getting

$$I_2(R_i + R_L) = V_i$$

The equivalence of these two expressions (if V is identified with V_i) shows that the two circuits are equivalent and thus proves Thévenin's theorem for any resistive load R_L. Repeated application will readily allow it to be extended to any more complicated load.

The parameters of the equivalent circuit can be calculated from the circuit equations, if desired; examples will be found in the next section. It is often more convenient to carry out certain operations at the two terminals, either by measurement or by calculation. The first operation is to find the open-circuit voltage, which is equal to V_i; if it is to be measured, a potentiometer may be used. For the second operation, two alternatives exist: the short-circuit current can be measured or calculated; or the terminal resistance can be calculated with all voltage sources replaced by short circuits. These procedures also are illustrated in the next section.

1.6 CALCULATION OF THÉVENIN PARAMETERS

First, we consider the *voltage divider* shown in Fig. 1.7. The first version is the actual circuit; the second is an abbreviated version in which it is understood that all potentials are measured with respect to the common point at the bottom. This convention will be followed in most of the circuits from now on. The reference point is usually called *ground*, although it is often not actually connected to the earth.

The output potential V_o can be found in several ways. The simplest is to recognize that the input potential V_i distributes itself across the two resistors in proportion to their resistance; then $V_o = V_iR_1/(R_1 + R_2)$. Or one can observe that the current through R_1 and R_2 is $V_i/(R_1 + R_2)$, and V_o is this current multiplied by R_1. This is the open-circuit potential to be used in the Thévenin equivalent circuit. To find the resistance R_i, we can apply either of the two methods just discussed. The first is

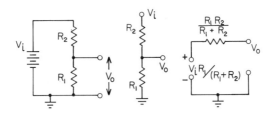

Fig. 1.7 Potential divider, showing the actual circuit, the simplified circuit with potentials measured from "ground," and the Thévenin equivalent.

to find the short-circuit current; if the output terminals are connected, the current flowing through them will be V_i/R_2. Then R_i is open-circuit voltage divided by short-circuit current, or $R_1R_2/(R_1 + R_2)$. In the other method, we replace V_i by a short circuit and calculate the resistance between the output terminal and ground. It is seen that R_2 is thrown in parallel with R_1, so that R_i is the parallel resistance of R_1 and R_2, in agreement with the first result. Fig. 1.7 shows the equivalent circuit that can be used to find the terminal voltage for any load resistance or current drain. The third method, solving the circuit equations, will be illustrated later.

The *potentiometer* has the same circuit as the voltage divider; the difference is in the application, the potentiometer being used to measure potential differences, as the name implies. (In electronics, however, the name is commonly applied to a variable voltage divider, such as the volume control in a radio.) Only one of the two important aspects of the potentiometer is considered in elementary discussions—that is, the output potential as given by the potential-divider equation just derived. The other is the highly practical matter of the amount of current that will flow in the galvanometer when the instrument is slightly off balance. This consideration governs the choice of galvanometer required for a given sensitivity. Fig. 1.8 shows the circuit, with the unknown represented by its Thévenin equivalent, as well as the reduced circuit when the potentiometer is also represented by its equivalent. The current flowing when the potentiometer voltage differs from V_x can now be found by inspection. If it is specified that the galvano-

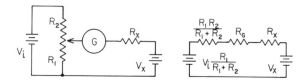

Fig. 1.8 Potentiometer and its Thévenin equivalent.

meter must show an observable deflection for a 0.1 per cent unbalance, the net voltage driving the current is 0.1 per cent of V_x, and it is easy to see whether a particular galvanometer is suitable.

The *Wheatstone bridge* provides a good example of the circuit-analysis method of finding Thévenin parameters, because it is almost impossible to find the internal resistance R_i in any other way. The situation just discussed arises again: it is easy to find the balance condition, but the off-balance sensitivity can be found only by a careful analysis. The balance condition can be found by regarding R_1, R_2 and R_3, R_4 (Fig. 1.9) as potential dividers; if they have an equal division ratio, then the potentials at the two ends of the galvanometer will be zero and no current will flow in it. Thus $R_1/R_2 = R_3/R_4$, or

$$R_1 R_4 = R_2 R_3$$

This "product" form of the balance condition is the most useful and will be used later in our discussion of impedance bridges. In words, it is simply stated: "The products of opposite arms are equal".

The next step is to find the mesh equations. In choosing the meshes we note that the required answer is the galvanometer current, and that the other two currents need not be found. Therefore, only one mesh current should traverse the galvanometer, as shown in Fig. 1.9; other sets of mesh currents are equally good as long as this condition is satisfied. The internal resistance of the battery has been omitted for simplicity, but it can readily be added if necessary. The circuit equations are

$$I_1(R_1 + R_2) + I_2(R_1 + R_2) + I_3R_1 = V$$
$$I_1(R_1 + R_2) + I_2(R_1 + R_2 + R_3 + R_4) + I_3(R_1 + R_3) = 0$$
$$I_1R_1 + I_2(R_1 + R_3) + I_3(R_1 + R_3 + R_G) = 0$$

and the determinant D is

$$D = \begin{vmatrix} R_1 + R_2 & R_1 + R_2 & R_1 \\ R_1 + R_2 & R_1 + R_2 + R_3 + R_4 & R_1 + R_3 \\ R_1 & R_1 + R_3 & R_1 + R_3 + R_G \end{vmatrix}$$

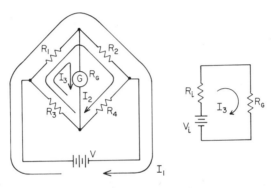

Fig. 1.9 Wheatstone bridge, and the Thévenin equivalent of the galvanometer circuit.

Notice that the determinant is symmetrical about the main diagonal. This is a consequence of the definition of mutual resistance as the resistance common to two meshes; it is always true that $R_{ij} = R_{ji}$. To find I_3 we also require the substituted determinant D_3, in which the right-hand side of the system is substituted for the third column. Since this column contains only one nonzero element (the source voltage V), the determinant immediately reduces its order by 1:

$$D_3 = V \begin{vmatrix} R_1 + R_2 & R_1 + R_2 + R_3 + R_4 \\ R_1 & R_1 + R_3 \end{vmatrix}$$

This may be simplified by subtracting, first, the second row from the top, and second, the left column from the right, yielding successively

$$D_3 = V \begin{vmatrix} R_2 & R_2 + R_4 \\ R_1 & R_1 + R_3 \end{vmatrix} = V \begin{vmatrix} R_2 & R_4 \\ R_1 & R_3 \end{vmatrix} = V(R_2R_3 - R_1R_4)$$

This is zero at balance, as it should be. We must now evaluate D itself; again, the algebra may be simplified by suitable subtractions. First, subtract the top row from the middle one, then the second column from the third and the first from the second:

$$D = \begin{vmatrix} R_1 + R_2 & R_1 + R_2 & R_1 \\ 0 & R_3 + R_4 & R_3 \\ R_1 & R_1 + R_3 & R_1 + R_3 + R_G \end{vmatrix}$$

$$= \begin{vmatrix} R_1 + R_2 & 0 & -R_2 \\ 0 & R_3 + R_4 & -R_4 \\ R_1 & R_3 & R_G \end{vmatrix}$$

Expansion about the first column then gives:

$$D = (R_1 + R_2)[R_G(R_3 + R_4) + R_3R_4] + R_1R_2(R_3 + R_4)$$
$$= (R_1 + R_2)(R_3 + R_4)R_G$$
$$+ R_1R_2R_3 + R_2R_3R_4 + R_3R_4R_1 + R_4R_1R_2$$

The galvanometer current I_3 is equal to D_3/D. However, before we write this down, we must consider the form in which we want it. The circuit equation for the Thévenin equivalent in Fig. 1.9 is

$$I_3 = \frac{V_i}{R_G + R_i}$$

and our result should be in the same form. Therefore, the factor $(R_1 + R_2)(R_3 + R_4)$ is extracted from D to get the following:

$$I_3 = V \frac{R_2R_3 - R_1R_4}{(R_1 + R_2)(R_3 + R_4)}$$

$$\times \frac{1}{R_G + \dfrac{R_1R_2R_3 + R_2R_3R_4 + R_3R_4R_1 + R_4R_1R_2}{(R_1 + R_2)(R_3 + R_4)}}$$

Comparison of these two expressions immediately yields the values of V_i and R_i, which can be used as before to find the galvanometer current for any prescribed degree of unbalance.

It is interesting to note that we have just repeated the proof of Thévenin's theorem for this particular case; what the theorem tells us is that an expression of this form can always be found, and that we can find it by any convenient method.

PROBLEMS

1) Find all of the currents in the network of Fig. 1.10. All resistances are given in ohms. Use the mesh method and check your results by the series-parallel method.

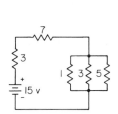
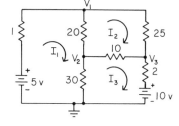

Fig. 1.10 Problem circuit.   Fig. 1.11 Problem circuit.

2) Find the mesh currents and the potentials at points 1, 2, and 3 in the network of Fig. 1.11. *Answers: D* = 34,410;

No.	1	2	3	
I	−0.216	−0.157	−0.430	amp
V	5.22	6.39	9.13	volts

1.7 NODE METHOD

We now consider a method which is complementary to the mesh method in the same way that the two forms of Ohm's law discussed in Section 1.1 are complementary. In the node method, the unknowns to be found are potentials rather than currents, the resistances are represented as conductances, and the power sources are represented as current generators. Despite the fact that the node method is less easily grasped than the mesh method because of its greater unfamiliarity, there are cases in which it can simplify the analysis of a circuit appreciably. For example, the required quantity is often a potential rather than a current, especially in circuits used with vacuum tubes and transistors; or the node method may lead to a smaller number of equations, as is often the case in vacuum-tube circuits.

The node method eliminates the equations of Kirchhoff's first law by assuming a potential for each node in the circuit. Because only potential *differences* have a physical significance, it is possible to set the potential of the *reference node* equal to zero and refer all the other potentials to it, as in Fig. 1.7. Assumption of these node potentials satisfies the first law, because the sum of all the potential differences around any loop must automatically be zero. Only the equations of the second law remain to be solved, and their number is $J - 1$, the number of nodes (or junctions) not counting the reference node. In many circuits this is the same as $B - J + 1$, the number of mesh equations, but in circuits of a predominantly "parallel" nature it may be less. A somewhat trivial example is Fig. 1.10, which has three meshes but only one or two node equations, depending on whether the 3- and 7-ohm resistors are considered together or separately.

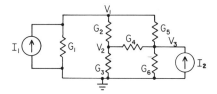

Fig. 1.12 The same circuit as Fig. 4 set up for solution by the node method.

The node method will now be applied to the familiar circuit of Fig. 1.4, which is repeated in Fig. 1.12 with the voltage sources replaced by current sources. As we have seen in Fig. 1.2 and Section 1.2, the strength of the current source is just the short-circuit current; for example, $V_1/R_1 = I_1$. (Note that in this section V_1 will be a node potential and I_1 the strength of a current source.) Kirchhoff's second law applied at node 1 gives

$$\text{Current leaving} = \text{Current entering}$$

or

$$(V_1 - 0)G_1 + (V_1 - V_2)G_2 + (V_1 - V_3)G_5 = I_1$$

Notice that the current leaving along each branch is the potential difference multiplied by the conductance. For the other two nodes the equations are

$$(V_2 - V_1) G_2 + (V_2 - 0) G_3 + (V_2 - V_3) G_4 = 0$$
$$(V_3 - V_1) G_5 + (V_3 - V_2) G_4 + (V_3 - 0) G_6 = I_2$$

Now, as with the mesh method, the terms in each V are collected systematically to give:

$$(G_1 + G_2 + G_5) V_1 - G_2 V_2 - G_5 V_3 = I_1$$
$$- G_2 V_1 + (G_2 + G_3 + G_4) V_2 - G_4 V_3 = 0$$
$$- G_5 V_1 - G_4 V_2 + (G_4 + G_5 + G_6) V_3 = I_2$$

Just as with the mesh method, these equations can and should be written down directly from the diagram. The coefficient of V_1 in the first equation is the sum of all the conductances connected to node 1, its *self-conductance*; the coefficient of V_2 is the conductance joining nodes 1 and 2, taken negative; and so on. The *mutual conductances* are always negative, and the determinant of the coefficients is symmetrical. The fact that each self-conductance is the sum of all the conductances connected to the node seems at first sight to imply that these are all connected in parallel, and this often worries those who have just met this method. In fact, there is no such implication; the rule for finding the self-conductance has been derived from Kirchhoff's laws and this is the only justification it needs. The complete set of rules may be summarized as follows:

(1) Choose a reference node. In many circuits there is a ground, which is the natural choice; in others, it can be chosen to give a desired potential difference most simply. Assume a potential for each of the other nodes.

(2) Write down one equation for each node. The coefficient of the node's own potential is the sum of all the conductances connected to it; the coefficient of each of the other potentials is the conductance joining it to the node in question, always taken negative.

(3) The right-hand side of each equation is the algebraic sum of all the currents entering the node from current generators. Each power source must be represented by its current-generator equivalent circuit.

The equations will be in the following form:

$$G_{11} V_1 + G_{12} V_2 + \cdots + G_{1n} V_n = I_1$$
$$G_{21} V_1 + G_{22} V_2 + \cdots + G_{2n} V_n = I_2$$

.   .   .   .

.   .   .   .

.   .   .   .

$$G_{n1} V_1 + G_{n2} V_2 + \cdots + G_{nn} V_n = I_n$$

In form, this set is identical with the set of mesh equations discussed in Sections 1.4, 1.5, and 1.6. It is merely necessary to replace Rs by Gs, and to exchange Vs with Is; it should also be remembered that this exchange is accompanied by a change of meaning for both symbols. Because of this identity of form, the solutions and the circuit theorems derived for the mesh case can be taken over without further ado. Determinants are just as useful in nodal analysis as in mesh analysis.

Circuit Theorems. The superposition theorem applies here; its interpretation is the same and it need not be discussed further. The analog of Thévenin's theorem is known as *Norton's theorem*, and is stated as follows: Any two-terminal linear network can be represented by a constant-current generator in parallel with a conductance. This representation has already been used for power sources in Section 1.2 and is illustrated in Fig. 1.2(b). The transformation from the Thévenin to the Norton equivalent circuit was also discussed there, but may be recalled briefly: The conductance represents the same resistance; the strength of the current source is equal to the short-circuit current.

PROBLEMS

1) Find the Thévenin and Norton equivalents of a potential divider (Fig. 1.7) with $V_i = 5$ volts, and R_1 and R_2 both equal to 10 ohms.

2) Solve the Wheatstone bridge of Fig. 1.9 by the node method and find the voltage across the galvanometer. To make this as easy as possible, choose the reference node at the bottom of the galvanometer and assume that the battery is replaced by a pure constant-current source I. Remember that this current will flow into one node and out of another, and will therefore appear in two equations.

3) Solve the network in Fig. 1.11 and compare the results with the answers obtained by the mesh method.

1.8 ATTENUATORS

We study an example of these devices now for several reasons: it is a good illustration of nodal analysis; it gives a natural introduction to decibel notation; and it allows us to discuss the use of attenuators in electronic measurements. An *attenuator* is a device for producing an accurately known voltage ratio, and since the output of a passive network must be less than the input, the output is reduced or attenuated. The simplest kind of attenuator is the potentiometer, and its uses illustrate the applications which may be made; these normally require production of a known voltage ratio, or of a known small voltage that cannot be measured directly to the required accuracy. A potentiometer will deliver an accurate voltage only if no current is drawn from it. The devices that actually use the name "attenuator" are designed to deliver their specified fraction of the input when loaded by a specified resistance. If the input resistance of the device has this same value, it can serve as the load for another attenuator if desired, and thus several devices can be combined at will to give large or easily variable ratios. In audio-frequency work this resistance is commonly made equal to 600 ohms. (It is customary to call this the *impedance* of the attenuator; this term will be introduced in the next chapter.)

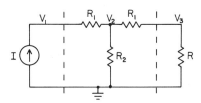

Fig. 1.13 T attenuator with source and load.

The circuit to be studied is shown in Fig. 1.13. The part between the dotted lines is the attenuator, the resistance R is the load, and a constant-current source is considered to be connected to the input. The attenuator is made symmetrical and designed to have an input resistance equal to R when loaded by a resistance R. We must choose R_1 and R_2 to satisfy this condition and to give the desired attenuation $\beta = V_3/V_1$.

Since $V_3 = D_3/D$ and $V_1 = D_1/D$,

$$\beta = \frac{D_3}{D_1} \tag{1}$$

The input resistance is the resistance which would be measured between the input terminal (node 1) and ground; since the current I is flowing into this terminal, it must develop a potential difference IR_i; with $R_i = R$ as specified, this gives the second condition

$$V_1 = IR = \frac{I}{G} \tag{2}$$

The use of these two conditions will give the required values of R_1 and R_2 in terms of R and β. The node equations are:

$$\begin{aligned} G_1 V_1 \qquad\quad - G_1 V_2 \qquad\qquad &= I \\ - G_1 V_1 + (2G_1 + G_2) V_2 - G_1 V_3 &= 0 \\ - G_1 V_2 + (G_1 + G) V_3 &= 0 \end{aligned}$$

and the determinant D is

$$D = \begin{vmatrix} G_1 & -G_1 & 0 \\ -G_1 & 2G_1 + G_2 & -G_1 \\ 0 & -G_1 & G_1 + G \end{vmatrix}$$

This may be reduced, by adding the top row to the middle, and then expanded:

$$D = \begin{vmatrix} G_1 & -G_1 & 0 \\ 0 & G_1 + G_2 & -G_1 \\ 0 & -G_1 & G_1 + G \end{vmatrix} = G_1 \begin{vmatrix} G_1 + G_2 & -G_1 \\ -G_1 & G_1 + G \end{vmatrix}$$

Finally, the upper row is added to the lower, and the determinant expanded:

$$D = G_1 \begin{vmatrix} G_1 + G_2 & -G_1 \\ G_2 & G \end{vmatrix} = G_1[G(G_1 + G_2) + G_1 G_2]$$

The first substituted determinant D_1 is found by replacing the first column of D with the right-hand side. It is well to remember that the original version of D before reduction must be used:

$$D_1 = I \begin{vmatrix} 2G_1 + G_2 & -G_1 \\ -G_1 & G_1 + G \end{vmatrix}$$

$$= I[(2G_1 + G_2)(G_1 + G) - G_1^2] = I[G_1(G_1 + G_2 + 2G) + GG_2]$$

Finally,

$$D_3 = I \begin{vmatrix} -G_1 & 2G_1 + G_2 \\ 0 & -G_1 \end{vmatrix} = IG_1^2$$

Conditions (1) and (2) both involve D_1, which is the most complicated of all the expressions; let us eliminate it as follows:

$$\frac{I}{G} = \frac{D_1}{D} = \frac{D_3}{\beta D}$$

Substitution of D_3 and D into this gives one relation giving R_1 and R_2 in terms of β and R; then, substitution of D_1 and D_2 into (1) gives another. Algebraic manipulation finally yields the two expressions for R_1 and R_2 separately:

$$R_1 = R\frac{1 - \beta}{1 + \beta} \quad \text{and} \quad R_2 = R\frac{2\beta}{1 - \beta^2}$$

Adjustable attenuators are made either by switching the three resistors together, or by switching in and out a number of sections in cascade. In the latter case, the attenuation of the system is the product of the individual attenuations, and it is not convenient to have to carry out such multiplications while making measurements. For this and other reasons, it is customary to express the attenuations on a logarithmic scale; they may then be added, with much less chance of error. The logarithmic unit used is called the *decibel* (one-tenth of a *bel*, named for Alexander Graham Bell). This unit is designed for expressing power *ratios*, and it is only by some convention that it can be extended to other purposes. Its use with acoustic power levels is well known; this is made possible by the general acceptance of a reference power level of 10^{-16} watt per cm^2. Its further extension to cover voltage ratios depends on the use of Joule's law in the form $P = V^2/R$.

Suppose we have two powers P_1 and P_2; then their ratio in decibels is given by

$$\text{Ratio (db)} = 10 \log_{10}\frac{P_2}{P_1}$$

If P_2 is the larger, the decibel ratio is positive; if smaller, it is negative. Substituting Joule's law, we get

$$\text{Ratio (db)} = 10 \log \frac{V_2^2 R_1}{V_1^2 R_2} = 20 \log \frac{V_2}{V_1}$$

The latter equality is true only if $R_1 = R_2$, but the convenience of the decibel scale is so great that it is widely used even when the resistances are not equal. Many attempts have been made to introduce a new unit to eliminate the resulting confusion, but none of these proposals has become popular. We will make a practice of calling these modified decibels by the name *voltage decibel*, with the abbreviation db$_V$.

Decibel ratios can be worked out with the aid of special tables or log tables; but it is wise to memorize the decibel equivalents of certain key ratios, remembering that the logarithms of 10 and 2 are, respectively, 1 and very nearly 0.3 (actually 0.30103). The following table should be memorized:

db	10	20	3	6
Power ratio	10	100	2	
Voltage ratio	$\sqrt{10}$	10		2

As an example of its use, consider a voltage ratio of $50 = 100/2$. In voltage decibels, this is $40 - 6 = 34$ db$_V$.

Let us return to the subject of the T attenuator we have been considering; the name T comes from the shape of the circuit formed by the three resistors. The attenuation has been expressed by a number β which is the ratio of output to input voltages, and is therefore less than 1. The corresponding decibel ratio will be negative, but it is customary to take it as positive; this is equivalent to expressing the reciprocal ratio $1/\beta$ in db. Thus, a 20-db section produces an attenuation of 0.1. If we refer back to the design equations, we see that for $R = 600$ ohms, the resistors have the values

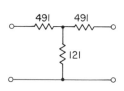

Fig. 1.14 20-db attenuator for a 600-ohm load.

$R_1 = 600 \times 9/11 = 491$ ohms, and $R_2 = 600 \times 2/9.9 = 121$ ohms; see Fig. 1.14.

Other useful types of attenuator exist; the T type has been chosen for illustration, and the π type forms the basis for a problem, but they do not exhaust the list.

PROBLEMS
1) Complete the derivation of the design equations for the T attenuator.
2) Design a T attenuator to give steps of 2 db from 0 to 100 db; take R equal to 600 ohms.

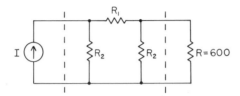

Fig. 1.15 π attenuator with source and load.

3) Find the design equations for the π attenuator shown in Fig. 1.15.

Answer:

$$R_1 = R\frac{1 - \beta^2}{2\beta} \quad \text{and} \quad R_2 = R\frac{1 + \beta}{1 - \beta}$$

1.9. POWER MATCHING

The object of most electronic design is to handle signals of some sort. Let us consider as an example an audio-frequency amplifier, which might be part of a radio receiver or a phonograph system. Only power that gets into the loudspeaker is of interest to us, and the amplifier must be designed to be able to deliver the required amount of power. It is, therefore, useful to inquire into the conditions under which a given power source delivers the greatest possible power to a load. Although this example involves an a-c circuit, the same principles are important in both d-c and a-c systems.

The power source may be represented by its Thévenin equivalent, as in Fig. 1.16. We wish to know what value should be chosen for R_L so that it receives the largest possible amount of power. If R_L is very large, only a small current flows and the power is small; if R_L is small, most of the available potential difference appears across R_i instead of

R_L and the power is again small. A maximum should appear for an intermediate value; we shall proceed to show that this value is $R_L = R_i$.

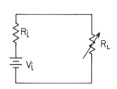

Fig. 1.16 Power matching.

The current flowing in Fig. 1.16 is $V_i/(R_i + R_L)$; the power in R_L is $I^2 R_L$, which is equal to

$$P_L = V_i^2 \frac{R_L}{(R_i + R_L)^2}$$

We must now differentiate this with respect to R_L and set the result equal to zero. The preceding discussion assures us that we will find a maximum.

$$\frac{dP_L}{dR_L} = V_i^2 \frac{(R_i + R_L)^2 - 2R_L(R_i + R_L)}{(R_i + R_L)^4} = 0$$

$$R_i + R_L - 2R_L = 0$$

$$R_L = R_i$$

Let us now calculate the efficiency of the system; this is the ratio of power delivered to power generated. Inasmuch as the same current flows through the internal and external resistances, if they are equal they must dissipate equal amounts of power. We conclude that when the load is *matched* to the source, the efficiency is only 50 per cent. Such a situation would be intolerable to a power company, which wants to sell as much as possible of the power it generates; in such a case, the appropriate condition is $R_i \ll R_L$, so that the power wasted in R_i is small. The power engineers are able to vary V_i and R_i in making their design so that this condition is satisfied. In handling signals, however, one is usually required to get as much power as possible out of a specified source without regard to efficiency, and it is here that matching is appropriate.

1.10 GALVANOMETERS

A brief discussion of galvanometers serves to illustrate the importance of power matching, and also points up some of the factors that are important in choosing a meter for a particular application. The principles to be developed are not restricted to galvanometer coils, but apply generally to almost all devices using a coil of wire to produce a magnetic effect; some examples are relay coils, chokes, and electro-magnets.

One does not usually think of power in connection with galvano-meters, because they are current-operated devices. However, it must be remembered that Ohm's law applies to the coil, and a potential difference is necessary before current will flow. In power circuits this potential drop is so small that it can usually be ignored; but if a gal-vanometer is being used with a bridge or thermocouple, the potential drop may be very important.

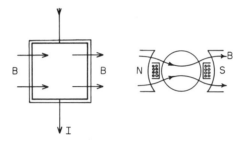

Fig. 1.17 Sketches of a galvanometer coil.

Consider a galvanometer coil, as in Fig. 1.17, containing N turns of wire filling the available space, and carrying a current I. In the magnetic field B produced by a suitable structure, the torque on the coil is proportional to NIB. The deflection of the pointer or light beam is also proportional to this product, but depends as well on the stiffness of the suspension or restoring springs. Let us compare a series of meters having similar magnetic structures and restoring torques; the deflection then depends only on the product NI. The fine wire will have a certain resistance R, so that the potential drop across the coil is $IR = V$ and the power required to drive it is $P = VI$. Suppose the coil is rewound with different wire having a cross-sectional area larger by a factor a; since the area of the winding remains the same, the number of turns N varies as $1/a$. The resistance per unit length of wire also varies as $1/a$. The total coil resistance is proportional to N and thus varies as $1/a^2$. For the same deflection, NI must remain constant; therefore I varies as a, and by Ohm's law, V varies as $1/a$. The product VI remains constant. Thus, we conclude that in a series of similar galvanometers having coils wound with different sizes of wire, the power required for a given deflection is the same for all. It is, therefore, possible to design meters for a small potential drop but a relatively large current; or for a small current but a relatively large potential drop. The former would be useful with a source such as a thermocouple; the latter would find wide use with vacuum tubes, which carry small currents at high voltage. This is merely a roundabout way of saying that, for optimum results, the resistance of the meter coil should match the source resistance as nearly as possible. We have already discussed in Section 1.6 the calculation of source resistance for a potentiometer and a bridge.

Because the magnetic field produced by a coil also is proportional to NI, the same principle applies to any electromagnetic device. For example, a magnet may be designed for low current and high voltage by using many turns of fine wire, or for high current and low voltage with few turns of heavy wire. As long as the wire fills the same space, the power required is the same.

Of course, there are certain practical limitations on this result. We have neglected the space taken up by insulation; this will be greater for finer wires. Moreover, very fine wire cannot be wound in as neatly as the larger sizes, and more space will be wasted. Thus, the power actually required will begin to rise for the smallest sizes of wire. At the other end, it is difficult (though not impossible) to have less than one turn; however, such low resistances are seldom of interest in any case. Moderately large wire can be made with a square or rectangular cross section and wound with almost no waste space; this technique is widely used in building large magnets and favors operation with low voltage and high current.

The following table gives an indication of the power required by a number of typical instruments: a common panel or portable meter, a portable mirror galvanometer with a taut suspension; and a sensitive, fixed mirror galvanometer with a hanging suspension. The values have been estimated from manufacturers' catalogs and are intended only as a guide to the orders of magnitude.

Panel meters:	50 microwatts full scale
Portable galvanometer:	10^{-12} to 10^{-10} watt for 10 cm
Fixed galvanometer:	3×10^{-14} watt for 10 cm

Any meter that is shunted to increase its current range, or supplied with a multiplier to increase its voltage range, will dissipate additional power in proportion to the increase in range.

CHAPTER 2

Alternating-current Circuit Analysis

2.1 INTRODUCTION

Alternating-current circuit analysis is concerned with the behavior of circuits in which the voltages and currents vary with time in simple-harmonic fashion, or sinusoidally. If a more complicated, periodic wave is of interest, it may be broken down into sine waves; then the individual waves can be studied and if necessary combined again at the output. This is possible because of the superposition theorem, which will be proved later for the a-c case, and because of the possibility of Fourier analysis, which permits any repetitive wave to be broken up into sine waves. Certain types of signal, often called *transients*, can be handled in this way only with a great deal of trouble; we shall consider transient analysis briefly at the end of this chapter. For the present we shall be concerned entirely with pure sine waves.

An a-c wave is characterized by three quantities: its amplitude or peak value, its frequency, and its phase. The last is arbitrary to the extent of an additive constant, as with potential, but phase differences between different waves can be important. Thus, a voltage wave may be represented as follows:

$$v = V \sin (2\pi\, \text{ft} - \theta) \qquad or \qquad v = V \cos (2\pi\, \text{ft} - \theta')$$

where θ and θ' differ by $\pi/2$ or 90 degrees. The capital letter V or I will be used for peak values, as well as for d-c values when they are encountered; the small letter v or i represents an instantaneous value in a varying quantity. It is customary and convenient to replace the quantity $2\pi f$ in such equations by ω, which is called *angular frequency*, by analogy to the angular velocity of a rotating object; by the same analogy, its units are radians per sec.

Suppose this voltage wave is applied to a resistance R; Ohm's law is obeyed at each instant and therefore

$$i = \frac{v}{R} = I \cos(\omega t - \theta')$$

where

$$I = \frac{V}{R}$$

Thus the peak, as well as the instantaneous values, obey Ohm's law. Now, let us consider Joule's law. The instantaneous power is readily written down, but the average power, which is of greater interest, can only be found by the following calculation. In a short time interval dt, the energy dissipated is

$$dW = vi \ dt$$

and over a longer interval T it is

$$W = \int_0^T vi \ dt$$

If we average this over one cycle of the wave, we will get the required result; thus, we set T equal to the period $1/f$ and divide by T to get the average power:

$$\bar{P} = \frac{1}{T} \int_0^T vi \ dt = \frac{VI}{T} \int_0^T \cos^2 \omega t \ dt = \frac{VI}{2T} \int_0^T (1 + \cos 2\omega t) dt$$

$$= \frac{VI}{2T}\left[t + \frac{\sin 2\omega t}{2\omega} \right]_0^T = \frac{VI}{2}$$

With the aid of Ohm's law, we can also see that $\bar{P} = I^2R/2 = V^2/2R$.

Therefore, Joule's law has an entirely different appearance using peak voltages and currents of an a-c wave, as compared with the constant values of a d-c signal. Since Joule's law is of fundamental importance, it is customary to define *effective* amplitudes of voltage and current that will satisfy Joule's law in its d-c form. For the sine wave we are considering now, these effective values are the peak values divided by $\sqrt{2}$, or

$$V_e = \frac{V}{\sqrt{2}} \quad \text{and} \quad I_e = \frac{I}{\sqrt{2}}$$

From the way in which they are derived, these values are also known as *root-mean-square* or *rms*. The relation between peak and rms amplitudes depends on the shape of the wave, and must be evaluated by direct integration for each case.

Thus, for any periodic wave $v(t)$ the rms amplitude is given by

$$V_e^2 = \frac{1}{T} \int_0^T v^2(t) \, dt$$

The power calculations given here apply only if the voltage and current are in phase. The more general case is considered in Section 2.7.

PROBLEMS

1) Two commonly found rms voltages are 115 and 6.3; give the corresponding peak amplitudes.
2) Find the rms amplitudes of the square and sawtooth waves shown in Fig. 2.1.

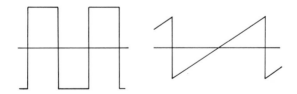

Fig. 2.1 Square and sawtooth waves for rms calculation.

3) Consider the wave $V_1 + V_2 \sin \omega t$ (d-c and a-c voltage superposed). Show that the power dissipated in a resistance R is $V_1^2/R + V_2^2/2R$, the sum of the powers corresponding to each component alone. (The same is true for two or more superposed sine waves.)

2.2 COMPLEX NUMBERS

A brief review of the relevant aspects of complex algebra is convenient at this point and will serve to introduce the notation to be used. In circuit theory the symbol i is so well established in its meaning of current that the symbol j is universally used for $\sqrt{-1}$. Thus, a complex number is written

$$z = a + jb$$

in which a and b, both real numbers, are called the real and imaginary parts. Addition, subtraction, multiplication, and division are carried out by the usual rules, merely remembering that $j^2 = -1$.

The correspondence between complex numbers and points or vectors in a plane is so close that the terms "vector" and "complex number" are used almost interchangeably in circuit theory. Also, a and b correspond exactly to x and y. A vector may be represented in polar as well as rectangular form, by its magnitude and angle, often called *phase angle*. The magnitude $|z|$ of the complex number is equal to $\sqrt{a^2 + b^2}$ and may be readily found if it is so expressed that a and b can be separated easily. If not, it is often easier to multiply z by its *complex conjugate* $z^* = a - jb$, which is found by reversing the sign of every coefficient of j. The result of the multiplication is just $a^2 + b^2$. The phase angle is given by the relation $\tan \theta = b/a$.

The algebraic representation corresponding to the polar form of the vector is found as follows, using the relations just given:

$$z = a + jb = |z|(\cos \theta + j \sin \theta) = |z|e^{j\theta}$$

The last equality follows by comparison of the series expansions for $e^{j\theta}$, $\cos \theta$, and $\sin \theta$. This form is convenient for multiplication and division of complex numbers; in multiplication, for example, the magnitudes are multiplied and the angles added. If the angle θ is allowed to increase steadily while $|z|$ is kept constant, a vector rotating in the counterclockwise direction is generated. The projection of this on the real axis is a sine wave and can be used to represent an a-c signal. This is the reason for the interest in complex numbers in a-c circuit analysis. The analogy between circular and simple-harmonic motions is widely exploited in mechanics; complex notation allows us to benefit from the same analogy in circuit analysis.

PROBLEMS

1) Prove that $e^{j\theta} = \cos\theta + j\sin\theta$, using the series expansions.
2) If your memory of complex arithmetic is rusty, make up a few complex numbers and practice on them. Plot the corresponding graphical operations.

2.3 ALTERNATING CURRENT AND ROTATING VECTORS

The expression $e^{j\omega t}$ represents a unit vector rotating with angular velocity ω. Its real part, $Re(e^{j\omega t})$, is equal to $\cos\omega t$, and represents the projection of the vector on the real axis. The alternating voltage $v = V\cos(\omega t - \theta)$ can be written $v = Re(Ve^{j(\omega t - \theta)})$. Because it is clumsy to carry the notation "the real part of" through algebraic manipulations, it is usual to omit it, understanding that only the real part of any solution has physical meaning. Thus we write

$$v = Ve^{j(\omega t - \theta)}$$

with the above understanding always in mind. More often, the phase factor $e^{-j\theta}$ will be absorbed into the amplitude V, making it complex, so that

$$v = Ve^{j\omega t}$$

If products of variables occur, as in power calculations, it is necessary to be more careful and to retain *only* the real part.

Inductance and Capacitance. The properties, *inductance* and *capacitance*, are of importance when energy is stored in magnetic and electric fields. This storage does not affect the steady-state conditions in a d-c circuit, but can greatly change the behavior of a circuit with the varying fields of an a-c wave. Every circuit contains at least some inductance and some capacitance, even a straight piece of wire, but such *strays* can usually be ignored at frequencies below about 100 mc (megacycles per second).

A coil of wire, especially if it has an iron core, exhibits a much larger inductance. As the current through it varies, so does the magnetic field. Because it stores energy, the latter is difficult to vary rapidly and a retarding effect is produced on the changes of current. The *inductance*, L, is defined by Faraday's law of induction:

$$v_L = L\frac{di}{dt}$$

where v_L is the voltage across the inductance, assuming zero resistance. The treatment of actual coils with resistance is discussed in Section 2.5. For the normal units of v, i, and t, the unit of L is the *henry*. Milli-henries (mh) and microhenries (μh) are also commonly used.

Two metallic conductors in close proximity can store energy in electric fields if their potential is different. If their areas are large and the spacing small, the effect can be large; the device is called a *con-denser* or *capacitor*. This time, it is the potential difference which is difficult to vary rapidly. The *capacitance*, C, is defined by the charge q which it can store:

$$q = Cv_c$$

With q in coulombs and v_c in volts, C is in farads. The farad is such a large unit as to be almost useless; instead, the microfarad (μf) and picofarad (pf) [or micromicrofarad ($\mu\mu$f)] are in common use.

Reactance and Impedance. The quantities known as reactance and impedance, analogous to resistance, appear in an a-c circuit as the result of the presence of inductance or capacitance. Let us first consider *inductive reactance*. We take the equation defining inductance

$$v_L = L\frac{di}{dt}$$

and substitute the following expressions, which assume steady-state sinusoidal voltage and current:

$$i = Ie^{j\omega t} \quad \text{and} \quad \frac{di}{dt} = j\omega Ie^{j\omega t}$$

Then

$$V_Le^{j\omega t} = j\omega LIe^{j\omega t}$$

Canceling the exponential, we find

$$V_L = j\omega LI$$

This expression resembles Ohm's law, with the quantity ωL playing a part analogous to resistance; it is called reactance, and in particular, inductive reactance, or X_L. In d-c circuits, ω is zero and so is the inductive reactance. The factor j in the expression relating V and I implies a 90 degree phase shift between them, with the current lagging the voltage.

The other form of reactance is *capacitive*, and is derived from the definition

$$q = Cv_c$$

Solving for v_c,

$$V_c e^{j\omega t} = \frac{q}{C} = \frac{1}{C} \int i \, dt = \frac{I}{j\omega C} e^{j\omega t}$$

$$V_c = \frac{I}{j\omega C}$$

Again we note the resemblance to Ohm's law; this time the reactance is $-1/\omega C = X_C$. The factor j in the denominator again implies a 90 degree phase shift, but this time in the opposite direction, with the current leading the voltage. At first sight it is a puzzle that the "effect" should precede the "cause" in this way. The explanation is again that we are considering a steady state which has taken many cycles to set up; the current is the result of a large number of preceding cycles of voltage.

Circuit Equations and Impedance. Consider now a series circuit containing inductance L, capacitance C, and resistance R, as well as a power source v (Fig. 2.2). (When a power source is shown without a

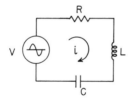

Fig. 2.2 Series *R-L-C* circuit

reference polarity, as here, the positive terminal is always on top.) If we assume a current i to be flowing, we can set up a circuit equation according to Kirchhoff's first law and the fundamental equations for potential drops:

$$Ri + L\frac{di}{dt} + \frac{1}{C} \int i \, dt = v$$

If this is differentiated once, it becomes a second-order differential equation for i, and it can be solved by the usual methods if v is specified.

This is not particularly difficult, but a circuit containing more than one mesh would lead to simultaneous differential equations. The assumption of a complex exponential form of current and voltage transforms the differential equation into an algebraic one, which is much easier to solve. However, it gives only the steady-state part of the solution; if the transient parts are required, some other method must be used. When the substitution is made, the result is:

$$\left(R + j\omega L + \frac{1}{j\omega C}\right) I e^{j\omega t} = V e^{j\omega t}$$

or

$$V = \left[R + j\left(\omega L - \frac{1}{\omega C}\right)\right] I = (R + jX)I = ZI$$

The quantity $Z \equiv R + jX$ is called the *impedance* of the circuit and limits the current in a-c circuits in the same way that resistance does in d-c circuits. Resistance and reactance, which we have already discussed separately, are the real and imaginary parts of impedance. Since the impedance of the circuit we are discussing is complex, there is a phase shift between V and I, equal to the phase angle of Z and therefore given by

$$\tan \theta = \frac{X}{R}$$

If we compare the final equation with the circuit in Fig. 2.2, we see that it can be written down directly without going through the differential equation. It is merely necessary to write the mesh equation, using the appropriate resistance or reactance for each element. As we have just seen, the solution contains information about phases as well as amplitudes, and this must be remembered, especially when mesh currents are being combined to give branch currents.

There is one other circuit element we have not considered—that is, mutual inductance, as found in transformers. It is treated in much the same way as inductance, but since we shall have little occasion to use it, it will not be discussed further.

2.4 VECTOR DIAGRAMS

If a number of sine waves of different phases are plotted together, the diagram can be confusing. A vector diagram is a compact method of representing the same information in a form which is easily grasped.

The diagram is a plot of the set of rotating vectors which generate the sine waves by their projections on the real axis, "photographed" at some instant to give a fixed pattern.

Consider the series R-C circuit shown in Fig. 2.3; the mesh equation is

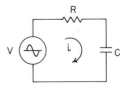

$$V = \left(R + \frac{1}{j\omega C}\right)I = \left(R - \frac{j}{\omega C}\right)I$$

The first term is V_R and the second is V_C; the former is in phase with I, and the latter lags it by 90 degrees. The total voltage V is the vector sum

Fig. 2.3   Series R-C circuit.

of these two, and lags I by some intermediate angle; for example, 45 degrees if $1/\omega C = R$. The corresponding waves are sketched in Fig. 2.4(a), and the vector diagram in Fig. 2.4(b). It is constructed using the complex amplitudes V, I; for this series circuit it is convenient

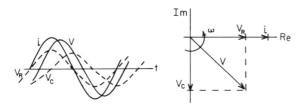

Fig. 2.4 Wave and vector diagrams for the circuit of Fig. 2.3.

to take I as real and plot it along the real axis. V_R, being in phase with I, is plotted in the same direction; V_C, with its factor $-j$, goes along the negative imaginary axis; and V is simply the vector sum of these two. The actual waves may be generated by multiplying these amplitudes by $e^{j\omega t}$, so that the vectors rotate counterclockwise at angular velocity ω; the waves are their projections on the real axis. The vector diagram is easier to draw and easier to grasp than the wave diagram. Notice that there is no need to remember whether the voltage on the capacitor lags or leads the current; the correct result comes out automatically.

Impedance Diagram. If each vector in Fig. 2.4(b) is divided by I, the result is a set of stationary vectors having the dimensions of V/I, or

impedance, as shown in Fig. 2.5. The corresponding equation is produced in the same way, and is

$$\frac{V}{I} = Z = R - \frac{j}{\omega C}$$

Now consider a series R-L-C circuit, as in Fig. 2.2. The mesh equation, already discussed in the preceding section, is

$$V = \left[R + j\left(\omega L - \frac{1}{\omega C} \right) \right] I$$

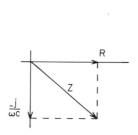

Fig. 2.5 Impedance diagram for the
circuit of Fig. 2.3.

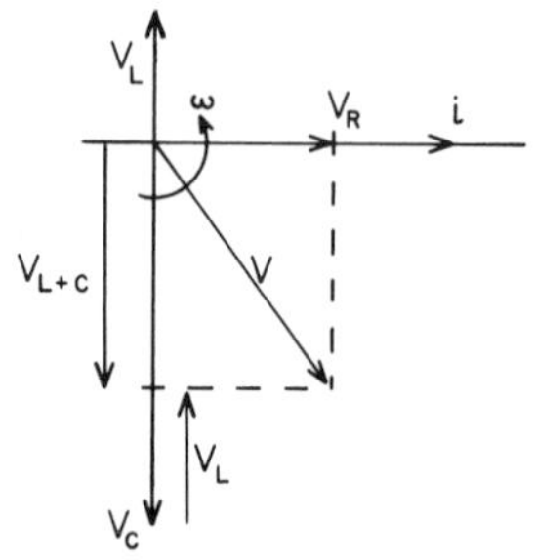

Fig. 2.6 Vector diagram for the circuit
of Fig. 2.2.

The vector diagram is shown in Fig. 2.6 for a frequency low enough so
that $X_C > X_L$. Notice that the voltage on the capacitor is larger than
the applied voltage; this is possible because of the energy storage in the
coil and capacitor. If the frequency is increased, V_L will rise and
V_C will fall until their magnitudes become equal at some frequency,
called the *resonant frequency*. At this frequency, given by $\omega^2 LC = 1$, the
net reactance is zero, the total voltage is in phase with the current, and
the current is a maximum. At higher frequencies, the total voltage
swings around into the first quadrant as V_L continues to rise and V_C
to fall.

PROBLEM

Draw the voltage and impedance diagrams to scale for the resonant
frequency, and for frequencies half and twice as great.

2.5 REAL INDUCTORS AND CAPACITORS

It is impossible to realize an actual circuit element that acts as a pure inductance or a pure capacitance, although the approach to perfection can be very close in a capacitor. In this section we consider the imperfections and discuss their representation by equivalent circuits.

Capacitors. In capacitors, energy losses can occur by means of leakage currents through the dielectric, and by energy losses within the dielectric caused by the rapidly oscillating electric fields. These losses can be represented by an equivalent circuit containing resistance as well as capacitance; the two simplest possibilities are shown in Fig. 2.7. If the

Fig. 2.7 Series and parallel representations of a capacitor with dissipation.

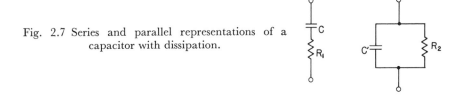

losses are caused primarily by leakage, the parallel circuit is physically more reasonable; if they are caused by an imperfect dielectric, or by the resistance of the conducting surfaces in the capacitor, the series circuit may be more reasonable. But at any one frequency, the circuits are interchangeable, and the representation may be chosen as a matter of convenience. In general, the resistance will be a function of frequency, but one representation may give a nearly constant resistance over a certain range of frequencies.

Since most capacitors are nearly ideal, the losses are small, and therefore the series resistance R_1 will be small and the parallel resistance R_2 will be large. In either case, the impedance vector will point almost straight down, making a very small angle with the negative imaginary axis. The tangent of this angle is known as the *dissipation factor D*. For the series circuit, D is simply the ratio R/X, or $\omega R_1 C$. For the parallel circuit, it is necessary to combine the two impedances in parallel, using the same rule as for resistances, and then find the phase angle of the resulting expression. For the very small values of D usually encountered, the result is $D = 1/\omega R_2 C$, and $C' = C$. For all but the most critical applications, D can usually be taken as zero.

PROBLEM

Derive the last results for D and C'.

Inductors. The most obvious cause of energy loss in an inductor is the ordinary resistance of the wire, but it is not the only cause. At higher frequencies, the "skin effect" will keep the currents near the surface of the wire and increase its effective resistance. If there is an iron core, energy will be dissipated by the hysteresis effect and by eddy currents induced in the iron. However, at low frequencies the wire resistance may dominate the others. For circuit analysis, the losses may again be represented by including a resistance along with the inductance, using either a series or a parallel circuit as in Fig. 2.8. Losses in an inductance can rarely be neglected, especially at frequencies below 1000 cps.

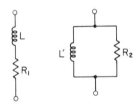

Fig. 2.8 Series and parallel representations of a coil with dissipation.

The presence of dissipation causes the vector representing an inductor to lean into the first quadrant; instead of using the dissipation factor to characterize this, it is customary to use its reciprocal, the quality factor Q, which is the tangent of the phase angle. Thus, for the series circuit in Fig. 2.8, $Q = \omega L/R_1$. For the parallel circuit, the impedance is given by

$$\frac{1}{Z} = \frac{1}{R_2} + \frac{1}{j\omega L'}$$

$$Z = \frac{j\omega L' R_2}{R_2 + j\omega L'} = \frac{j\omega L' R_2^2 + \omega^2 L'^2 R_2}{R_2^2 + \omega^2 L'^2}$$

The last form was produced by rationalizing—that is, multiplying top and bottom by the complex conjugate of the denominator. From the definition of Q, it is equal to the ratio of imaginary to real parts; thus

$$Q = \frac{R_2}{\omega L'}$$

Note that this is just the reciprocal of the form involving the series parameters L and R_1. One is usually interested only in coils with a fairly high Q; for these, the first term in the denominator of Z is dominant. For example, if $Q = 10$, R_2^2 is 100 times larger than $\omega^2 L^2$. Then we can write

$$Z \doteq j\omega L' + \frac{\omega^2 L'^2}{R_2}$$

If the same coil is to be represented by either a series or parallel circuit $L \doteq L'$.

The Q of a high-quality coil is usually in the range from 100 to a few hundred. Generally speaking, the Q increases with the size. The best type of construction depends strongly on the frequency. At audio frequencies, iron cores are used, normally in a toroidal shape. At higher frequencies, ferrite cores are useful, and in the range above a few megacycles per second no core is needed.

PROBLEM

Find the effective series and parallel resistances for a 30-henry inductor whose Q is 20 at 1000 cps.

2.6 PARALLEL CIRCUITS

Parallel d-c circuits are most easily treated by using the concept of conductance, G. This is still useful in a-c circuit analysis, along with the quantities related to impedance and reactance. These are the following:

Admittance is the reciprocal of impedance; its real and imaginary parts are conductance and susceptance; the unit of all three is the mho.

The susceptance of a perfect capacitor is ωC and of a perfect inductor is $-1/\omega L$. The reason for the reversal of sign is seen as follows: Consider an impedance $Z = R + jX$; its admittance is

$$Y = \frac{1}{Z} = \frac{1}{R + jX} = \frac{R - jX}{R^2 + X^2} = G + jB$$

Then $G = R/|Z|^2$ and $B = -X/|Z|^2$. For pure resistances and reactances, these reduce to the simpler forms already given.

Let us now consider a simple example, the parallel R-L-C circuit shown in Fig. 2.9. The node equation is

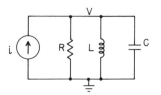

$$I = \left[G + j\left(\omega C - \frac{1}{\omega L}\right)\right]V$$

Fig. 2.9 Parallel R-L-C circuit.

where $G = 1/R$. This circuit exhibits resonance at the same frequency as the series circuit, given by $\omega^2 LC = 1$; for a constant-current input, the terminal voltage is a maximum at this frequency having the value I/G. At resonance the circuit behaves as if L and C are not present; although they draw no current from the source, they contain a large circulating current, driven by the energy stored alternately in the capacitor and the coil.

2.7 MESH AND NODE EQUATIONS

These equations are set up in the same way as for d-c circuits, using the appropriate expressions for impedance, resistance, and reactance—or admittance, conductance, and susceptance. The manipulation of the equations is the same in principle, as long as the rules of complex algebra are kept in mind. One important point is often forgotten: in combining mesh currents to give branch currents, or node potentials to give potential differences, one must use vector addition and subtraction, and not merely combine the magnitudes. This is especially easy to overlook when numerical values have been substituted for the symbols.

Circuit Theorems. The set of mesh equations for a circuit has exactly the same form as the d-c equations discussed in Section 1.4; it is only necessary to remember that I, V, and Z are complex. This fact does not affect any of the proofs in that chapter; the superposition theorem can be taken over unchanged. Thévenin's theorem can be restated as follows: At any one frequency, a two-terminal linear circuit can be represented by an a-c voltage generator in series with an impedance; in general, different parameters will be required at each different frequency. There is nothing to prevent the impedance being a resistance independent of frequency in particular cases, at least to a high degree of approximation, and such cases are probably the commonest when the theorem is used.

All these remarks can be adapted to the a-c node equations, which lead again to the appropriate form of the superposition theorem and to Norton's theorem.

Power and Power Matching. So far we have considered Joule's law only when there is no phase shift between current and voltage. The importance of the phase shift can be seen by considering the power dissipation in a pure reactance which produces a 90-degree phase shift. For example, if $v = V \sin \omega t$ and $i = I \cos \omega t$, the power is zero since the integral of sin x cos x over one cycle is zero. If the current i passes through an impedance $Z = R + jX$, the voltage is

$$v = IR \cos \omega t + IX \sin \omega t$$

If we now integrate the product vi over one cycle, we find

$$P = \frac{I^2 R}{2} = I_e^2 R$$

Thus, only the real part of Z is to be used in calculating the power.

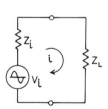

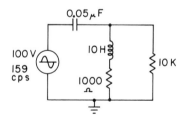

Fig. 2.10 Power matching for an
a-c circuit.

Fig. 2.11 Problem circuit.

Let us now reconsider the power-matching theorem for an a-c circuit as the one in Fig. 2.10. The power dissipated by the load Z_L is $I_e^2 R_L$, and I is equal to $V_i/(Z_i + Z_L)$. For any particular value of R_L, the current is a maximum when $X_L = -X_i$; that is, when a reactance provided is tuned to resonance with the reactance in the generator at the frequency generated. With this condition satisfied, the reactances play no further part in the circuit, and the proof for the d-c case applies; the value of R_L that absorbs maximum power is equal to R_i. Thus, a matched load in an a-c circuit has a resistance equal to the generator resistance, and a reactance equal and opposite to the generator reactance.

PROBLEMS

1) Show that $P = V_e I_e \cos \theta$, if θ is the phase angle between V and I.
2) Solve the circuit in Fig. 2.11 by both mesh and node methods, finding all branch currents and the voltage at A. The frequency of 159 cps is chosen to make things easy, since the angular frequency is 1000 radians per sec.

2.8 ALTERNATING-CURRENT BRIDGES

We shall now consider several generalizations of the Wheatstone bridge for a-c operation with capacitors and inductors. Besides offering excellent illustrations for analysis, they are useful in their own right. Many kinds of bridges are in use for special purposes; the ones to be discussed are the relatively simple circuits found in the common laboratory impedance bridge.

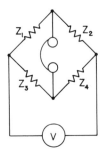

Fig. 2.12 Wheatstone bridge.

A four-arm bridge of the Wheatstone type is illustrated in Fig. 2.12; it uses an a-c generator, and the detector is indicated as a pair of earphones, although other detectors may be used in practice. By analogy with the d-c bridge, the balance condition is

$$Z_1 Z_4 = Z_2 Z_3$$

Since some or all of the Z's are complex, this condition is really two conditions; they may be on amplitudes and phases, or on real and imaginary parts, whichever is convenient. For the most satisfactory bridges, both these balances must be independent of frequency. There are two reasons for this: (1) the result for the unknown impedance should depend on the bridge arms only, and not on the generator frequency; (2) even the best generator produces some harmonics; if the fundamental is balanced out but the harmonics left, balance is difficult to detect accurately. However, this rule can be relaxed slightly in special cases, usually those in which the unknown is an almost pure reactance with a phase angle close to 90 degrees. The phase angle of the corresponding bridge balance can then be allowed to vary with frequency in a different way.

In the impedance bridge, it is convenient to have two arms made up of pure resistances, one of which is variable. The third arm is a high-quality capacitor with a very small dissipation factor. If the unknown is a capacitor, the only way to have equal phase angles on both sides of the balance condition is to have one resistor and one capacitor on each side; if dissipation can be neglected, the condition is just

$$R_1 X_4 = R_2 X_3 \qquad \text{or} \qquad \frac{R_1}{C_4} = \frac{R_2}{C_3}$$

If the unknown is an inductor, it must be on the same side of the equation as the capacitor, and the two resistors must be on the other side; again, for negligible dissipation, the result is

$$R_1 R_4 = X_2 X_3 \qquad \text{or} \qquad R_1 R_4 = \frac{L_3}{C_2}$$

Since a useful bridge must be able to allow for and measure dissipation let us now consider the circuits that accomplish this. The general principle is to add dissipation to the standard capacitor by means of a resistor.

Capacitance Bridge. The capacitance-bridge circuit is shown in Fig. 2.13, with the source and detector omitted to simplify the diagram. The dissipation of the unknown capacitor C_3 is represented by a shunt resistance R_3. It is balanced by R_4 in series with the standard capacitor C_4. We first work out an expression for the impedance of the parallel arm, number 3:

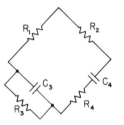

$$Z_3 = \frac{R_3/j\omega C_3}{R_3 + 1/j\omega C_3} = \frac{R_3}{1 + j\omega R_3 C_3}$$

Then the balance condition is

$$Z_1 Z_4 = Z_2 Z_3$$

$$R_1\left(R_4 + \frac{1}{j\omega C_4}\right) = \frac{R_2 R_3}{1 + j\omega R_3 C_3}$$

Fig. 2.13 Capacitance bridge.

Dividing by R_1 and multiplying by $(1 + j\omega R_3 C_3)$, we get

$$R_4 + \frac{R_3 C_3}{C_4} + j\left(\omega R_3 R_4 C_3 - \frac{1}{\omega C_4}\right) = \frac{R_2 R_3}{R_1}$$

The real and imaginary parts of this equation must be satisfied separately; the real part is

$$R_4 + \frac{R_3 C_3}{C_4} = \frac{R_2 R_3}{R_1}$$

$$C_3 = C_4\left(\frac{R_2}{R_1} - \frac{R_4}{R_3}\right) \doteq \frac{C_4 R_2}{R_1}$$

The last approximation is a very good one if the dissipation is small, for then R_3 is very large and R_4 is very small. The imaginary part is

$$\omega^2 R_3 R_4 C_3 C_4 = 1$$

In terms of the dissipation factor D, this becomes

$$D \equiv \frac{1}{\omega R_3 C_3} = \omega R_4 C_4$$

The main balance, for C_3, is seen to be strictly independent of frequency, as required; it also agrees, as it should, with the result found for the case of negligible dissipation. The subsidiary balance, which gives D, is dependent on frequency, but the effect is not serious, so long as D is small. The frequency appears in the calibration of R_4 in terms of D, but again this is not important, since accurate values of D are not needed in ordinary laboratory work.

Inductance Bridges. Since it is common to encounter inductances of large dissipation, or low Q, the impedance bridge must allow for their measurement. The Maxwell bridge, Fig. 2.14, does this by putting a resistor in parallel with the standard condenser; when a high-Q coil

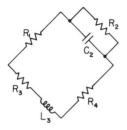
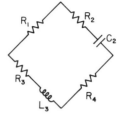

Fig. 2.14 Maxwell bridge.　　　　Fig. 2.15 Hay bridge.

is to be measured, the Hay bridge, Fig. 2.15, is used, with the resistor in series as in the capacitance bridge. First we consider the Maxwell version; with the expression already developed for a parallel R-C arm, the balance condition is

$$(R_3 + j\omega L_3)\left(\frac{R_2}{1 + j\omega R_2 C_2}\right) = R_1 R_4$$

Multiplying to clear the fraction, and dividing by R_2, we get

$$R_3 + j\omega L_3 = \frac{R_1 R_4}{R_2}(1 + j\omega R_2 C_2)$$

The main balance comes from the imaginary part:

$$L_3 = C_2 R_1 R_4$$

and the real part gives

$$R_3 = \frac{R_1 R_4}{R_2}$$

These may be combined to give

$$Q \equiv \frac{\omega L_3}{R_3} = \omega R_2 C_2$$

For the Hay bridge in Fig. 2.15, the balance condition is

$$(R_3 + j\omega L_3)\left(R_2 + \frac{1}{j\omega C_2}\right) = R_1 R_4$$

$$R_2 R_3 + \frac{L_3}{C_2} + j\left(\omega R_2 L_3 - \frac{R_3}{\omega C_2}\right) = R_1 R_4$$

The real part gives

$$L_3 = C_2(R_1 R_4 - R_2 R_3) \doteq C_2 R_1 R_4$$

As with the capacitance bridge, the approximation is a very good one as long as Q is at least 10. The main balance condition is the same for both Maxwell and Hay bridges, and for the simple bridge without dissipation. The imaginary part must be zero; therefore

$$\omega R_2 L_3 = \frac{R_3}{\omega C_2} \quad \text{or} \quad Q \equiv \frac{\omega L_3}{R_3} = \frac{1}{\omega C_2 R_2}$$

Again, this subsidiary balance depends on frequency, but for the range of Q appropriate for this bridge, the effect is not serious.

The practical problems of realizing a bridge that conforms to these circuits are considerable. The principal difficulty is that it is impossible to ground both the source and detector, so that unless special precautions are taken, appreciable capacitances will appear across certain bridge arms. It is usual to use a special transformer to couple the source to the bridge, and the shielding must be carried out with care and understanding. The developments given above allow us to understand the operation of an existing bridge, but more study in specialized works would be needed before we could build one that would give accurate results.

2.9 FREQUENCY RESPONSE OF R-C NETWORKS

We turn now to a somewhat different aspect of a-c network theory: the study of frequency response, or variation of attenuation with frequency. This study is often called *filter theory*, but the simple R-C networks to be considered do not really deserve the name "filter." The basic R-C networks, the *lag* and the *lead*, are found as parts of almost all electronic circuits, and it is well to discuss them by themselves first. Methods will be developed to allow rapid estimation and plotting of their characteristics. The more complicated *phase-advance* and *phase-retard* networks are important in connection with negative-feedback amplifiers, and are also useful for adjusting the frequency response of a system such as a phonograph.

Time Constant. We first digress slightly to recall the meaning of the term "time constant." Consider the behavior of the circuit in Fig. 2.16, when the switch is turned to the battery side. Current will flow through

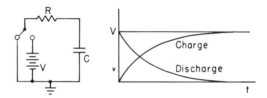

Fig. 2.16 Time constant of an *R-C* circuit.

R and into *C*, charging up the capacitor until eventually the potential *V* is reached. If the switch is returned to the ground side, the capacitor discharges slowly according to the equation

$$v_C = Ve^{-t/RC}$$

The product *RC* is called the time constant of the network; after a time equal to this, the voltage has decreased to $1/e$ of its initial value. The charge and discharge curves are shown in Fig. 2.16. Although inductive time constants will not be discussed in detail here, it is well to recall that the time constant of an *R-L* circuit is L/R.

PROBLEM

Set up the differential equation for Fig. 2.16 and derive the equations for charge and discharge.

Lag or Low-pass Network. The low-pass network is the same as the type just discussed (Fig. 2.17), but now we are interested in its steady-state frequency response instead of its time response. It can be considered as an a-c potential divider, and the attenuation β can be written down as follows:

$$\beta = \frac{V_o}{V_i} = \frac{1/j\omega C}{R + 1/j\omega C} = \frac{1}{1 + j\omega\tau}$$

In the last form, the time constant RC has been written as the Greek letter τ. The subscripts o and i stand for output and input; thus, the former should be pronounced as a letter, not a number. The appearance of the time constant in this expression for frequency response

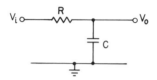

Fig. 2.17 Lag network.

should not occasion surprise. For frequencies whose periods are longer than about one time-constant, the rises and falls illustrated in Fig. 2.16 do not appreciably affect the wave, but for shorter periods they do.

The frequency response can be discussed most easily by breaking up the frequency range into parts and observing the asymptotes approached by the curve; the phase shifts θ are also given.

Low-frequency range: $\omega\tau \ll 1$ $\quad \beta \simeq 1$ $\qquad\qquad\qquad \theta \simeq 0$

High-frequency range: $\omega\tau \gg 1$ $\quad \beta \simeq \dfrac{1}{j\omega\tau}$ $\qquad\qquad \theta \simeq -90°$

Corner frequency: $\quad \omega\tau = 1$ $\quad \beta = \dfrac{1}{1 + j}$ $\qquad\qquad \theta = -45°$

These asymptotes are most conveniently plotted on a log-log scale, by using a decibel scale for β and a logarithmic frequency scale. An attenuation of 1 corresponds to 0 db$_v$. The $1/f$ variation in the high-frequency range means that β falls 20 db$_v$ per decade of frequency, or 6 db$_v$ per octave (factor of 2 in frequency). Both these ways of expressing the slope are in use; we shall use the former, or 20 db$_v$ per decade, version. The asymptotes intersect at the corner frequency, as the name implies; the actual attenuation here is $1/\sqrt{2}$, or -3 db$_v$. The convention used with resistive attenuators is not followed here; the decibel attenuations are written negative, as they actually are. Thus, the actual slope in the high-frequency region is -20 db$_v$ per decade.

A plot of the response curve is shown in Fig. 2.18. It may be sketched rapidly and easily by plotting the asymptotes, locating their intersection at the corner frequency $f_c = 1/2\pi\tau$. The actual curve passes 3 db_v below this corner, and about 1 db_v below the lines at frequencies half and twice as great.

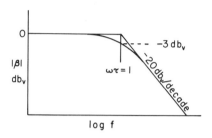

Fig. 2.18 Frequency response of the lag network.

The phase shifts are responsible for the name "lag" given to the network. At very low frequencies, the phase shift is close to zero; its departure from zero is noticeable long before the magnitude changes appreciably. For example, one decade below the corner, the output lags the input by about 0.1 radian, or 5.7 degrees. There is a 45 degree lag at the corner frequency, and above this the lag approaches 90 degrees in a similarly slow fashion.

Lead or High-pass Network. Comparison of Fig. 2.19 with Fig. 2.17 shows that the lag can be turned into a lead by changing the reference

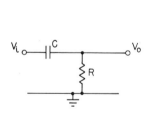

Fig. 2.19 Lead network.

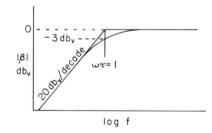

Fig. 2.20 Frequency response of the lead network.

point or ground to the other side of the generator. Therefore, a vector addition of their two outputs should give the input voltage, and it may be surmised that the frequency responses are complementary. In fact, it is merely necessary to reverse the frequency scale of Fig. 2.18 to convert it into the response of the lead network. The attenuation may be derived from the circuit in the same way as before, giving

$$\beta = \frac{R}{R + 1/j\omega C} = \frac{j\omega\tau}{1 + j\omega\tau} = \frac{1}{1 + 1/j\omega\tau}$$

The last form demonstrates that this response is indeed complementary to that of the lag, because they differ only in replacing $j\omega\tau$ by $1/j\omega\tau$; that is, in reading the logarithmic frequency scale in the opposite direction and in reversing the sign of the phase shifts. We now proceed to develop the expressions for the asymptotes directly.

Low-frequency range: $\omega\tau \ll 1$ $\quad \beta \simeq j\omega\tau$ $\quad\quad \theta \simeq +90°$

High-frequency range: $\omega\tau \gg 1$ $\quad \beta \simeq 1$ $\quad\quad \theta \simeq 0$

Corner frequency: $\omega\tau = 1$ $\quad \beta = \dfrac{j}{1 + j}$ $\quad\quad \theta = +45°$

The attenuation in the low-frequency range is proportional to f; the slope is then $+20$ db$_\text{v}$ per decade (or 6 db$_\text{v}$ per octave). The response is plotted in the same way as for the lag, with the appropriate minor changes; the result is shown in Fig. 2.20. The phase of the output leads that of the input by 90 degrees at very low frequencies, by 45 degrees at the corner frequency, and by amounts approaching zero at high frequencies.

PROBLEMS
1) Show that the phase shifts are $\theta = -\tan^{-1}\omega\tau$ for the lag network and $\theta = +\tan^{-1}(1/\omega\tau)$ for the lead network.
2) Plot the asymptotes of $|\beta|$ for a lag and a lead network with corner frequency 1000 cps. Work out the actual response for several frequencies near the corner, and plot the amplitude and phase.

Phase-retard Network. The circuit of a phase-retard network is shown in Fig. 2.21, and the response in Fig. 2.22; it produces a "bump" of phase shift, and a transition of amplitude to a plateau at high frequencies. The development of the attenuation function is straightforward and is left as a problem; the result is

$$\beta = \frac{1 + j\omega R_1 C}{1 + j\omega(R_1 + R_2) C} = \frac{1 + j\omega\tau}{1 + j\omega\tau/k}$$

where

$$\tau = R_1 C$$

$$k = \frac{R_1}{R_1 + R_2}$$

At the lowest frequencies there is no attenuation; at the highest, the attenuation is equal to k. In between, there is a transition, with an "asymptote" joining these two lines at two corners, where $\omega\tau/k = 1$

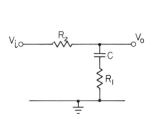 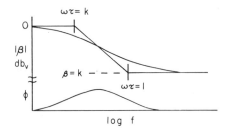

Fig. 2.21 Phase-retard network.   Fig. 2.22 Its frequency response.

and $\omega\tau = 1$. Actually, as shown in Fig. 2.22, the slope of the curve does not approach that of this "asymptote" unless k is considerably less than 0.1. To find the actual maximum slope, we assume, omitting the proof, that the curve is antisymmetrical about a frequency that is the geometric mean of the corner frequencies (the arithmetic mean on a log scale). This frequency is given by $\omega\tau = \sqrt{k}$. Now we form the natural log of $|\beta|$ and differentiate it with respect to log ω:

$$|\beta|^2 = \beta\beta^* = \frac{1 + \omega^2\tau^2}{1 + \omega^2\tau^2/k^2}$$

$$\log |\beta| = \tfrac{1}{2} \log |\beta|^2 = \tfrac{1}{2} \log (1 + \omega^2\tau^2) - \tfrac{1}{2} \log (1 + \omega^2\tau^2/k^2)$$

$$\frac{d(\log |\beta|)}{d(\log \omega)} = \omega \frac{d(\log |\beta|)}{d\omega} = \frac{\omega}{2} \frac{2\omega\tau^2}{1 + \omega^2\tau^2} - \frac{\omega}{2} \frac{2\omega\tau^2/k^2}{1 + \omega^2\tau^2/k^2}$$

Substituting the frequency of maximum slope just derived, we find

$$\frac{d(\log |\beta|)}{d(\log \omega)} = \frac{k}{1 + k} - \frac{1/k}{1 + 1/k} = \frac{k}{1 + k} - \frac{1}{k + 1} = -\frac{1 - k}{1 + k}$$

For a slope of $1/\omega$, this would be just -1, which must therefore correspond to -20 db$_v$ per decade. Therefore, the maximum slope must be

$$-20\,\frac{1-k}{1+k}\ \text{db}_v\ \text{per decade}$$

For example, if k is 0.2, this is -13.3 db$_v$ per decade, only 2/3 the slope of the "asymptote."

The maximum phase shift occurs at the same frequency as the maximum slope, and may be found from the expression for β at that frequency:

$$\beta = \frac{1+j\sqrt{k}}{1+j/\sqrt{k}} = \frac{2+j(\sqrt{k}-1/\sqrt{k})}{1+1/k}$$

The second form, found by rationalizing the denominator, looks clumsier but gives a better expression for the phase shift:

$$\tan\theta = \tfrac{1}{2}(\sqrt{k}-1/\sqrt{k})$$

Typical values of phase shift are given in the following table:

k	0.05	0.2	0.5
Maximum phase	$-65°$	$-42°$	$-20°$

These developments are a little complicated, but the results allow rapid approximate plotting of amplitude and phase curves.

Phase-advance Network. The complementary network is the phase advance; an example is shown in Fig. 2.23, and the frequency characteristics in Fig. 2.24. With a little manipulation, the attenuation can

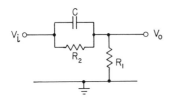

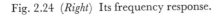

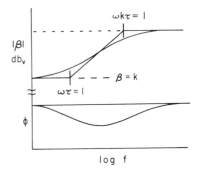

Fig. 2.23 (*Above*) Phase-advance network.

Fig. 2.24 (*Right*) Its frequency response.

be put in the form

$$\beta = \frac{R_1}{R_1 + R_2} \frac{1 + j\omega R_2 C}{1 + j\omega R_p C} = k\frac{1 + j\omega\tau}{1 + j\omega k\tau}$$

where

$$R_p = \frac{R_1 R_2}{R_1 + R_2}$$

$$\tau = R_2 C$$

$$k = \frac{R_1}{R_1 + R_2}$$

Replacement of $j\omega\tau$ by $1/j\omega\tau$ converts this into the equation for the phase-retard network. All of the results for it may thus be taken over by reversing the frequency scale and the sign of the phase shifts.

PROBLEM

Derive the equations for the phase-advance and phase-retard networks. Carry out the replacement just mentioned.

2.10 TRANSIENT RESPONSE OF R-C NETWORKS

A transient, as the name implies, is a signal that lasts only a short time, and therefore the steady-state treatment does not apply—although it can be adapted with some awkwardness. The best way is to return to the original differential equation and solve it with the appropriate initial conditions. The usual practice is to carry out the solution by the method of Laplace transforms, which has many points of resemblance to the steady-state analysis with complex exponentials; indeed, the latter can be regarded as a special case of the former. We shall not have time to consider this excellent technique, and must content ourselves with some simple examples that can be solved directly.

R-C Integrator. Return to Fig. 2.17 and suppose a mesh current i to be flowing. With no assumptions as to the form of the input voltage v_i, we can write the mesh equation

$$iR + \frac{1}{C} \int i\, dt = v_i$$

The second term on the left is equal to v_o. Now if we restrict ourselves to signals for which $v_o \ll v_i$, we can write $iR \doteq v_i$; substituting this value of i into the expression for v_o, we get

$$v_0 \doteq \frac{1}{RC} \int v_i \, dt$$

This result is not restricted to steady-state conditions and sinusoidal signals; any signal for which the attenuation of the network is large will satisfy the conditions. The commonest example is a high-frequency signal; another is the initial part of a transient. The name *integrator* is commonly applied to the network; if it is desired to give emphasis to the restriction, it may be called *quasi-integrator*.

R-C Differentiator. The lead network of Fig. 2.19 can be used as a differentiator under the same conditions. The mesh equation is the same, but now the output voltage v_o is taken across R and is equal to iR. If this is small compared with v_i, then

$$v_i \doteq \frac{1}{C} \int i \, dt \quad \text{and} \quad i \doteq C \frac{dv_i}{dt}$$

Then

$$v_0 = iR \doteq RC \frac{dv_i}{dt}$$

Again, because of the restriction to signals for which the attenuation is great, the network is sometimes called a "quasi-differentiator."

EXAMPLES

The application of these circuits may be illustrated by using a square wave as the input. First consider the integrator as in Fig. 2.25. If the frequency of the wave is well below the corner frequency (for the same circuit considered as a lag), it will be transmitted with only a slight rounding of the corners by the exponential rises and falls. As the time constant is increased, the exponentials become more and more noticeable, until they begin to cause an appreciable decrease in the wave amplitude. The resemblance to a triangular wave is already marked, and gets closer and closer as the time constant is further increased. When the output amplitude is one tenth that of the input, the triangular wave is perfect as far as the eye can tell.

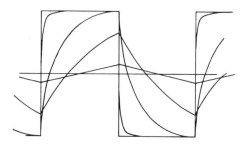

Fig. 2.25 Square wave applied to integrating networks with various time constants.

With the differentiator, the results appear poorer at first sight, as illustrated in Fig. 2.26. If the corner frequency is low enough, the wave is transmitted unchanged; as the corner frequency is raised, a slight sag appears. A further rise makes the sag more pronounced, and then produces a series of spikes, which are tending to resemble the derivative.

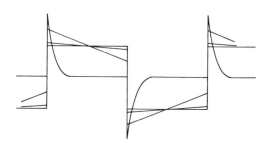

Fig. 2.26 Square wave applied to differentiating network with various time constants.

Further shortening of the time constant shortens the exponential tails but does not noticeably affect anything else. But we should not expect accurate differentiation yet, because the output amplitude is actually greater than the input, rather than much less. Now, consider Fig. 2.27, in which the rise of the wave has been stretched out to make it visible. If the time constant of the differentiator is made short enough, the output amplitude will finally decrease, and when it is small enough, the wave will be the derivative of the finite rise.

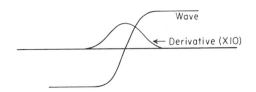

Fig. 2.27 The rise of the square wave on a magnified time scale, showing true differentiation with a short enough time constant.

If the triangular wave produced by the integrator in Fig. 25 is amplified and applied to a differentiator, the square wave can be recaptured easily under the right conditions.

PROBLEMS

1) Discuss this in detail and draw a diagram similar to Fig. 2.26.
2) Consider qualitatively the results of applying a square wave to a phase-retard and a phase-advance network.

Discussion. These simple examples show that transient response of a network is best handled by a direct attack. In more complicated networks, the best method is that of Laplace transforms. The square-wave response of a network can also be found by dissecting the wave into a Fourier series, calculating the steady-state response to each harmonic, and reassembling them with due regard to phase shifts. This is a clumsy and unnatural technique, but it is found all too often in the older literature, and still very much in the literature of sound reproduction. Some of the hardest things to reproduce in music are transients, such as drum beats and the attack of piano notes; their reproduction should be discussed in terms of good transient response, not in terms of extended high-frequency response and small phase shift.

Compensated Voltage Dividers. High-impedance voltage dividers are needed in measuring equipment, such as oscilloscopes and high-frequency voltmeters. Such a divider is shown in Fig. 2.28, along with

.the small "stray" capacitance introduced by the following amplifier and the connecting wires. Application of Thévenin's theorem to the resistors allows the circuit to be shown as a simple lag, and with the typical values given the time-constant is 3.6 μsec, far too long for any

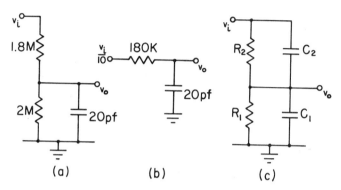

Fig. 2.28 (a) High-impedance voltage divider with 20pf stray capacitance loading it. (b) Its equivalent circuit. (c) A compensated voltage divider.

kind of high-quality test equipment. The remedy, as shown in Fig. 2.28(c), is to shunt the upper resistor R_2 by a small capacitor C_2 chosen so that the voltage division ratio produced by the capacitors is the same as that of the resistors. The ratio of the whole divider is the same for short times (or high frequencies) and long times (or low frequencies). Therefore, the impedance ratio of the capacitors is the same as that of the resistors:

$$\frac{1/\omega C_1}{1/\omega C_2} = \frac{R_1}{R_2} \quad \text{or} \quad R_1 C_1 = R_2 C_2$$

The principle is readily extended to dividers with more than two sections by keeping the time constant of each section the same. Usual practice is to make the capacitors variable and adjust them for best response to a square wave.

References

An excellent treatment of Laplace-transform analysis from the viewpoint of the physicist will be found in *Linear Feedback Analysis* by J. G. Thomason (New York: Pergamon Press, Inc., and McGraw-Hill Book Company, Inc., 1955).

CHAPTER 3

Physics of Vacuum Tubes

3.1 THERMIONIC EMISSION

The operation of nearly all tubes depends on the phenomenon of emission of electrons into a vacuum by hot bodies. Although a complete theory of this effect is beyond our scope, we can make a qualitative discussion and justify the kind of result obtained.

Electron Theory of Metals. According to the modern theory of metals, their characteristic properties are mainly due to the presence of "free" electrons. Each atom contributes one or more of its outermost electrons to the piece of metal as a whole, and these electrons are able to wander through the crystal lattice almost unimpeded. However, they are still tightly bound to the whole piece, and cannot ordinarily leave it except into another piece of metal in close contact. The motion of the electrons under an applied electric field is an electric current. The drift of electrons in the presence of a temperature gradient is responsible for the large heat conductivity of a metal. The remarkable mechanical and optical properties are also due to the presence of the electron "gas."

The binding of an electron to the piece of metal can be overcome by giving it enough energy; the minimum amount required is called the *work function*, and represented by the symbol W. The energy can be provided by the absorption of a suitable light quantum; this effect is the basis of the photoelectric cell. However, we are more interested in heat as the source of the energy. It is well known that, at any temperature, particles have a range of energies, which may be described by a suitable distribution function. For particles in a gas, this is the familiar Maxwell-Boltzmann distribution; Fig. 3.1 shows it plotted against energy rather than velocity (as is more common), so that the rise from the origin has a different shape. For electrons in a metal, however, the

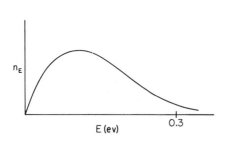

Fig. 3.1 Maxwell–Boltzmann energy distribution.

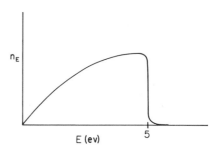

Fig. 3.2 Fermi–Dirac energy distribution. Note the difference in the energy scale compared with Fig. 3.1.

distribution is entirely different because of the important quantum effect known as the *Pauli exclusion principle*, which limits the way in which the electrons can fill the available energy states. The resulting *Fermi-Dirac* distribution is shown in Fig. 3.2; it rises steadily with energy until it approaches a rather high energy called the *Fermi energy*, then drops rapidly and forms a tail. Notice that the energy scales are very different in Figs. 3.1 and 3.2; the Fermi energy is far above the mean energy of the Maxwell distribution. However, if the two are superposed with the zero of the Maxwell function at the Fermi energy, the high-energy tails are the same. The work function is so large that any electrons that are able to escape are in the region in which the two curves coincide; the correct result for thermionic emission can therefore be obtained from either distribution function. The result we shall use is that the probability of an electron's having energy E is given by the *Boltzmann factor* $e^{-E/kT}$, in which k is Boltzmann's constant and T is the absolute temperature.

Suppose that the three components of velocity of an electron are u, v, and w, so that $E = \frac{1}{2}m(u^2 + v^2 + w^2)$, and that the surface of the metal is perpendicular to u. To find the flux of escaping electrons, we can take the velocity component u, weight by the Boltzmann factor, and integrate over u, v, and w. The integration over u is taken with a lower limit corresponding to the work function W; the others are from $-\infty$ to $+\infty$. Since each electron carries the same charge, the emission current is proportional to this flux, and we may write

$$I \propto \int_{-\infty}^{\infty} \int_{-\infty}^{\infty} \int_{u_w}^{\infty} u e^{-E/kT} \, du \, dv \, dw$$

$$\propto \int_{-\infty}^{\infty} \int_{-\infty}^{\infty} \int_{u_w}^{\infty} u e^{-m(u^2+v^2+w^2)/2kT} \, du \, dv \, dw$$

The integrations over v and w resemble the integral of the error function, and each yields a factor $\sqrt{T}$. Then we have

$$I \propto T \int_{u_w}^{\infty} u e^{-mu^2/2kT} \, du = \frac{T}{2} \int_{u_w}^{\infty} e^{-mu^2/2kT} \, d(u^2)$$

$$\propto -T^2 [e^{-mu^2/2kT}]_{u_w}^{\infty} = T^2 e^{-W/kT}$$

This is usually written

$$J = A_0 T^2 e^{-W/kT}$$

and is called Richardson's equation; J is the *current density* or current per unit area of surface. The complete theory yields a value for A_0 of about 60 amp per cm^2 · (degree K)^2, but many emitters are found to have much smaller values, perhaps because only very small parts of the total area are actually emitting. It is usual to write $W = e\phi$, where e is the electronic charge and ϕ is the work function in electron volts; it is commonly in the range of 1 to 5 volts.

Practical Emitters. The three surfaces that are most used as electron emitters are shown in the table along with their constants and a typical operating temperature.

SURFACE	A_0 amp cm^{-2}(°K)$^{-2}$	ϕ volts	T °K
Tungsten	60	4.52	2600–2800 (white)
Thoriated tungsten	3	2.63	1800 (bright red)
Oxide	0.01	approx. 1	1000 (dull red)

Since the power required to keep a *cathode* at temperature T is proportional to T^4 (Stefan's law), the efficiency increases rapidly as one goes down the table; however, the efficient cathodes are also relatively fragile.

Tungsten cathodes are used mostly in tubes operated at very high voltages, such as x-ray tubes and their rectifiers. They operate at about the same temperature as a lamp bulb and have a similarly limited life; but during that life, they are nearly indestructible. Thoriated tungsten cathodes contain a small amount of thorium and are treated so as to produce a monatomic layer of thorium on the surface, which greatly reduces the work function. However, the layer can be destroyed by positive-ion bombardment with ions that are produced from the residual gas in the tube under some conditions. Oxide cathodes have a layer of barium and strontium oxides on a metal base, usually nickel; they are even more sensitive to ion bombardment and are normally used in small tubes of the "receiving" variety. These form the vast majority of all tubes in use. Oxide cathodes are also used in beam-type tubes, such as cathode-ray and traveling-wave tubes.

There are two fundamental physical forms of cathode: directly and indirectly heated. The former is usually called a *filament*, by analogy with an electric lamp; it is heated by passing current through it and may be made with any of the three surfaces. The indirectly heated cathode, or *heater-cathode*, is always oxide-coated; the nickel base is in the form of a tube containing an insulated heating wire. This construction has two advantages: it offers more freedom in setting the cathode potential; and that potential is uniform along the whole cathode, in particular having no a-c component even if the heating current is alternating.

Other Sources of Electrons. Although none of the other electron sources competes with thermionic emission in electron tubes, they are useful for special purposes. In *field emission* the electrons are "drawn out" of the metal by a very strong field. To produce such a field with a moderate potential difference, the cathode must be made with a very sharp point. In the *photoelectric effect*, light quanta provide the energy necessary for electron emission; the effect is widely used for light detection and measurement. In *secondary emission* the energy is provided by incident fast electrons; some special surfaces will emit as many as five secondaries for each primary. This effect is most useful for amplifying photoelectric currents; the secondary-emission electrodes are called *dynodes*, and *photomultiplier* tubes with nine or more dynodes are very useful for measuring small light intensities. *Positive-ion bombardment* can produce electrons just as electron bombardment can; the ions normally are produced from gas in the tube and often must be accelerated by more than a thousand volts to give enough emission. This effect is used in discharge tubes, such as neon signs.

3.2 DIODES AND SPACE CHARGE

The simplest of all vacuum tubes is the *diode*, or two-electrode tube. It contains a cathode and a second electrode to which the electrons can flow through the vacuum; it is called the *anode* or, more usually, the *plate*. The plate is normally in the form of a cylinder with a circular, elliptical, or rectangular cross section, and the cathode is on or near the axis. However, it is easier to think of the diode as made in parallel

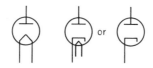

Fig. 3.3 Symbols for a diode.

planes, as in the conventional symbols shown in Fig. 3.3. Symbols are given for directly and indirectly heated cathodes; since a heater must be present in the latter but plays no direct part in the operation, it can and usually will be omitted from the symbol, as shown on the right. It is also possible to omit the bulb from the symbol, but this has a serious disadvantage: a tube circuit is centered around the tube, and the circle helps to draw the eye towards this center. Electronic circuits are complicated enough that any such aid to their understanding is well worthwhile.

We must now consider the principles that control the electron flow in the diode. Under certain conditions, the current flowing to the anode is *temperature limited*; it is controlled by Richardson's equation as discussed in Section 3.1. However, these conditions are not normal in most tubes, which are usually operated in such a way that the current is *space-charge limited* instead. This means that the flow of electrons is controlled by the negative charge of the electron cloud formed in the vacuum near the cathode. Suppose that a diode is set up in a circuit as in Fig. 3.4. The cathode temperature can be varied, and the plate

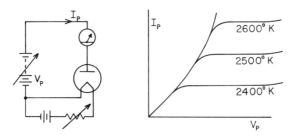

Fig. 3.4 Plate characteristics of a diode and a circuit for measuring them.

current may be measured as a function of plate voltage for a series of temperatures. When the voltage is high enough, an almost constant current flows; the small slope is caused by an effect of the electric field in aiding the thermionic emission. The series of constant currents is described by Richardson's equation. But at lower voltages, the plate current follows a universal curve that does not depend on the cathode temperature as long as it is high enough. This is the region of space-charge-limited current; the current is found to vary as the 3/2 power of V_p. This law will now be derived for a simple case.

To make the problem as easy as possible, we make it one-dimensional by taking a small section of a large plane-parallel diode; if it is large enough, the electric field lines will be straight, and all quantities will vary only with x, the distance from the cathode. We suppose that the anode is at $x = d$. At some point in the middle at a distance x, the variables to be considered are:

> potential V
> electric field E
> electron velocity u
> electron density n

The presence of the electrons in the space modifies the potential distribution and the electric field and, in turn, controls the flow of the electrons and the charge distribution. We then set up four equations relating the unknowns and solve for the one we want. From the law of conservation of energy, the kinetic energy of an electron is derived from the electric field:

$$\tfrac{1}{2}mu^2 = eV \tag{1}$$

where m and e are the mass and charge of the electron; e is considered to be positive. The current density must be independent of x; this is essentially Kirchhoff's second law. Since eu is the current carried by one electron, the current density is

$$J = neu = \text{constant} \tag{2}$$

The electric field is equal to the potential gradient:

$$E = -\frac{dV}{dx} \tag{3}$$

Gauss' theorem gives the effect of the space charge on the field:

$$\frac{dE}{dx} = -4\pi ne* \tag{4}$$

Putting (3) into (4) gives Poisson's equation, which is readily reduced by successive substitution of (2) and (1):

$$\frac{d^2 V}{dx^2} = 4\pi ne = 4\pi \frac{J}{u}$$

$$\frac{d^2 V}{dx^2} = 4\pi J \sqrt{\frac{m}{2e}} V^{-1/2}$$

This differential equation relates V and J, when the correct boundary conditions are imposed; in particular, it will give a relation between J

---

* This is obtained from Gauss' theorem as follows: the net flux diverging from a volume enclosing charge q is $4\pi q$ (in electrostatic units). Take the volume as a thin slice parallel to the electrodes, of area A and thickness dx.

                   Flux in   = AE
                   Flux out   = $A(E + dE)$
                   Net flux out = $AdE = 4\pi(-neA\,dx)$
which is the same as (4).

and V_p, the applied plate voltage. Before we solve it, let us discuss these boundary conditions.

Fig. 3.5 illustrates several possible potential distributions across the tube. We have already taken the cathode potential V_k equal to zero by writing equation (1), and this is our first boundary condition: $V = 0$ for $x = 0$. If there is no space charge, the field E is uniform

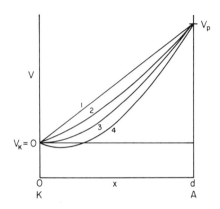

Fig. 3.5   Potential distributions in a diode.

across the tube, and the potential curve is straight (curve 1). The presence of electrons depresses the potential, especially near the cathode, and could produce curves like 2, 3, and 4. In fact, the actual curve will be like curve 3, starting out with a horizontal tangent, so that the field E at the cathode is zero. If the curve is like curve 2, E is in the direction to aid emission and hinder the return to the cathode of electrons from the space charge; therefore, the density of the space charge will increase. If it is like curve 4, the field impedes emission and aids return, and the density will decrease. Thus, the second boundary condition is: $dV/dx = 0$ at $x = 0$.

This discussion and equation (1) have assumed that the electrons are emitted with no initial velocity. This is a fairly good approximation for most tubes, in which the final velocity near the anode is much larger, but it is worth examining. The emission velocity is the same as would be produced by an accelerating potential of about one volt (or the energy is about one electron volt). An equilibrium will then be set up resembling curve 4 in Fig. 3.5, with the depth of the minimum equal to this voltage. Equation (1) and the second boundary condition then apply strictly at this point, the *virtual cathode*, rather than at the actual cathode; similarly, the applied voltage V_p must include this extra amount.

We now return to the differential equation. It is readily solved by the trick of multiplying both sides by $2(dV/dx)$; this converts the left-hand side to

$$\frac{d}{dx}\left(\frac{dV}{dx}\right)^2$$

which integrates immediately. The variable part of the right side becomes $V^{-1/2}(dV/dx)$, equally easy to integrate. Then

$$\left(\frac{dV}{dx}\right)^2 = 16\pi J \sqrt{\frac{m}{2e}}\, V^{1/2} + \text{constant}$$

According to the second boundary condition, V and its derivative are both zero at the cathode; therefore the constant is zero. After taking the square root, we may separate the variables:

$$V^{-1/4}dV = \left(16\pi J\sqrt{m/2e}\right)^{1/2}dx$$

Upon integration, this becomes

$$\frac{4}{3}V^{3/4} = \left(16\pi J\sqrt{m/2e}\right)^{1/2}x + \text{constant}$$

The first boundary condition shows the constant to be zero. This equation gives the potential distribution across the tube for any assumed current density J; we are usually more interested in the J corresponding to an applied plate potential V_p. Let us, therefore, substitute $V = V_p$ at $x = d$, and solve for J:

$$J = \frac{1}{9\pi d^2}\sqrt{\frac{2e}{m}}\, V_p^{3/2}$$

This equation gives the observed dependence on the three-halves power of plate voltage, and is usually known as Child's law. It gives the current per cm² of a large plane-parallel diode. Because these diodes are never used in practice, it becomes necessary to enquire what changes are necessary in other forms. Langmuir was able to find the solution for a diode in the form of coaxial cylinders; this is again a one-dimensional problem in cylindrical coordinates. The three-halves power law is found again, with a different constant of proportionality. Furthermore, Langmuir showed that this will be true for *any* configuration, though in general the constant cannot be calculated exactly. Thus, any diode will obey the law.

$$I = K V_p^{3/2}$$

The constant K, called the "perveance," is a quantity resembling a conductance, but does not have quite the same dimensions. For the plane diode, K varies inversely as the square of the spacing d; a similar result is found for other shapes.

Application of Diodes. The commonest application of the diode is as a *rectifier* or one-way conductor, usually for converting alternating into direct current. The techniques will be discussed later, but first let us consider the conditions governing the choice of a particular diode. The closer the spacing, the smaller the voltage drop for a given current; this is desirable, because all the power given to the electrons by the electric field must be dissipated as heat by the anode. On the other hand, a useful rectifier must be able to withstand a large *inverse voltage* (plate negative, no current flowing) without breaking down, and this is favored by a large spacing. A variety of tubes are available in which this compromise has been reached at different points. Some closely spaced tubes may be able to pass a very large current without over-heating the plate; in such a case, the emitting capacity of the cathode, rather than the plate dissipation, may set the maximum allowed current.

In practice, the majority of rectifiers put into service are semi-conducting, rather than vacuum, diodes. However, vacuum diodes are still used for special purposes, and in any case must be studied as an introduction to amplifying tubes.

Transit Time. Tubes are sometimes used with high-frequency signals, and it is useful to know approximately the response time to a change in the applied voltage. When the electron *transit time* becomes appreciable in comparison with the period of the wave, the tube can no longer be considered as responding instantly. For typical small tubes, the transit time is about 10^{-8} sec or somewhat less. As long as the frequencies of interest are less than about 100 mc, the effect can usually be ignored.

PROBLEM

Calculate the transit time, in the absence of space charge, for a plane diode with a 3-mm spacing and 100 volts between cathode and plate.

3.3 TRIODES

Although the diode is a useful device, it is not in itself responsible for the enormous applications of electronics. These rest upon the ability to control the flow of electrons, and in the tube this control is by means of the *grid*. The addition of a third electrode gives a tube called a *triode*; it was introduced by de Forest in 1907. The grid, as its name implies, was originally made of wire screening; but the usual construction now is in the form of a helix of fine wire, coaxial with the cathode, and supported by welding to two heavier wires parallel to the cathode. In most tubes, the grid is much closer to the cathode than is the plate.

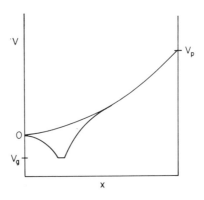

Fig. 3.6 Potential distribution in a triode, neglecting space charge.

Let us consider the potential distribution in a plane-parallel triode, as illustrated in Fig. 3.6. The grid is wound coarsely enough that it does not completely shield the cathode from the plate; potential distributions are sketched for a section through a grid wire, and for one between wires. The slope near the cathode is affected by both grid and plate potentials. If a space charge is introduced, it will change the potential distributions, but the current flowing will be controlled primarily by the electric field near the cathode. It is thus reasonable to suppose that the current will depend on the three-halves power of this field. For a given tube, the field can be written as proportional to

$$V_p + \mu V_g$$

where μ is a number greater than unity, which expresses the fact that the grid has more effect than the plate. This is partly because it is closer to the cathode, and partly because of its shielding effect on the field from the plate. The value of μ will thus depend on the grid-to-cathode distance and on the closeness of mesh of the grid; it is usually in the range from 20 to 100, but values outside this range are used for special purposes. For reasons which will become apparent later, μ is called the *amplification factor*. The plate current may be written

$$I_p = k(V_p + \mu V_g)^{3/2}$$

However, if the grid should be positive, the grid current is included in I_p. As indicated in Fig. 3.6, all potentials are measured with respect to the cathode.

This relation does not hold exactly for actual tubes, but is a very good and useful approximation. This can be verified by comparing it with a set of characteristic curves taken from a tube manual.

Triode Characteristics and Parameters. The most useful way to express the characteristics of an actual triode is graphically. Because the plate current is a function of two variables, one must be taken as a parameter; when this is the grid potential, as in Fig. 3.7, we get the *plate characteristics*. If the three-halves power law were strictly correct, each curve would be the same shape, differing only by a horizontal translation, and the curve for $V_g = 0$ would be identical to a diode curve. The main deviation from this is that the curves for the more negative grid potentials tend to come in almost tangent to the voltage axis. In normal operation, the grid potential is always negative with respect to the cathode, and therefore it draws virtually no current. A constant potential applied to the grid is often called the *grid bias*, or just *bias*. For any given plate potential, there is always a grid potential that is able to reduce the plate current to zero; the tube is said to be *cut off*, and the bias required is called the *cutoff* bias. From the three-halves power law, the cutoff bias is equal to $-V_p/\mu$; while this is not

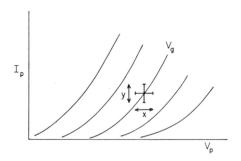

Fig. 3.7 Triode plate characteristics.

strictly true for actual tubes, it is a useful approximation. (The potentials in Fig. 3.6 show the cutoff condition.)

Let us represent the characteristics of Fig. 3.7 by the following equation:

$$I_p = f(V_p,\ V_g)$$

It is clear that this equation is nonlinear, in the sense that the term takes in circuit analysis; therefore, linear circuit analysis cannot be used with it. However, suppose that we are concerned only with very small changes about a certain point on the graph, the *operating point* or *quiescent point*. If we draw a small circle around this region, and then magnify the part of the characteristics within the circle, they will look like straight parallel lines. In other words, for *small signals* the tube is approximately linear, and the powerful methods of linear circuit analysis can be applied. The algebraic equivalent of this geometrical operation is expansion in a Taylor series about the operating point, ignoring all derivatives higher than the first. The result is

$$\Delta I_p = \left(\frac{\partial I_p}{\partial V_p}\right)\Delta V_p + \left(\frac{\partial I_p}{\partial V_g}\right)\Delta V_g$$

The two partial derivatives are called *tube parameters* and are given special symbols and names. The reciprocal of the first is the (variational) *plate resistance*, r_p; the second is the *mutual conductance* or *transconductance*, g_m. The amplification factor μ is also a tube parameter;

it can be defined as

$$\mu = - \frac{\partial V_p}{\partial V_g}$$

A relation between the three parameters may be found from the Taylor expansion by setting ΔI_p equal to zero, so that

$$-\frac{\Delta V_p}{\Delta V_g} = g_m r_p \text{ (when } I_p \text{ is constant)}$$

As ΔV_g approaches zero, this becomes

$$\mu = g_m r_p$$

This fundamental relation is most easily remembered by recalling that the product of a conductance and a resistance is a pure number.

Approximate values of the parameters can be found from a set of plate characteristics, as in Fig. 3.7, by measuring the small increments of I_p and V_p indicated by y and x; for convenience they may be taken for a change in grid voltage ΔV_g of 1 volt. Then

$$\mu \doteq x/1 \qquad g_m \doteq y/1 \qquad \text{and} \qquad r_p \doteq x/y$$

Also r_p is the reciprocal of the slope of the line, evaluated at the operating point.

For a given tube, the parameters vary somewhat according to the operating point chosen. However, μ is very nearly independent of operating point, as can be seen from the fact that the curves are nearly a constant distance apart in the horizontal direction. The variation of the other two may be estimated by assuming the three-halves power law; it is readily shown that

$$g_m \propto I_p^{1/3} \qquad \text{and} \qquad r_p \propto I_p^{-1/3}$$

PROBLEM

Prove this last statement.

Other Characteristic Plots. The plate characteristics which we have been studying are the most generally useful and the most commonly found, but two other plots are used for special purposes. The *transfer characteristics* plot I_p against V_g, with V_p as parameter; the *constant-current characteristics* plot V_p against V_g, with I_p as parameter. All three graphs contain the same information, and the other two can always be produced if one is available. The transfer characteristics are useful in the study of distortion of large signals, and we shall meet them later in that connection. The constant-current characteristics are used in the design of radio-frequency power amplifiers; a brief discussion is given in Chapter 11.

3.4 TETRODE

Any two conductors in close proximity have a certain mutual capacitance; this applies to the plate and grid of a triode, for which a typical capacitance is 10 pf (or $\mu\mu$f). At high frequencies this has a reactance sufficiently small to cause a serious *feedback* of energy from the plate to the grid, and at radio frequencies (above a few hundred kc) a triode amplifier can be used only in very special circuits. The tetrode was invented to eliminate this difficulty. The fourth electrode is another grid, the *screen grid* or *screen*, between the *control grid* and the plate. It is so constructed as to shield (or screen) these two electrodes from each other; therefore, they each have a considerable capacitance to the screen, but practically none directly to each other. As a natural consequence, the electric field from the plate no longer penetrates to the space-charge region, and the screen must therefore be kept at a positive potential to accelerate the electrons; a typical value is 100 volts. Variations in the plate potential have very little effect on the plate current; in other words, the variational plate resistance r_p is very high. The transconductance of a triode (or any other tube) is measured at constant plate voltage; that is, the conditions near the cathode are just like those in the tetrode. The transconductance g_m will then be about the same as that of a similar triode; since $\mu = g_m r_p$, the amplification factor will be very large.

The plate characteristic for zero bias of a typical tetrode is shown in Fig. 3.8. Our discussion would lead us to expect a curve like the dotted one, in which the plate current rises rapidly with plate voltage, quickly reaching a plateau. The observations show a dip, which can go very low in some tubes, followed by a recovery and then a line with a marked slope. The recovery takes place at a plate voltage equal to the screen voltage as shown. The explanation is found in the process of secondary emission. Electrons accelerated by more than 20 volts or so can dislodge a slow electron upon hitting the plate; if the screen potential is higher, these secondary electrons will go to the screen, increasing the screen current and decreasing the net plate current. As soon as the plate is at a higher potential than the screen, the slow

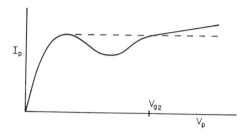

Fig. 3.8 Zero-bias characteristic of a tetrode; the dotted line shows the ideal shape that would be expected in the absence of secondary emission.

secondaries must return to the plate and the effect disappears. However, a small converse effect is now present, with secondaries from the screen going to the plate, thus explaining the noticeable slope in this region. The tetrode could still be used with due regard for its limitations, but there is no need for this; the *pentode* and the *beam tetrode* can perform the same duties without the disadvantages.

3.5 PENTODE

This tube has still a third grid, the *suppressor*, between the screen and the plate; its function is to return all secondary electrons to their point of origin. It is a coarse grid, nearly always connected to the cathode; because of its coarseness, the potential in its plane does not fall all the way to zero and the electrons from the cathode are not stopped. But the slow secondary electrons come from electrodes at a positive potential, and they cannot pass this plane with its lower potential. The resulting characteristics are very much like the ideal tetrode characteristics, except that the *knee* at low plate voltages is not quite so sharp (Fig. 3.9). The discussion of tetrode parameters applies equally to the pentode.

The beam tetrode produces the potential minimum by a controlled space charge instead of by a third grid. Careful control of the electron flow is required, but the details need not concern us. The principle is used only in power tubes, in which the plate current is large enough to provide the space charge between the screen and plate. At low plate currents the suppressor action is not as good, and tetrode dips can be

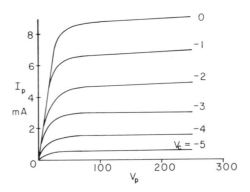

Fig. 3.9 Pentode plate characteristics.

seen in this region for most beam tetrodes. The beam tetrode has the sharp knee of the plain tetrode; this advantage over the pentode is important in power amplifiers and will be discussed along with that topic.

Symbols. The conventional symbols for triode, tetrode, and pentode are shown in Fig. 3.10; the beam tetrode is often represented as a pentode. The heater symbol may be included if it is required.

Triode   Tetrode   Pentode

Fig. 3.10 Symbols for triode, tetrode, and pentode.

3.6. GAS-FILLED TUBES

Although we have considered only "vacuum" tubes up to now, there is another class that contains low-pressure gas. In fact, there is some gas in any tube; but in a vacuum tube, there is not enough to have an appreciable effect on the motion of the electrons. This requires that the mean free path of an electron should be large compared with the distance it must travel. In a gas tube the mean free path is very short, and positive ions are produced in large numbers. These can be used both to bombard the cathode, thus producing electrons, and to neutralize the space charge. In most tubes, the latter function is the important one; in *cold-cathode* tubes, ion bombardment is also important. A cold-cathode diode containing one of the rare gases forms a voltage-regulator tube by virtue of the characteristic sketched in Fig. 3.11. Over a range of currents from 5 to about 40 ma, the voltage

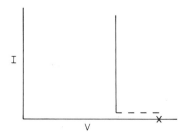

Fig. 3.11 Characteristic of a voltage-regulator tube.

drop across the tube is nearly independent of the current. The commonest voltages are 105 and 150 volts, but 75 and 90 volts are also available. As with diode rectifiers, voltage-regulator tubes are being replaced by an equivalent semiconductor device, in this case the *breakdown diode* or *Zener diode*. These can be made in a much wider range of voltage and can also handle more current.

    Gas-filled hot-cathode tubes use the positive ions to neutralize the space charge; they can therefore carry very large currents with a low voltage drop, usually about 15 volts, just enough to ionize the gas. The positive ions, with their large mass, move much more slowly than the electrons and are able to accumulate in any region that tries to build up a negative space charge. Gas-filled diodes are widely used as high-power rectifiers. Because there is no internal mechanism to limit the current, the external circuit must provide for keeping the current within the rating of the cathode. When the rating is exceeded, the plate voltage starts to increase and the cathode is bombarded by faster ions, which will quickly destroy it.

Gas-filled triodes and tetrodes are called *thyratrons*. Once they are conducting, they act like diodes, and the foregoing remarks still apply. The grid has no control over the current; if it is made more negative, it attracts more positive ions, which shield the discharge from it. The purpose of the grid is to keep the tube cut off until a specific time. To turn the tube off, the plate voltage must be made zero or negative for a short time. The simplest way to do this is by using an unrectified a-c

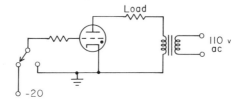

Fig. 3.12 Circuit for controlling a large power
with a thyratron.

source for the plate supply voltage. Fig. 3.12 illustrates a simple thyratron relay, which conducts during the positive half-cycles when the grid is at ground and stays off when it is negative. This circuit is useful, for example, with a thermostat to avoid arcing at the contacts; the load is then a heating coil. The resistor in the grid circuit limits any grid current to a very small value. Thyratrons are available with very high power ratings; they are used for controlled rectification in such applications as welding.

CHAPTER 4

Vacuum-tube Amplifiers

4.1 INTRODUCTION

The analysis of many vacuum-tube circuits can be made in two steps. First, by reference to the plate characteristics, an operating point is chosen, and the parameters for that point looked up or estimated. Second, a small-signal equivalent circuit is set up; it can then be analyzed by the usual methods. Even for large signals, these results are a useful first approximation. More information, if required, may be found by suitable operations on the plate characteristics. These operations will be outlined in this chapter, and a more detailed treatment will be given under "power amplifiers". We shall primarily be interested in the small-signal approximation.

Notation. The voltages and currents in a tube circuit can be divided into two classes: supply and signal. The total voltage on an element is usually the sum of these two. It is useful to have a notation that distinguishes them, and the following conventions will be used here. Total voltages and currents are represented by capital letters V and I, with subscripts as required to distinguish them. Signal voltages and currents are represented by lower-case letters v and i, and their subscripts. Supply voltages have capital letters with the subscripts a, b, and c, inherited from the days of battery-operated radios. These had an A battery for the filaments, a B battery for the plates, and a C battery for grid bias; the first two are still in use. With a-c operated heaters, there is no need for an A battery, and in any case the heater circuit

77

plays no direct part in the operation of the circuit as a whole. But the B supply, represented by V_b, is always important, and a C supply is present in some circuits. Common values for these are $V_b = +300$ and $V_c = -300$ volts, measured with respect to "ground" as always. Let us recall that the reference node of a circuit may be called "ground" even if it is not connected to earth.

4.2 GROUNDED-CATHODE AMPLIFIER

We shall now analyze the circuit shown in Fig. 4.1. A triode is used for simplicity, but the same results apply to a pentode with a fixed screen voltage. Batteries or d-c power supplies are understood to be connected to the terminals marked V_b and V_c. Because V_c is negative,

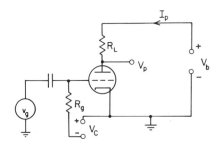

Fig. 4.1 Circuit of a grounded-cathode amplifier.

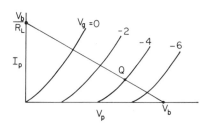

Fig. 4.2 Plate characteristics and load line.

the grid is also negative and draws no current. Therefore, no current flows through R_g and the average value of V_g is the same as V_c. The input signal v_g is connected to the grid by a capacitor, which is chosen to present a low impedance (small compared with R_g) at the frequency concerned. Then the total voltage on the grid is

$$V_g = V_c + v_g$$

For a start, we take $v_g = 0$ so that we can determine the operating point, represented on the plate characteristics (Fig. 4.2) by Q, for *quiescent*. This point is known if two of the three values V_p, V_g, and I_p are known; however, we only know V_g, since there is an unknown voltage drop across the load resistance R_L. One possibility is to assume a value of I_p; the voltage drop is then $I_p R_L$, and V_p is less than V_b by this amount. We can then consult Fig. 4.2 to see whether this plate voltage and current are consistent with the bias V_g that we have chosen. If not, we try another value. A much better way is to draw the *load line*, which is the locus of all these trial values, given by

$$V_p = V_b - I_p R_L$$

The point where this intersects the characteristic for the chosen V_c is the one we want. The load line is easily drawn by plotting its intercepts—that is, $V_p = V_b$ when $I_p = 0$, and $I_p = V_p/R_L$ when $V_p = 0$. In effect, this procedure gives a graphical solution of two simultaneous equations in V_p and I_p: the load line for R_L, and the tube function $I_p = f(V_p, V_g)$ represented by the characteristics.

The load line is useful not only for finding the operating point, but also for analyzing the operation of the amplifier. No matter what the grid voltage, the point representing the plate voltage and current must be somewhere on the load line. If the grid voltage is varied, this point moves along the load line. For each instantaneous value of V_g, the corresponding values of V_p and I_p can be read from the axes. For a

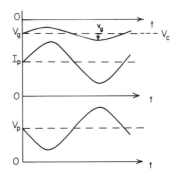

Fig. 4.3 Voltage and current waveforms in the amplifier
of Fig. 4.1.

sinusoidal input, the result is of the kind shown in Fig. 4.3. The plate-current wave closely resembles the input; the plate-voltage wave has exactly the same shape as the current wave, but is inverted.* It is also

---

* This inversion is often loosely called a 180 degree phase shift, but this is incorrect. An inversion is *equivalent* to this phase shift for a sine wave, but not for any nonsymmetrical wave.

much larger than the input wave, by a factor slightly less than μ in most cases; the circuit is therefore an amplifier, and the name "amplification factor" for μ is justified.

For a large-signal amplifier, it is often useful to replot the load line on the transfer characteristics, where it is known as the *dynamic characteristic*. From the amount of its deviation from a straight line, it is possible to estimate the distortion of the amplified wave (Section 5.2). However, for the present we are concerned with the small-signal treatment with the aid of an equivalent linear circuit.

PROBLEM

Using the characteristics of a 6SN7, plot the load line for $V_b = 300$ volts, $R_L = 75$ K (kilohms). Find the operating point for $V_c = -8$ volts, and plot a diagram similar to Fig. 4.3 for a sinusoidal input of 2 volts peak.

4.3 EQUIVALENT PLATE CIRCUITS

The graphical treatment is not suitable for small signals, because the variations are too small to be measured accurately from the graph. We then turn to the equivalent plate circuit, which represents the tube by its three parameters, taken at the chosen operating point. A more important reason for this is to permit the use of linear circuit analysis, which allows a wide variety of circuits to be treated. In fact, this method is not restricted to small signals, but is satisfactory for medium signals (output signal around 10 volts) and useful even for large signals. This is because the characteristics of a tube, triode or pentode, are not far from a set of parallel, equally spaced straight lines, for which the small-signal analysis applies exactly.

The small-signal analysis applies to *variational* quantities, such as v_g in Fig. 4.1; fixed quantities, such as the supply voltages V_b and V_c, do not appear. Any fixed voltage is to be regarded as a variational ground. The tube parameters are variational quantities; this is why lower-case letters are used to represent them. The analysis is based on the Taylor expansion set up in Section 3.3:

$$\Delta I_p = \left(\frac{\partial I_p}{\partial V_p}\right)\Delta V_p + \left(\frac{\partial I_p}{\partial V_p}\right)\Delta V_g$$

The partial derivatives are replaced by $1/r_p$ and g_m; the increments are replaced by the corresponding variational quantities i_p, v_p, and v_g. Thus, the equation becomes

$$i_p = \frac{v_p}{r_p} + g_m v_g$$

Remembering that $g_m r_p = \mu$, we may also write this as

$$v_p = r_p i_p - \mu v_g$$

These two forms can be represented by the variational equivalent plate circuits shown in Fig. 4.4. Notice that they are Norton and Thévenin

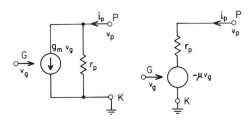

Fig. 4.4 Equivalent plate circuits for a tube.

equivalents of the same generator. The grid does not appear in the circuit at all, but it is sometimes convenient to represent it with an arrow pointing at the generator which it controls.

The procedure for setting up an equivalent circuit is the following:

(1) Replace all constant voltages by short circuits. Supply voltages usually have one terminal grounded and will therefore become variational grounds.

(2) Replace all tubes by one of the circuits shown in Fig. 4.4, according to whether node or mesh analysis is to be used. Remember that v_g must be measured with respect to cathode; if the cathode is not grounded, the voltage to be used is v_{gk}, the grid-to-cathode voltage.

Once the equivalent circuit has been set up, ordinary circuit analysis can be applied, and the properties of the system can be found by simple algebra. The difficult part for most people is to get the equivalent circuit right in the first place. You are therefore advised to practice by setting up the equivalents for each circuit we treat, and check against the one given. Let us now return to the grounded-cathode amplifier of Fig. 4.1, remembering that the coupling network at the grid is supposed to be chosen so that v_g appears on the grid with no attenuation. The series equivalent circuit appears in Fig. 4.5, which shows the generator μv_g feeding a potential divider. Then the variational plate voltage must be

$$v_p = -\mu v_g \frac{R_L}{r_p + R_L}$$

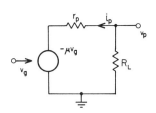

Fig. 4.5 Equivalent circuit of Fig. 4.1.

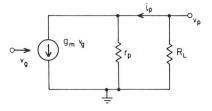

Fig. 4.6 Equivalent circuit of Fig. 4.1, using the parallel representation.

The negative sign indicates the inversion that we have already noted. The *gain* of an amplifier is defined in the same way as the attenuation of a passive network, and represented by the symbol K; thus,

$$K = \frac{v_p}{v_g} = -\frac{\mu R_L}{r_p + R_L}$$

As R_L becomes considerably larger than r_p, the gain approaches μ, which is therefore the upper limit to the gain. This condition can usually be approached with a triode, for which r_p is usually in the range 10 K to 100 K, but for a pentode r_p is greater than 1 M (megohm) and the gain is normally much less than μ. Since neither μ nor r_p can be determined accurately for a pentode, this equation is not very useful, and we turn to the parallel equivalent circuit shown in Fig. 4.6. The node equation is

$$v_p(g_p + G_L) = -g_m v_g$$

and the gain is

$$K = -\frac{g_m}{g_p + G_L} = -\frac{g_m r_p R_L}{r_p + R_L} = -\frac{g_m R_L}{1 + R_L/r_p}$$

Notice that the second form is the same as the equation we derived from the series circuit. In many cases the plate resistance of a pentode is much greater than the load resistance, and a good approximation to the gain is then

$$K \doteq -g_m R_L$$

These results are easily generalized to the case of a complex load impedance Z_L, such as the parallel tuned circuit found in radio receivers. R_L may be replaced by Z_L in any of the expressions without affecting their validity, since nothing in their derivation required the load to be real. The gain K will in general be a complex number, implying a phase shift between input and output in addition to the inversion produced by the tube. It will also be a function of frequency

PROBLEM

Estimate the parameters of the 6SN7 at the operating point used for the problem of the last section. Calculate the gain and compare with your graphical result.

Stray Capacitances. Miller Effect. At high frequencies, it is necessary to consider the effect of the small *stray capacitances* between the elements of a tube, and also the wires leading to them. These are typically from 5 to 10 pf, which is certainly small, but the reactance of

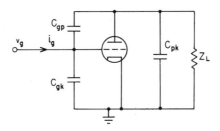

Fig. 4.7 A triode with its stray capacitances.

10 pf at a frequency of 1 mc is only about 16 K. A triode with its stray capacitances is shown in Fig. 4.7. C_{pk} is effectively in parallel with Z_L and can be treated as part of the load. The two grid capacitances will form part of the load on the signal source; C_{gk} is straight-

forward, but C_{gp} requires careful consideration, because it is not connected to ground. Suppose that the gain K is real and negative; a rise of 1 volt at the grid will produce a fall of K volts at the plate, and the change of voltage across C_{gp} will be $(1 - K)$ volts. Therefore, the transient current that flows into it from the source is $(1 - K)$ times larger than one would expect for a 1-volt signal, and the capacitance observed is $(1 - K)C_{gp}$. Since K is a negative number, this capacitance is much larger than C_{gp}.

Let us now treat this subject quantitatively by setting up a node equation for the grid current i_g:

$$i_g = v_g(j\omega C_{gk} + j\omega C_{gp}) - v_p(j\omega C_{gp})$$

If $v_p = Kv_g$, this equation may be written as:

$$i_g = v_g j\omega[C_{gk} + (1 - K)C_{gp}]$$

The expression in square brackets can be called the effective input capacitance C_i. The fact that this is much larger than the "static" input capacitance $(C_{gk} + C_{gp})$ is known as the *Miller effect*. It is one aspect of the energy feedback from plate to grid that makes the triode unsuitable for grounded-cathode amplifiers at high frequencies. In pentodes, C_{gp} is extremely small and, even with the Miller multiplication, can be neglected. There is still an appreciable capacitance from grid to screen, but the screen is effectively grounded for a-c voltage and there is no multiplication.

So far we have assumed that K is real; if it is complex, the input admittance will not be purely capacitive but will have a real or resistive part. This is positive if the load impedance is capacitive, and negative if it is inductive; the latter condition is met in tuned amplifiers below their resonant frequency. A negative input resistance implies energy feedback to the grid, and the usual result is that the amplifier oscillates. This is another difficulty with triodes at high frequencies.

Screen Circuit for Pentodes. As we have just mentioned, the screen of a pentode must be connected to a variational ground; it must also be at a positive d-c potential of 100 to 150 volts. Because the screen current is only a few milliamperes, the power can be provided by a voltage divider connected to V_b; the variational ground is produced by a large capacitor connected to ground (Fig. 4.8). This kind of capacitor is often called a *bypass capacitor*, because it passes the alternating currents that would otherwise flow through the resistors. Because the voltage divider is loaded, the screen voltage will be less than the no-load value; if the current is known, the effect is readily calculated by applying Thévenin's theorem as shown in Section 1.6.

A more usual arrangement is to use a single resistor to drop the voltage to the desired value. This has the effect of providing a nearly constant screen *current*, which may be desirable in some cases. The bypass capacitor is still included.

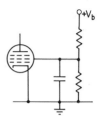

Fig. 4.8   Screen supply for a pentode, using a bypassed voltage divider.

4.4 RESISTANCE-COUPLED AMPLIFIER

Most amplifiers contain more than one tube, or *stage*; it is then necessary to consider the means of *coupling* one stage to the next. The plate of the first stage cannot ordinarily be connected directly to the grid of the next, because of the large difference in d-c potentials. The usual way of coupling the a-c signal and blocking the d-c signal is by means of a coupling (or blocking) capacitor, as was already discussed in connection with Fig. 4.1. This scheme might logically be called *capacitance coupling*, but the accepted name is *resistance coupling*, which historically served to distinguish it from transformer coupling. The latter was once widely used for audio-frequency amplifiers, but is now found only for special purposes and in tuned radio-frequency amplifiers.

The analysis of a multistage amplifier is greatly simplified if it is possible to apply the following assumption: The behavior of the whole amplifier can be found by combining the behaviors of the individual stages; each one acts as it would by itself, and the output of one stage is the input to the next. It is then possible to consider the amplifier stage by stage, and not necessary to treat it as a whole. This assumption is never strictly satisfied in practice, but can be a good approximation under certain conditions. Part of the art of building good electronic devices lies in taking the measures necessary to prevent energy feedback from the output towards the input. In many cases this feedback can cause the amplifier to break into oscillation, and such oscillations are among the chief problems encountered with all types of amplifiers. The most obvious of the corrective measures is to isolate the output and input connections physically, and by shielding if necessary. It is also possible for signals to be fed back along the V_b line, which may be common to all stages and is never exactly the virtual ground it is supposed to be. Usually this condition can be cured by *decoupling filters*, as shown in Fig. 4.9. Common practice is to apply these filters to pairs of adjacent stages, since it takes three stages to give oscillation by this path. If the gain is very high, precautions may be necessary to eliminate other feedback paths, such as the heater wiring.

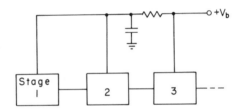

Fig. 4.9 Block diagram of a multistage amplifier, showing a decoupling filter.

Another kind of energy feedback gives the Miller effect, treated in the last section. Fortunately, this can be taken into account stage by stage, remembering that the input impedance of one stage forms part of the load on the preceding one. If the input impedance has a negative real part, the feedback will probably have to be reduced by use of a pentode.

When all these conditions are met, we can consider the stages individually. A two-stage amplifier is shown in Fig. 4.10, in which the necessary grid-bias sources have been omitted for simplicity. The coupling capacitor is C; the grid resistor R_g is necessary to define the average grid potential, and for most tubes should not exceed one megohm, because of small residual grid currents. The first stage is considered to include the first tube with its load resistor R_L, and all the additional load impedances contributed by the coupling network and the second tube. Its equivalent circuit is shown in Fig. 4.11; the tube contributes the equivalent plate circuit and part of the output capacitance C_o, the rest of which comes from the wiring. Similarly, the next stage and the wiring contribute the input capacitance C_i. The other components are taken directly from Fig. 4.10, remembering that the plate-supply line is a virtual ground. The subscript has been omitted from the coupling capacitor for simplicity. A complete analysis of this circuit could best be done by nodal analysis, since it has four meshes but only two nodes, and since the required variable is a voltage. Instead, we shall write simplified circuits valid in certain frequency ranges, thus making the analysis easier and giving a much better physical idea of what is happening.

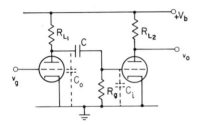

Fig. 4.10 Resistance-coupled amplifier with relevant stray capacitances.

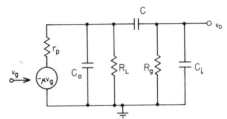

Fig. 4.11 Equivalent circuit of the first stage of Fig. 4.10.

First, let us examine the circuit and see what kind of behavior to expect. In most amplifiers, C is much larger than $C_o + C_i$, and therefore there is a region of frequency in which C can be regarded as a short circuit, whereas the other two are open circuits; in this range the gain is constant. At lower frequencies the impedance of C becomes appreciable, and the output voltage v_o is attenuated as in a lead network. At high frequencies, the shunt capacitances are effectively in parallel with the load, and reduce the gain; it is not surprising to find that the response is that of a lag network. This treatment gives accurate results only if the mid-frequency range is wide enough to separate the corner frequencies by at least two decades, but this condition is usually met in practice.

Mid-frequency Range. With C a short circuit and the shunt capacitances neglected, the circuit (Fig. 4.11) reduces to Fig. 4.12. The effective load is the parallel combination of R_L and R_g, which we shall call R; thus, $R = R_L R_g/(R_L + R_g)$. As for Fig. 4.5, the gain is simply

$$K_0 = -\frac{\mu R}{r_p + R}$$

The "zero" subscript is used because this gain is a fundamental one in terms of which the gains for the other ranges are expressed. If the parallel equivalent circuit is used, the corresponding expression for K_0 is found; the other results given in terms of K_0 are unchanged.

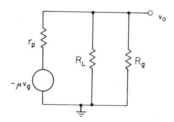

Fig. 4.12 Simplified circuit valid for the mid-frequency range.

Low-frequency Range. At low frequencies the impedance of C can no longer be neglected, and Fig. 4.11 reduces to Fig. 4.13. This circuit can be analyzed by the mesh or node method, but a simpler way is to apply Thévenin's theorem to the part on the left of the dotted line.

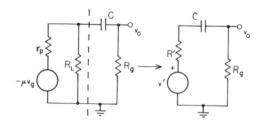

Fig. 4.13 Circuit for the low-frequency range, and reduced version derived by Thévenin's theorem.

The equivalent resistance R' is the parallel resistance of r_p and R_L, or $r_p R_L/(r_p + R_L)$; the generator voltage v' is the open-circuit voltage $-\mu v_g R_L/(r_p + R_L)$. Note that the polarity of the generator has been reversed, giving the expression a minus sign. The reduced circuit may be treated as a voltage divider, with

$$v_0 = v' \frac{R_g}{R' + R_g + 1/j\omega C} = v' \frac{j\omega R_g C}{1 + j\omega(R' + R_g)C}$$

Substitution of the expressions for v' and R' gives the following, in which a small manipulation has been made to give the same time-constants in numerator and denominator:

$$\frac{v_0}{v_i} = K = -\mu \frac{R_L}{r_p + R_L} \frac{R_g}{R' + R_g} \frac{j\omega\tau_1}{1 + j\omega\tau_1}$$

where the time constant τ_1 is equal to $(R' + R_g)C$. Since this gain must reduce to K_0 at the higher frequencies, where $\omega\tau_1 \gg 1$, the expression becomes

$$K = K_0 \frac{j\omega\tau_1}{1 + j\omega\tau_1}$$

This can also be shown directly.

PROBLEM

Manipulate the expression into this form, and also derive the result directly from Fig. 4.13 (left) by nodal analysis. The tube must be replaced by a current generator to do this.

The frequency dependence is that of a lead network having an equivalent circuit as shown in Fig. 4.14. A simple approximation often used is to replace the resistance by R_g alone; this gives the time constant that the coupling network would have if it were fed directly by a voltage generator. In the actual circuit, the effective load impedance rises as the impedance of C becomes appreciable; the voltage at the plate rises just as the coupling network begins to attenuate, and the result is a longer effective time constant. With triodes, the difference is usually small because of the small value of r_p.

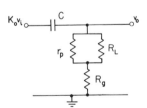

Fig. 4.14 Equivalent time constant for the low-frequency cutoff.

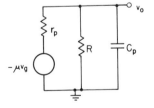

Fig. 4.15 Circuit for the high-frequency range.

High-frequency Range. At high frequencies the coupling condenser is an effective short circuit, but the shunting effect of C_o and C_i must be considered. The simplified circuit is shown in Fig. 4.15. As in Fig. 4.12, R_L and R_g appear in parallel as R; and C_o and C_i are in parallel as C_p. The total load impedance is the parallel combination of R and C_p, or

$$Z_L = \frac{R/j\omega C_p}{1/j\omega C_p + R} = \frac{R}{1 + j\omega C_p R}$$

Then the gain is

$$K = -\mu \frac{Z_L}{r_p + Z_L} = -\mu \frac{R}{R + r_p(1 + j\omega R C_p)}$$

This equation must be placed in the form $K_0 f(\omega)$, with $f(\omega)$ in the standard form, containing terms like $(1 + j\omega\tau)$. This is done by factoring the quantity $(R + r_p)$ out of the denominator:

$$K = -\mu \frac{R}{R + r_p} \frac{1}{1 + j\omega\tau_2}$$

where

$$\tau_2 \equiv \frac{R r_p}{R + r_p} C_p$$

This is the required result, since the first part is equal to K_0. The high-frequency response is that of a lag network having an equivalent circuit as shown in Fig. 4.16.

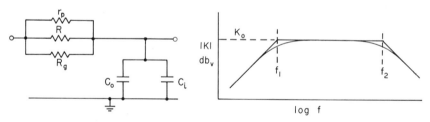

Fig. 4.16 Equivalent time constant for the high-frequency cutoff.

Fig. 4.17 Complete frequency response of the amplifier of Fig. 4.10.

The complete frequency response is shown in Fig. 4.17, with the magnitude of K in voltage decibels plotted against log of frequency. The curve is described completely by the mid-frequency gain K_0 and the two time constants τ_1 and τ_2 (or the corresponding corner frequencies f_1 and f_2). The slopes of the asymptotes are the usual $+20$

and -20 db$_v$ per decade. The "bandwidth" of the amplifier is often taken to be $f_2 - f_1$, although appreciable gain still exists outside this range.

PROBLEM

Consider the 6SN7 amplifier already studied in Sections 4.2 and 4.3, supposing that it feeds a similar stage with $C = 0.1\ \mu f$ and $R_g = 1$ M. Assume $C_o = 5$ pf, $C_{gk} = 5$ pf, and $C_{gp} = 4$ pf, and calculate the frequency response of the first stage. Repeat the calculation, this time ignoring the Miller effect.

4.5 CATHODE BIAS

The grid bias V_c can be provided from a separate supply as shown in Fig. 4.1; however, this is often inconvenient, and another method known as *cathode bias* is commonly used. As shown in Fig. 4.18, a resistance R_k is inserted between cathode and ground; the plate current

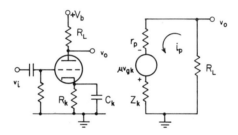

Fig. 4.18 Actual and equivalent circuits of an amplifier with cathode bias.

flowing through this generates a potential drop $I_p R_k$, so that the cathode is above ground by this amount. If the grid is *returned* to ground through R_g, it will be at a negative potential with respect to the cathode, as required. In effect, the bias has been derived from the plate supply and the available plate voltage is slightly diminished.

As the varying plate current flows through R_k, it will generate a varying voltage, resembling the signal and with the same sign. The result is to diminish the effective input to the tube, which depends on the difference between grid and cathode potentials. The bypass capacitor C_k eliminates this effect by carrying the variational current with a negligible voltage change. If it is chosen large enough, it will have this action even at the lowest audio frequencies; but at a sufficiently low frequency, the action of the capacitor will disappear. Let us now consider this phenomenon quantitatively with the aid of the equivalent circuit, also shown in Fig. 4.18. Since the cathode is not grounded, it is necessary to remember that the generator voltage is $-\mu v_{gk}$. Two equations are needed to define the plate current

$$i_p = \frac{\mu v_{gk}}{R_L + r_p + Z_k}$$

$$v_{gk} = v_i - v_k = v_i - i_p Z_k$$

Combining these and cross multiplying, we get

$$i_p(R_L + r_p + Z_k) = \mu(v_i - i_p Z_k)$$

We now collect all the terms in i_p on the left and solve for i_p:

$$i_p = \frac{\mu v_i}{R_L + r_p + (\mu + 1)Z_k}$$

Since i_p flows up through R_L, the output voltage is $v_o = -i_p R_L$; then the gain is

$$K = -\frac{\mu R_L}{R_L + r_p + (\mu + 1)Z_k}$$

This equation reduces, as it should, to the familiar result when $Z_k = 0$.

Let us first consider the effect of a cathode resistance without the bypass capacitor, so that $Z_k = R_k$. We see that the gain is reduced, and the effect is as if r_p were replaced by $[r_p + (\mu + 1)R_k]$. For typical values of R_k, the gain will be reduced by about a factor of 2.

If C_k is included, then Z_k can be written as $R_k/(1 + j\omega R_k C_k)$, and K can be found by making this substitution. As usual, we then manipulate the result to isolate the frequency dependence in terms of the standard form.

$$K = -\frac{\mu R_L(1 + j\omega R_k C_k)}{(R_L + r_p)(1 + j\omega R_k C_k) + (\mu + 1)R_k}$$

$$= -\frac{\mu R_L}{R_L + r_p + (\mu + 1)R_k} \frac{1 + j\omega R_k C_k}{1 + j\omega R' C_k}$$

In this expression, R' represents the combination

$$\frac{(R_L + r_p)R_k}{R_L + r_p + (\mu + 1)R_k}$$

which is equivalent to

$$\frac{1}{R'} = \frac{1}{R_k} + \frac{\mu + 1}{R_L + r_p}$$

The frequency dependence is that of a phase-retard network, and K approaches K_0 at frequencies such that $\omega R_k C_k \gg 1$. The asymptotes are sketched in Fig. 4.19; since the ratio k (defined in Section 2.9) is

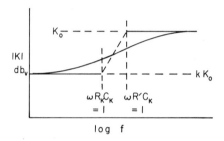

Fig. 4.19 Frequency dependence of the gain of an
amplifier with cathode bias.

about 0.5, the maximum slope is small, only about 6.7 db$_v$ per decade. Usually C_k is chosen large enough so that the transition is below the range of interest; for audio amplifiers, low-voltage electrolytic capacitors of 10 to 25 μf are common.

PROBLEM

Show that a suitable cathode resistor for the amplifier used for problems in previous sections is about 5 K, and estimate the loss in gain if the resistor is used without a bypass capacitor.

4.6 TRANSFORMER COUPLING

At one time, interstage coupling by transformers was widely used in audio amplifiers. However, they offer little advantage with high-μ triodes and pentodes, and have been replaced almost entirely by resistance coupling. Their chief use now is in impedance matching, where power must be delivered to a load such as a loudspeaker. Our main interest will be to examine the factors that control the frequency response of a transformer-coupled stage with a resistive load.

Let us first consider an appropriate equivalent circuit for a transformer. Fig. 4.20 shows an ideal transformer connected to a load R_L; a real transformer will be a good approximation to this at frequencies of a few hundred cycles per second. If a voltage v_o is developed across the load, the corresponding voltage across the primary is nv_o; the primary current is i_o/n. Therefore, the resistance which is observed at

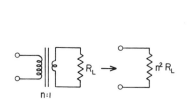

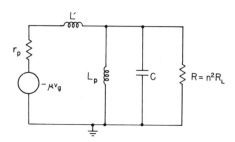

Fig. 4.20 Ideal transformer with a load R_L, and the equivalent load resistance.

Fig. 4.21 Equivalent circuit of a real transformer with driving tube and load.

the primary terminals is n^2R_L. A real transformer differs from this in several ways. First of all, the primary winding has a finite inductance, which appears in parallel with the reflected load; at low frequencies, more current may flow in the inductance than in the apparent load. Second, there is a *leakage inductance*, caused by *leakage flux* that is generated by the primary but does not link the secondary. It can be measured at the primary terminals when the secondary winding is short-circuited. Finally, there is appreciable shunt capacitance; there are several separate sources of this capacitance, but they can all be transformed so as to appear across the primary, if some approximations are allowed. Other imperfections, such as the resistance of the wire, may be important in power transformers but can usually be neglected in audio transformers. A suitable equivalent circuit of the real transformer, as viewed from the primary terminals, is shown in Fig. 4.21. Although an equivalent plate circuit of a tube has been included, most power stages will have to be discussed by large-signal analysis. Nevertheless, it is much easier to get the frequency response by small-signal analysis.

At mid-frequencies, the series impedance of the leakage inductance L' can be ignored, and so can the shunting effect of L_p and C. Then the gain is just $K_0 = -\mu R/(r_p + R)$ at the primary, or $\pm \mu R/n(r_p + R)$ at the secondary. Even if this is not accurate for large signals, a more appropriate value of K_0 can be used with the frequency-response equations.

At low frequencies, the shunt reactance of L_p must be taken into account. The effective load is R and L_p in parallel, or

$$Z_L = \frac{j\omega R L_p}{R + j\omega L_p}$$

and the gain is

$$K = -\mu \frac{j\omega R L_p}{r_p(R + j\omega L_p) + j\omega R L_p}$$

$$= -\mu \frac{R}{r_p + R} \frac{j\omega(r_p + R)L_p}{r_p R + j\omega(r_p + R)L_p}$$

$$= K_0 \frac{j\omega \tau_1}{1 + j\omega \tau_1}$$

where

$$\tau_1 = \frac{r_p + R}{r_p R} L_p$$

The time constant is seen to be formed by the primary inductance with the parallel resistance of r_p and R.

At high frequencies, the series impedance of L' becomes important; L_p can be ignored and, to a first approximation, so can C. To this approximation, we can write

$$K \doteq \frac{-\mu R}{R + r_p + j\omega L'} = \frac{K_0}{1 + j\omega \tau_2}$$

where

$$\tau_2 = \frac{L'}{R + r_p}$$

Here the time constant is formed by the leakage inductance with the series resistance of R and r_p. For good high-frequency response, the leakage inductance must be kept small by careful design of the coils and the use of a high-permeability core. At somewhat higher frequencies, the shunting effect of C becomes appreciable; the asymptotic gain may be found by considering $\omega L'$ and $1/\omega C$ as the dominant impedances, so that the gain finally approaches the line

$$K = +\mu/\omega^2 L'C$$

indicating a slope of -40 db$_v$ per decade and a phase shift of 180 degrees (in addition to the normal inversion). The final gain curve is sketched in Fig. 4.22.

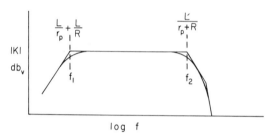

Fig. 4.22 Frequency response of a transformer-coupled amplifier with resistive load.

Interstage transformers are often used without any load resistance at all; let us briefly examine the behavior of Fig. 4.21 when R is omitted. The mid-frequency gain at the primary is $-\mu$, and at the secondary is μ/n, with the sign depending on which way the secondary is connected. The low-frequency time constant will be $\tau_1 = L_p/r_p$. At high frequencies, the gain will be

$$K = \frac{-\mu(1/j\omega C)}{r_p + j\omega L' + 1/j\omega C} = \frac{K_0}{1 - \omega^2 L'C + j\omega r_p C}$$

The ω^2 term in the denominator indicates an asymptotic slope of -40 db$_v$ per decade, but at the corner there may be a resonant peak. Let us examine the gain at the resonant frequency of L' and C; the peak will not be exactly here unless it is very high, but it will be close. When $\omega^2 L'C = 1$, the gain is $K_0/j\omega r_p C$. The Q of the system at resonance is given by $Q_0 = \omega_0 L'/r_p = 1/\omega_0 r_p C$; thus, the gain at ω_0 is $K = (-jQ_0)K_0$. If the leakage inductance is kept small enough, Q_0 will be

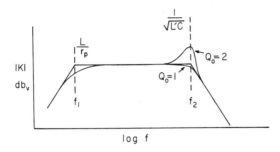

Fig. 4.23 Possible frequency responses of a transformer-coupled amplifier with no load resistance.

1 or less and there will be no peak; otherwise, a peak will occur with a gain higher by the factor Q_0 than the mid-frequency gain. Possible curves are sketched in Fig. 4.23.

4.7 WIDE-BAND (VIDEO) AMPLIFIERS

Amplifiers with a bandwidth of several megacycles are required for applications such as radar, nuclear-particle counting, cathode-ray oscilloscopes, and television. The amplifier in a television set is required for the picture or *video* signal, and the class of amplifiers takes its name from this. The important quality of the amplifier for all these purposes is not actually a good high-frequency response, but rather a good response to *transients* or rapid changes in voltage. But either quality implies the other, and it is often easier to discuss the frequency response than the transient response. When this is done, one should never lose sight of the fact that it is merely a convenience and should not be taken too seriously. As we have already mentioned, the same thing is true in the high-fidelity reproduction of music.

In discussing the requirements, let us use a television wave as an example. The picture is built up by scanning horizontally in 525 lines at 30 frames per second, so that 15,750 lines must be scanned per second. A simple picture is shown in Fig. 4.24, along with the wave produced by scanning once across it. This wave includes *synchronizing pulses* for the horizontal and vertical scanning of the electron beam, these do not concern us now. In the receiver, the video wave is used to control the current in the electron beam and thus the intensity of the spot. If the rises and falls of the video wave are not fast enough, the picture will be blurred. If the width of the picture is 4/3 its height,

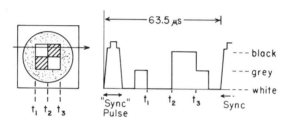

Fig. 4.24 A simple television picture and the video wave produced by scanning once across it.

the horizontal and vertical resolutions will be similar if the changes take place in about 1/700 of the width, since there are 525 lines in the vertical direction. The corresponding time is about 0.1 μsec; as we shall soon see, an amplifier that can reproduce this must have a bandwidth of at least 5 mc; the usual figure for a television receiver is 4.5 mc. Another requirement is that a scan across a line of constant brightness must be reproduced as a constant voltage to within a small tolerance; this is found to require a constant gain down to about 30 cps. If only short pulses are to be amplified, as in radar and nuclear physics, the corresponding frequency is much higher and the performance is easily achieved. But an amplifier with constant gain from 30 cps to 4.5 mc must be very carefully designed.

In testing and discussing a wide-band amplifier it is common to use a square wave, which allows defects in transient and flat-top responses to be observed easily. The leading edge of such a wave is shown in Fig. 4.25, very much spread out to indicate possible defects caused by an amplifier. Because of the rounded corners, the *rise time* can only be specified by adopting some convention. The usual one is to measure the time between the points at 10 and 90 percent of the final amplitude. Some amplifiers also exhibit an *overshoot*, possibly followed by damped oscillations; the result in a television picture will be "fringes" bordering the right-hand edge of large dark or light areas. The overshoot is usually expressed as a percentage of the final amplitude, and would be about 10 percent in Fig. 4.25.

The flat-top response is shown in Fig. 4.26; as long as the defect is fairly small, the top usually remains straight, but has a *sag* accompanied by an undershoot that has the same magnitude for a linear amplifier.

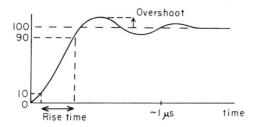

Fig. 4.25   Leading edge of a pulse showing possible defects.

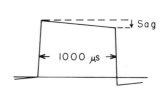

Fig. 4.26 Sag in the flat top of a pulse.

(This is in addition to any "overshoot," as in Fig. 4.25, that may be generated at the trailing edge.) The amount of the sag depends on the period of the wave or the length of the pulse.

The transient response of an amplifier is best treated by the method of Laplace transforms, but a single stage can easily be handled by inspection, as in our example. We shall ignore the complications introduced by cathode- and screen-bypass capacitors. The circuit treated is the one discussed in Section 4.4, and τ_1 and τ_2 are the time constants, defined there, which control the frequency response. Further details may be found in the references at the end of this chapter.

We have seen that the high-frequency response is identical with that of an R-C lag network. The response to the step is therefore

$$v = V(1 - e^{-t/\tau_2})$$

We are interested in very small values of τ_2, which can only be achieved by use of a pentode with a small load resistance R_L; under these conditions, the gain at mid-frequencies is accurately given by $K_0 = -g_m R_L$ and the time constant is $\tau_2 = R_L C_p$, with C_p representing the total interstage shunt capacitance. If $C_p = 10$ pf and $R_L = 10$ K, τ_2 is 0.1 μsec, which is in the range of interest. The calculation of the rise time T_r is carried out in the following table by finding the times at which $(1 - e^{-t/\tau_2})$ has the values 0.1 and 0.9.

v/V	$1 - e^{-t/\tau_2}$	e^{-t/τ_2}	t/τ_2
0.1	0.1	0.9	0.1
0.9	0.9	0.1	2.303

We see that T_r is equal to $2.2\tau_2$, or 0.22 μsec for the example. The corner frequency of the stage is $f_2 = 1/2\pi\tau_2$; then we can write

$$f_2 T_r = \frac{2.2}{2\pi} \doteq 0.37$$

It happens that this last expression holds fairly well for any amplifier, as long as f_2 is taken as the frequency at which the gain is down 3 db from the mid-frequency value. Thus, it is a very useful rule of thumb for linking the rise-time and the high-frequency response.

Another useful relation can be found by substituting the mid-frequency gain $K_0 = -g_m R_L$ into the expression for the time constant. This gives

$$\frac{K_0}{T_r} = -\frac{g_m}{2.2 C_p} \quad \text{and} \quad K_0 f_2 = -\frac{g_m}{2\pi C_p}$$

The second expression is called the *gain-bandwidth product*. In a multistage amplifier using several tubes of one type, the ratio g_m/C_p is characteristic of the tube; it is thus a useful figure of merit for this type of service. The designer of the tube tries to get a large transconductance without too large a capacitance; the best tubes have gain/rise-time ratios of about 200 per μsec.

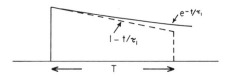

Fig. 4.27 An exponential decay and its initial tangent.

The low-frequency response of the single stage is the same as that of the RC lead network; the flat top will actually fall away according to the function e^{-t/τ_2}. For times that are short compared with τ_1, this is approximated by $(1 - t/\tau_1)$, as shown in Fig. 4.27. The amount of sag in time T is then just T/τ_1, and the percent sag is $100 T/\tau_1$. If the resulting wave is used as the input to a second stage, an additional sag will be produced and simply added to what is already present. Thus, the total sag of a number of stages is the sum of the individual sags. The lower 3-db frequencies do not combine in the same way; we conclude that there is no simple correlation between sag and lower 3-db point for an amplifier.

Shunt Peaking. An important improvement in the rise time of a stage can be made by this technique, in which a properly chosen coil is placed in series with the load resistance, as in Fig. 4.28. The effect on the frequency response is seen as follows: at frequencies where the

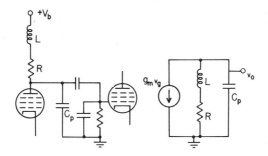

Fig. 4.28 Actual and equivalent circuits of a shunt-peaked amplifier. C_p represents the sum of the two stray capacitances.

shunting effect of C_p begins to be appreciable, the impedance of the R–L branch begins to rise. If L is chosen correctly, the effects can be made to compensate over a certain range, beyond which the gain falls towards the same asymptote as with L omitted. In terms of transient response, L allows all the available current from the tube to flow into C at the beginning; however, L must not be too large if an overshoot is not to develop. Fig. 4.28 also shows a high-frequency equivalent circuit; r_p and R_g have been omitted because they are usually about 100 times greater than R. The gain is $-g_m Z_L$ which reduces to the mid-frequency value $K_0 = -g_m R$. The load impedance is $(R + j\omega L)$ in parallel with $(1/j\omega C_p)$, or

$$Z_L = \frac{(R + j\omega L)/j\omega C_p}{R + j\omega L + 1/j\omega C_p} = \frac{R + j\omega L}{1 + j\omega R C_p - \omega^2 L C_p}$$

Then in terms of K_0, the gain is

$$K = K_0 \frac{1 + j\omega L/R}{1 + j\omega R C_p - \omega^2 L C_p}$$

For further analysis, this equation may be expressed in terms of two parameters; the first is $\tau_2 = R C_p$, and the second is $m \equiv L/R^2 C_p$, which gives the "normalized" value of L. With these substitutions, the gain is

$$K = K_0 \frac{1 + j\omega m \tau_2}{1 + j\omega \tau_2 - m\omega^2 \tau_2^2}$$

This expression is sometimes analyzed to give the condition for flattest frequency response, or *maximal flatness*. However, it is the step response that is really of interest, and it is preferable to make the analysis directly in terms of this. The analysis and results are shown in Valley and Wallman (see reference at the end of this chapter). The best value of m is 0.250 if no overshoot is allowed; the rise time is reduced to 70 percent of the value for no peaking. Larger values of m give more and more overshoot, along with even faster rise times.

Valley and Wallman also give the following rule for combining the rise times of successive stages: if these are denoted by τ_1, τ_2, $\cdots$, the rise time of the whole amplifier is given by

$$\tau^2 = \tau_1^2 + \tau_2^2 + \cdots$$

The same relation serves to estimate the lengthening produced by measuring equipment (such as an oscilloscope) and allows a correction to be made for it. Thus, a pulse of rise time τ_1 applied to an amplifier of rise time τ_2 will be reproduced with the rise time τ given above.

PROBLEMS

1) Consider an amplifier stage with $g_m = 5000\,\mu$mhos, $C_p = 10$ pf, and $R_L = 10$ K. Calculate the gain and rise time. If shunt peaking with $m = 0.25$ is added, what is the size of L?

2) A pulse is observed on an oscilloscope to have a rise time of 0.20 μsec. If the rise time of the oscilloscope is 0.10 μsec, show that the rise time of the original pulse is about 0.17 μsec.

4.8 CATHODE FOLLOWER

In this circuit, the output is taken from the cathode instead of the plate. The gain is always less than unity, but it has other characteristics that make it useful for certain purposes. The output impedance is so low that it is unaffected by almost any reasonable load; it is popular for transmitting signals along a cable from remote equipment. On the other hand, the input impedance is unusually high, a useful property when a signal source has a high impedance.

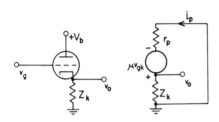 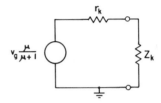

Fig. 4.29 Actual and equivalent circuits of a cathode follower.

Fig. 4.30 Equivalent output circuit of a cathode follower.

The actual and equivalent circuits are shown in Fig. 4.29. Because the plate is at a variational ground, the circuit is sometimes called a *grounded-plate* amplifier. As in Section 4.5, two simultaneous equations must be written for the plate current; when they are solved, the result is

$$i_p = \frac{\mu v_g}{r_p + (\mu + 1)Z_k}$$

The output voltage v_0 is $+i_p Z_k$, and the gain is

$$K = \frac{\mu Z_k}{r_p + (\mu + 1)Z_k}$$

$$= \frac{\mu}{\mu + 1} \frac{Z_k}{r_p/(\mu + 1) + Z_k}$$

$$= \frac{\mu}{\mu + 1} \frac{Z_k}{r_k + Z_k}$$

where

$$r_k \equiv \frac{r_p}{\mu + 1} \div \frac{1}{g_m}$$

An equivalent output circuit is shown in Fig. 4.30. Since μ is much greater than unity for most tubes, and usually Z_k is much larger than r_k, the gain is normally just less than unity. But the output impedance, r_k in parallel with Z_k, is very low; since g_m is usually in the range of 1,600 to 3,500 μmhos, r_k runs from 600 to 300 ohms. It can be made even lower by using tubes with higher transconductance or connecting tubes in parallel.

This low impedance also results in an excellent high-frequency response. Suppose that Z_k includes a capacitance of 50 pf; this is assumed rather large to include the cathode-heater capacitance. The time constant controlling the high-frequency corner is approximately equal to $r_k C_k$ or $(300)(50 \times 10^{-12}) = 15 \times 10^{-9}$ sec. This is so much shorter than the typical values for other types of amplifier that it can usually be ignored altogether.

Let us now consider the input impedance. The input capacitance is *less* than the "cold" value, because now the Miller effect reduces the apparent grid-to-cathode capacitance. If the gain were unity, this capacitance would disappear completely. With a gain K, the apparent capacitance is

$$C_i = C_{gp} + (1 - K)C_{gk}$$

If this is too large, a pentode can be used with the screen bypassed to the cathode so that it, too, follows the grid. Capacitance from the grid directly to ground can be reduced by shielding the grid lead and connecting the shield to the cathode. When a pentode is used as a cathode follower, it should be remembered that it will behave as a triode unless the screen is constrained to move with the cathode.

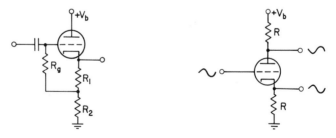

Fig. 4.31 Cathode follower with a small   Fig. 4.32 Split-load phase inverter.
bias resistor and a large load resistor.

A cathode resistor that is suitable for providing a gain near unity may give too large a bias if the grid is returned to ground. One answer is the circuit shown in Fig. 4.31, in which R_1 provides the bias, and $(R_1 + R_2)$ acts as R_k. Another may be to connect the grid directly to the preceding plate. The inverse Miller effect acts upon the grid resistance in Fig. 4.31, as well as the capacitance, increasing its value by the factor $1/(1 - K')$, where K' is the gain measured to the junction of R_1 and R_2.

A cathode follower is able to deliver large positive pulses to a load, and can be biased near cutoff in this service. But it is not nearly as good at delivering negative pulses, since it must be biased to carry a large plate current, which drops only during the pulses. Moreover, if the load has a high capacitance, it must be discharged through R_k, since the tube can do no more than cut off with a negative signal. The best answer to this problem is to use a White cathode follower, which will be considered presently.

Resistance in the Plate Circuit. For one reason or another, it is sometimes desirable to connect resistance between the plate and its supply. The effect on the gain and output impedance is easily found by noting that this resistance will appear in series with r_p in the equivalent circuit of Fig. 4.29. It is then merely necessary to replace r_p by $(r_p + R_p)$ in the equations; thus, r_k is replaced by $r'_k \equiv (r_p + R_p)/(\mu + 1)$. If the added resistance is small compared with r_p, the effect will be negligible; if it is comparable or larger, the gain will be reduced and the output impedance increased.

A useful case of this is the *split-load phase inverter*, shown in Fig. 4.32; it is used to produce two waves of the same shape but opposite sign (known as a *push-pull* signal). Because the same current flows through the two resistors, their equality guarantees identical waveforms, unless the frequency is high enough for capacitive effects to be important. The performance may be calculated by the equations just derived.

White Cathode Follower. A circuit consisting of two tubes in series and connected as in Fig. 4.33 is referred to as a *White cathode follower*. (The series connection is often called by the name *cascode*, and this can be called a *cascode cathode follower*.) The upper grid is biased at about half the plate-supply voltage, and the cathode follows to a slightly higher voltage; thus, the supply is distributed equally between the two tubes. An a-c equivalent circuit is given also; further reduction is left as a problem. To a first approximation, the upper tube is a cathode follower and the lower is its load impedance. However, the lower tube

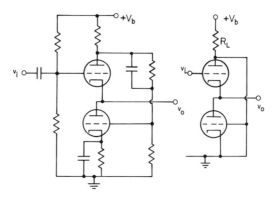

Fig. 4.33 White cathode follower.

helps out as follows: an inverted version of the signal appears on its grid, and it inverts again, trying to produce an output similar to that of the upper tube. In particular, if a large negative step cuts off the upper tube, the lower will be driven very hard and will conduct heavily, rapidly draining the current out of the load. If the two tubes have the same parameters, the gain is

$$K = \frac{\mu r_p + \mu^2 R_L}{(\mu + 2)r_p + (\mu^2 + \mu + 1)R_L} \doteq \frac{\mu}{\mu + 1}$$

The approximation is a very good one, since nearly the same amount is dropped from numerator and denominator.

PROBLEMS
1) Complete the equivalent circuit and derive the expression just given.
2) Find the gain and output resistance of a tube having $\mu = 70$ and $g_m = 1600\ \mu$mhos for the following load resistances R_k : 1 K, 5 K, 20 K, 50 K, in the circuit of Fig. 4.29.

4.9 ANODE FOLLOWER

This circuit has nearly the same gain and output impedance as a cathode follower, but it inverts the signal and has a much lower input impedance. It is used in the same kind of application, where the signal has the wrong polarity for a cathode follower, and where the source can supply the required signal current. The essence is to feed the signal through a resistance R and feed back from plate to grid through an equal resistance, as shown in Fig. 4.34. If the signal source has an

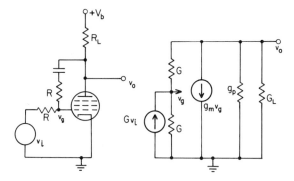

Fig. 4.34 Anode follower and its equivalent circuit.

appreciable output resistance, it must be allowed for in choosing the input R; we shall assume that it has been included in R. The equivalent circuit also is shown in Fig. 4.34; only the mid-frequency region will be treated. The node equations are

$$(g_p + G_L + G)v_o - Gv_g = -g_m v_g$$
$$- Gv_o + 2Gv_g = Gv_i$$

The second gives $v_g = (v_i + v_o)/2$, and substitution in the first yields

$$K = \frac{G - g_m}{2g_p + 2G_L + G + g_m} = \frac{G - g_m}{2G_p + g_m}$$

where G_p represents $g_p + G_L + G/2$, the effective total plate-load conductance; R_p will be the corresponding resistance. In many cases, r_p and $2R$ are large enough so that $R_p = R_L$ to a good approximation. A useful approximation to the gain is made by noting that R is usually much larger than $1/g_m$, so that $G = 1/R$ can be neglected, and further that $1/g_m$ is nearly equal to the r_k defined in the previous section. We then find

$$K \doteqdot - \frac{R_p}{2r_k + R_p} \doteqdot - \frac{R_L}{2r_k + R_L}$$

The similarity to the gain of the cathode follower is now obvious; the differences are in the negative sign and the replacement of r_k by approximately $2r_k$. The magnitude of the gain will be slightly less than that of the corresponding cathode follower, and the output impedance about twice as great.

The action may be understood in physical terms as follows. Any variation of v_i causes an opposite and slightly smaller variation of v_o; half the difference appears at the grid, giving the signal that causes v_o to change. The two equal Rs behave as an electrical "seesaw" with the fulcrum at the grid. The higher the gain of the tube, the closer to this is the actual behavior. The operational computing amplifier, to be discussed later, behaves in the same way and can be considered as a development of the anode follower.

Since the grid voltage varies only slightly, the grid can be considered a variational ground or *virtual ground* to a good approximation. The input impedance is therefore just equal to R, or even less if R includes a contribution from the source of v_i.

4.10 GROUNDED-GRID AMPLIFIER

So far we have treated two possible configurations of a tube: grounded cathode and grounded plate. A third possibility is to ground the grid and connect the input to the cathode. The resulting amplifier has a rather limited utility because of the very low input impedance, but does make an excellent radio-frequency amplifier, especially since it allows a triode to be used at the higher frequencies, at which transit-time effects may be important in a pentode. The distance across a triode can be made very small if necessary, and the grounded grid shields the input from the output. Another important application, arising when two independent signals must be fed into the same tube, will be treated in detail in the next section.

Fig. 4.35 shows actual and equivalent circuits. The resistance R normally represents the impedance of the generator, although it may also be chosen to give the correct bias if desired. Since the grid is grounded, the grid voltage is $-v_k$, as shown. The plate current is

$$i_p = -\frac{v_i + \mu v_k}{R + r_p + R_L}$$

With the substitution of $v_k = v_i + i_p R$, this becomes

$$i_p = -\frac{(1 + \mu)v_i + \mu i_p R}{R + r_p + R_L}$$

$$i_p[(1 + \mu)R + r_p + R_L] = -(1 + \mu)v_i$$

Since $v_o = -i_p R_L$, the gain is

$$K = +\frac{(1 + \mu)R_L}{(1 + \mu)R + r_p + R_L}$$

As always when voltages appear on the cathode, the factor $(1 + \mu)$ appears; the "one" comes from the change in plate-to-cathode voltage, and the μ from the change in grid-to-cathode voltage. Except for this

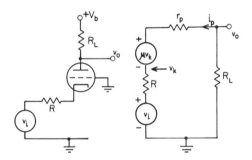

Fig. 4.35 Grounded-grid amplifier and its equivalent circuit.

change in the numerator, the gain is the same as that of a grounded-cathode amplifier with resistance R in the cathode circuit; the positive sign shows that there is no inversion of the signal.

Another useful form of the gain may be found by separating it into two factors, as follows:

$$K = \frac{(1 + \mu)R_L}{r_p + R_L} \cdot \frac{1}{1 + (1 + \mu)R/(r_p + R_L)} = \frac{(1 + \mu)R_L}{r_p + R_L} \cdot \frac{r'_k}{r'_k + R}$$

in which r'_k is defined as $(r_p + R_L)/(1 + \mu)$ as in Section 4.8. The first factor is the value of the gain when the source impedance R is zero; the form of the second factor shows that the input impedance of the amplifier is r'_k, which is roughly equal to $1/g_m$, unless R_L is much larger than r_p.

Because the input impedance is so low, the signal will usually have to be matched to it. In radio-frequency amplifiers this is easily done by means of a step-down transformer; at audio frequencies, a cathode follower is often used, as discussed in the next section.

PROBLEM

Derive the input impedance by calculating the ratio of source voltage to source current.

4.11 DIFFERENTIAL AMPLIFIERS

A differential amplifier is one having an output that depends on the difference between two signals and not on their common magnitude. The term is commonly extended to amplifiers that approximate this performance, even if they do not quite reach it. The most obvious applications are the combining of two independent signals, or the removal of an undesired component from a signal. In d-c amplifiers, an example of such a component is zero drift, a gradual change in the output even when there is no input. Drift may be greatly reduced by the use of differential stages.

Cathode Input. As discussed in the previous section, it is possible to take one input to the grid, and the other to the cathode; this is shown in Fig. 4.36. Since the equivalent circuit is linear, we may apply the

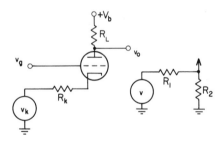

Fig. 4.36 Differential amplifier with cathode input.

superposition theorem and consider the output as the sum of two parts, each produced by one input acting by itself. From the grid, the circuit looks like a grounded-cathode amplifier with cathode resistance R_k;

from the cathode, it appears as a grounded-grid stage. Using results from Sections 4.5 and 4.10, we may write

$$v_0 = - \frac{\mu R_L v_g}{R_L + r_p + (1 + \mu) R_k} + \frac{(1 + \mu) R_L v_k}{R_L + r_p + (1 + \mu) R_k}$$

$$= - \frac{\mu R_L}{R_L + r_p + (1 + \mu) R_k} \left(v_g - \frac{1 + \mu}{\mu} v_k \right)$$

If $\mu \gg 1$, the quantity in the bracket is nearly $(v_g - v_k)$ and the coefficient is the differential gain of the amplifier. The disadvantage is the low input impedance at the cathode, or the small required value of R_k. The circuit is found in power-supply voltage regulators, and in cases where the cathode input can be greatly attenuated, as shown at the right of Fig. 4.36. R_1 can then be a substantial size, even when R_2 is fairly small. This arrangement is widely used for applying negative feedback.

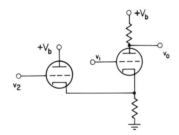

Fig. 4.37 Use of a cathode follower to drive the cathode input.

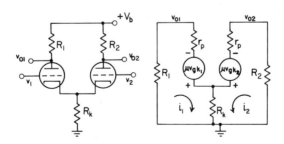

Fig. 4.38 Differential amplifier and equivalent circuit.

An obvious variation of cathode input is to use a cathode follower to match the source to the cathode. The two cathodes can be connected together as shown in Fig. 4.37. This arrangement is most easily treated as a special case of the balanced pair in Fig. 4.38, by setting R_1 equal to zero.

Balanced Pair. This circuit, also known as a *long-tailed pair*, is shown in Fig. 4.38 along with its equivalent circuit. We assume that the two tubes are identical. Although the two load resistors, R_1 and R_2, are often equal, we reserve the possibility of setting one of them equal to zero. We note that the cathode voltage is $v_k = (i_1 + i_2)R_k$, and then write the mesh equations:

$$(R_1 + r_p + R_k)i_1 + R_k i_2 = \mu v_{gk_1} = \mu[v_1 - (i_1 + i_2)R_k]$$

$$R_k i_1 + (R_2 + r_p + R_k)i_2 = \mu v_{gk_2} = \mu[v_2 - (i_1 + i_2)R_k]$$

All terms in i_1 and i_2 are now collected to give:

$$[R_1 + r_p + (1 + \mu)R_k]i_1 + (1 + \mu)R_k i_2 = \mu v_1 \qquad (1)$$

$$(1 + \mu)R_k i_1 + [R_2 + r_p + (1 + \mu)R_k]i_2 = \mu v_2 \qquad (2)$$

Two important cases may now be distinguished: differential output and output from one plate only. The former is encountered in vacuum-tube voltmeters and cathode-ray oscilloscopes, in which the indicator responds to the difference between two voltages, and also in amplifiers having a differential input in the next stage. For differential output we may assume $R_1 = R_2$ and call them both R_L; we then subtract (2) from (1):

$$(R_L + r_p)(i_1 - i_2) = \mu(v_1 - v_2) = \mu \Delta v_i$$

The difference between the plate voltages, which we may call Δv_o, is equal to $-(i_1 - i_2)R_L$, so that

$$\Delta v_o = -\frac{\mu R_L}{R_L + r_p}\Delta v_i$$

This circuit is truly differential, with a gain equal to that of a stage using the same triode with the same load.

The case of *single-ended* output is not quite so easy to treat. It is possible to eliminate i_2 from the two equations by multiplying them by suitable factors and subtraction, or by the determinant method; either way, the result is

$$i_1 = \frac{\mu(1 + \mu)R_k v_1 - \mu[R_1 + r_p + (1 + \mu)R_k]v_2}{[R_1 + r_p + (1 + \mu)R_k][R_2 + r_p + (1 + \mu)R_k] - (1 + \mu)^2 R_k^2}$$

To reduce this to a more useful form, we make the approximation $(1 + \mu)R_k \gg (R_1 + r_p)$; this is usually excellent in a well-designed circuit. Parts of both numerator and denominator can then be dropped, but the factors in the denominator must be multiplied out first, because there is some cancellation. A factor $(1 + \mu)R_k$ disappears, leaving

$$i_1 \doteq \frac{-\mu(v_1 - v_2)}{R_1 + R_2 + 2r_p}$$

$$v_{o_1} \doteq -\frac{\mu R_1}{R_1 + R_2 + 2r_p}\Delta v_i$$

By symmetry, the output at the other plate must be

$$v_{o_2} \doteq +\frac{\mu R_2}{R_1 + R_2 + 2r_p}\Delta v_i$$

To this approximation, the differential output is split equally between the two plates. Physically, the reason is that when R_k is large, a signal on one grid causes just half as much to appear on the cathode; this effectively generates a push-pull input signal at the two grids, and an amplified version appears at the plates. As we have already seen, no approximation is needed to get differential action when a differential output is used.

The degree to which the approximation can be satisfied in practice can be estimated. It is best to use a high-μ twin triode, so that μ can be taken as about 70, and r_p about 70 K. If R_L is 100 K and R_k at least 50 K, then we have:

$$(1 + \mu)R_k = 71 \times 50 \ K = 3550 \ K$$

$$R_L + r_p = 100 \ K + 70 \ K = 170 \ K$$

The ratio, then, is about 20. An adequate plate current through such a large cathode resistor can be obtained by providing for a large voltage drop across it; the grids can be given a positive bias (with respect to ground), or the cathode resistor can be connected to a negative power supply.

Four possible configurations of the basic amplifier are sketched in Fig. 4.39. At (a) is the perfectly differential circuit with differential output. Approximately differential circuits with single-ended outputs are shown in (b) and (c); the latter has the higher gain, but the former

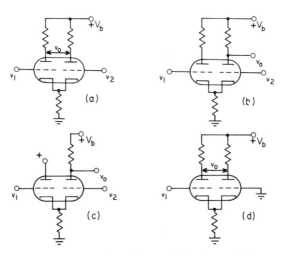

Fig. 4.39 Forms of the long-tailed pair amplifier.

may be easier to balance. For the best balance, the plate of the left-hand triode in (c) should be fed from a lower voltage than the right-hand one. At (d) is a phase-splitter, giving an approximate push-pull output from a single-ended input, the other grid being grounded or at a fixed positive potential. This circuit is found in many vacuum-tube voltmeters, and is also useful for providing a push-pull signal to a cathode-ray tube.

REFERENCES

Wide-band amplifiers are well treated in *Vacuum Tube Amplifiers*, edited by G. E. Valley and H. Wallman (New York: McGraw-Hill Book Company, Inc., 1948). An exposition from the viewpoint of the nuclear physicist is given in *Electronics* by W. C. Elmore and M. Sands (New York: McGraw-Hill Book Company, Inc., 1949). A basic treatment is given in *Electronic Amplifier Circuits* by J. M. Pettit and M. M. McWhorter (New York: McGraw-Hill Book Company, Inc., 1961).

CHAPTER 5

Power Amplifiers

5.1 INTRODUCTION

The small-signal analysis used in Chapter 4 is usually suitable for the first stages of an amplifier, but the last stages may operate on large signals. In many cases, the final stage is required to deliver appreciable power to the load. We shall now consider the kinds of analysis that are appropriate to these applications. The small-signal approximation is useful as a guide, but cannot be expected to give accurate results or to apply at all in some cases.

This is particularly true when the tubes spend part of the time with the plate current cut off. With suitable design, the result may be a higher efficiency and a higher power output for a given type of tube, along with moderately small distortion. Amplifiers are divided into classes according to the fraction of the time they spend cut off, in the following manner:

Class A—plate current flows all the time
Class AB—plate current flows more than half, but less than all, the time
Class B—plate current flows half the time
Class C—plate current flows less than half the time.

All the amplifiers treated up to now are Class A. With a push-pull connection, the missing part of the wave in Classes AB and B is supplied by the other tube; Class C is used for radio-frequency amplification with a tuned load which smooths out the waveform.

A subscript 1 indicates that no grid current flows, or in other words, that the signal never drives the grid positive. Subscript 2 shows that grid current does flow on the positive peaks of the signal. Class A is understood to be A_1, and B and C to be B_2 and C_2, although B_1 is possible. Thus, the chief use of the subscripts is with Class AB.

5.2 POWER TRANSFER

Since the power available from a given tube is limited, it is necessary to choose the best possible load impedance, transforming it if necessary by a transformer. The usual power-transfer theorem is not really relevant here, because it assumes that the source voltage is held constant as the load is varied. In an amplifier, the source voltage can have any required value and should be varied along with the load in such a way as to satisfy some suitable criterion. The output of an amplifier is limited by the distortion of the peaks or valleys of the wave as it becomes

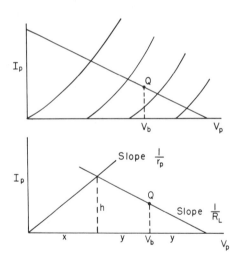

Fig. 5.1 Plate characteristics of a triode with an a-c load line. A simplified schematic version is shown at the bottom.

too large to handle. Thus, the useful criterion is to set a tolerance on this distortion and keep it constant as the load is varied. The optimum load resistance, therefore, may be very different from the plate resistance. As we carry out the variations, we shall hold V_b and V_c constant.

Let us first consider a triode, with the aid of Fig. 5.1. A load line has been indicated, with the operating point Q in the middle of the available range of instantaneous plate voltage, thus assuring that the largest possible wave can be produced without clipping either peak. Since most power amplifiers are transformer coupled, there is a very small d-c voltage drop between the plate supply and the plate; the quiescent plate voltage is thus nearly equal to V_b. The instantaneous plate voltage can rise above this by virtue of the self-inductance of the transformer primary. The a-c load line is drawn through the point Q with a slope appropriate for the reflected load resistance.

The essentials of the diagram for the present purpose are shown in Fig. 5.1, bottom half; the zero-bias plate characteristic has been replaced by a straight line with slope $1/r_p$. We wish to find the value of the other slope, $1/R_L$, that gives the largest output power without clipping. To do this, note that the power is proportional to the product of peak-to-peak voltage and peak-to-peak current, or $2yh$. As the slope of the load line is varied by rotating it around Q, h varies with x, and $(x + y)$ remains constant, essentially equal to V_b. Then the power output is

$$P_0 = kx(V_b - x)$$

where k is a suitable constant. If the derivative of this with respect to x is set equal to zero, the result is

$$V_b - 2x = 0$$
$$2x = V_b = x + y$$
$$x = y$$

This equality indicates that the slope of the load line is just half that of the tube line, or $1/2r_p$; the optimum load resistance is $2r_p$. The result is only rough, because a highly idealized triode has been used, but it does give a useful guide and is found in practice to be fairly accurate. With this load resistance, less than half the power generated appears in the load, but the power generated is larger than it is under matched conditions, and the actual available power is a maximum.

Most power amplifiers use beam tetrodes, loosely called pentodes, because a tube of a given size can deliver more power if it is a beam tetrode. As we have just seen, the minimum instantaneous plate voltage for the triode is about half the supply voltage; with a beam tetrode, the plate can go to a much lower voltage, delivering more power to the load and wasting less. The choice of optimum load resistance is illustrated by Fig. 5.2, which shows the zero-bias characteristic and three possible load lines. It is seen that line 1 offers a smaller voltage excursion, and therefore less power, than line 2. Line 3 gives a larger voltage excursion, but a smaller current change, than 2; in fact, it will also give

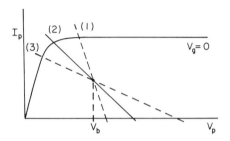

Fig. 5.2 Zero-bias characteristic of a beam tetrode and three possible load lines.

severe clipping of the negative peaks of the output voltage, unless the excursion is restricted. The optimum load line is line 2, which intersects the tube line just above the knee. The corresponding resistance is much lower than r_p and not related to it at all; its value also depends on the supply voltage used. The usual practice is to accept the optimum resistance tabulated in a tube manual; it has been determined by the manufacturer to give the greatest power output at a given distortion level.

PROBLEM

Refer to the description of a beam tetrode, such as the 6V6 or 6AQ5, in a tube manual. Estimate the optimum load resistance by drawing a line like (2) in Fig. 5.2, and compare your estimate with the value recommended in the manual. Also estimate the plate resistance for comparison.

Distortion. Because the power output of a linear amplifier is always limited by the onset of distortion, it is necessary to have a method of specifying the latter. The usual procedure is to assume a pure sine-wave input and then examine the harmonics produced in the output, as determined by Fourier analysis. Let V_n be the amplitude of the nth harmonic, with V_1 representing the fundamental; then the percent distortion is defined by

$$\text{Distortion} = \frac{100}{V_1} \left(\sum_{n=2}^{\infty} V_n^2 \right)^{1/2} \text{ percent}$$

If the second harmonic is predominant, this becomes approximately $100V_2/V_1$. For audio amplifiers it is customary to evaluate power output at a distortion level of 5 percent, which is reasonably tolerable to the ear. However, for some purposes this level is much too high and a different tolerance must be set; in high-fidelity amplifiers, for example, even 1 percent is considered large.

It is possible to estimate the distortion of a stage from the plate characteristics as follows. First, a load line is chosen and drawn. This is then replotted on the transfer-characteristic plane; as was mentioned in Section 4.2, it is then called the *dynamic characteristic*. The operation is sketched in Fig. 5.3 for a triode; the dynamic curve is fairly straight

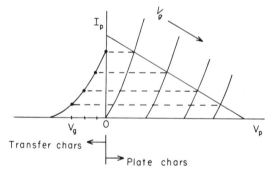

Fig. 5.3 To the right of the I_p axis, the plate characteristics and load line of a triode. To the left, the transfer-characteristic plane with only the load line plotted; it is now called the dynamic characteristic.

for its upper part, but its lower part curves slightly. It is seen from Fig. 5.3 that it gives the relation between plate current and grid voltage for that particular load resistance. Thus, if it is straight, the waveform of the plate current will be the same as that of the signal, and its curvature gives a measure of the distortion or nonlinearity.

Plate and dynamic characteristics for a beam tetrode are shown in

Fig. 5.4. The dynamic line is curved at both ends in this case, giving it an S shape, which results in a different kind of distortion from that produced by a triode. The process of selecting the optimum load line, discussed earlier in this section, is carried out by constructing the

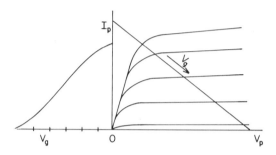

Fig. 5.4 Same as Fig. 5.3, for a beam tetrode.

dynamic characteristics for each, and comparing their power outputs and distortions. For example, line 1 in Fig. 5.2 will be more linear at high currents but will give a lower output; line 3 will be very non-linear at high currents. This effect is worse with a true pentode because the "knee" in the plate characteristics is more rounded.

If a signal amplitude is chosen, the distortion can be evaluated quantitatively from the dynamic characteristic by one of two methods. The first is to plot the output wave for a sinusoidal input, and then perform a graphical Fourier analysis. The whole process must be repeated each time the amplitude is changed. The second method, more elegant and probably easier, is to represent the dynamic line itself by a power series. Substitution of a sinusoidal input then permits a trigonometric evaluation of the output wave, which is readily placed in the form of a Fourier series. This will now be illustrated briefly; a more detailed treatment is given in Chapter 13.

Assume that the dynamic characteristic can be represented by the series

$$I_p = A + BV_g + CV_g^2 + \cdots$$

The coefficients can be evaluated by measuring the coordinates of several points well distributed along the line, substituting them, and taking the result as a set of simultaneous equations for A, B, C, and so on. The number of points required is equal to the number of coeffi-cients to be found. Suppose that D and higher coefficients are negli-gible; this is nearly true for a triode, for which Fig. 5.3 shows the curve to be similar to part of a parabola. Taking V_g as $V_c + V \sin \omega t$, we find

$$I_p \doteqdot A + B(V_c + V \sin \omega t) + C(V_c + V \sin \omega t)^2$$

Remembering that $\sin^2 x = (1 - \cos 2x)/2$, we thus get

$$i_p \doteqdot (B + 2CV_c) V \sin \omega t - \frac{V^2 C}{2} \cos 2\omega t$$

in which only the variational part has been kept. The parabolic curvature has produced some second-harmonic distortion, but no higher harmonics. Similarly, a series terminating at the cubic term can produce no harmonics above the third. The S curvature of a beam-tetrode characteristic requires at least a cubic term, and this type of tube must therefore produce considerable third-harmonic distortion. As will be seen shortly, even harmonics can be eliminated by a push-pull connection, and thus a push-pull triode amplifier can be expected to be useful when very low distortion is required.

PROBLEM

Construct a dynamic characteristic for the load line found in the last problem. From four well-spaced points on it determine the coefficients of a four-term power series and find the amplitude of the harmonics at full output.

5.3 POSSIBLE PLATE-CIRCUIT EFFICIENCY

We shall now discuss the efficiency with which the different ampli-fier classes can convert plate power input into useful output. The calculations will be for sinusoidal signals only; higher efficiency is possible with square waves, and lower efficiency is to be expected with "peaked" waves, such as those found in music and speech. Thus, the results for sine waves are fairly representative.

Class A, Series Fed. In a series-fed amplifier, the plate current flows through the load resistance, dissipating part of the power and reducing the efficiency. Fig. 5.5 shows the load line and a possible zero-bias plate curve; the operating point Q is chosen in the middle of the linear operating range. The maximum and minimum plate voltages are V_b and V_m; the corresponding minimum and maximum

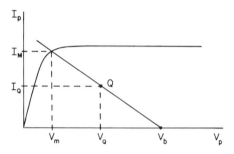

Fig. 5.5 Load line and maximum and minimum voltages
and currents for a series-fed Class A amplifier.

currents are 0 and I_M. The average plate current is I_Q. The power input is then simply

$$P_i = V_b I_Q$$

To calculate the maximum power output, we note that the rms value of a sine wave is the peak-to-peak amplitude divided by $2\sqrt{2}$; the output power is therefore

$$P_o = \frac{V_b - V_m}{2\sqrt{2}} \frac{I_M}{2\sqrt{2}} = \frac{(V_b - V_m)I_Q}{4}$$

Then the percent efficiency E is 100 P_o/P_i, or

$$E = \frac{100(V_b - V_m)}{4V_b} = 25\left(1 - \frac{V_m}{V_b}\right)\text{percent}$$

For a beam tetrode, V_m can be very small, and 25 percent efficiency can be approached; for a triode with the optimum load, V_m is one-third of V_b with series feed, and the best efficiency is less than 17 percent. The commonest example of a series-fed power amplifier is probably a cathode follower, to which this analysis applies.

Class A, Transformer Fed. With transformer coupling, the plate current does not flow through the load, and the d-c voltage drop between power supply and plate is very small. The same effect is occasionally produced by *shunt feed* when no impedance transformation is needed: a choke is connected between plate and V_b, and the load is coupled by a capacitor. With the average plate voltage equal to V_b,

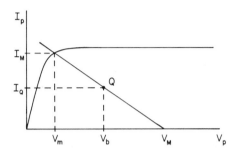

Fig. 5.6 Load line and maximum and minimum voltages
and currents for a transformer-fed Class A amplifier.

the load line is shown in Fig. 5.6; the stored energy in the primary inductance allows the voltage to rise above V_b to a maximum of V_M. Thus,

$$P_i = V_b I_Q \qquad \text{and} \qquad P_0 = \frac{(V_M - V_m)I_M}{8} = \frac{(V_b - V_m)I_Q}{2}$$

so that

$$E = 50\left(1 - \frac{V_m}{V_b}\right) \text{ percent}$$

The efficiency is exactly twice that of the series-fed arrangement.

Class B. In a Class B amplifier, two tubes are used in a push-pull arrangement, illustrated in Fig. 5.9 and discussed in the next section; each tube is biased to cutoff. Then one supplies the positive half cycles, and the other the negative, with the two parts being combined in the output transformer. (A Class AB amplifier works on a similar principle, but is not so heavily biased; its properties are intermediate between those of Classes A and B.) The load line and operating point for one tube are shown in Fig. 5.7. The peak value of the sine wave is $V_b - V_m$, and the peak current is I_M; the total power output is therefore

$$P_o = \frac{(V_b - V_m)I_M}{2}$$

To find the power input, we note that the current from the power supply is a series of half sine waves as in Fig. 5.8; the average current may be found by integrating sin ωt over a half cycle:

$$I = \frac{2}{T} \int_0^{T/2} \sin \omega t \, dt = \frac{2}{T} \left[\frac{-\cos \omega t}{\omega} \right]_0^{T/2} = \frac{4}{\omega T} = \frac{2}{\pi}$$

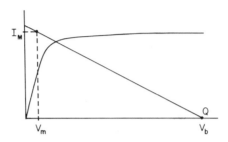

Fig. 5.7 Load line for one tube of a Class B amplifier.

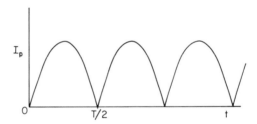

Fig. 5.8 Power-supply current of a Class B amplifier
with sine wave signal.

If the peak value is I_M instead of 1, the average current is $2I_M/\pi$ and the power input is

$$P_i = \frac{2 I_M V_b}{\pi}$$

The efficiency is

$$E = 100 \frac{\pi}{4} \frac{V_b - V_m}{V_b} \doteqdot 78.5 \left(1 - \frac{V_m}{V_b} \right)$$

For the highest efficiency the minimum voltage V_m should be as small as possible. It is normal practice to drive the grids positive at the peaks of the input wave so that V_m can approach zero, as Fig. 5.7 suggests. Under these conditions, beam tetrodes lose much of their advantage over triodes.

The improvement over the Class A circuit is greater than would appear at first sight, because the power input decreases when the signal decreases, whereas it remains at its full value in a Class A arrangement. For this reason, the Class B arrangement is widely used in high-power amplifiers and in the output circuit of portable radios.

As would be expected, the Class C amplifier attains even greater efficiency, because it draws current only when the plate voltage is near its minimum; very little power is dissipated by the plate and most of the input power goes to the load. Even a push-pull arrangement will not give a complete wave, and so the Class C circuit is only used with a tuned load at a fixed frequency; the resonant circuit smooths out the wave. A brief discussion is given in Chapter 11.

PROBLEM

The efficiencies calculated in this section are for maximum output. Suppose that the output voltage is a fraction k of the maximum; show that the efficiency is proportional to k^2 for Class A and to k for Class B.

5.4 PUSH-PULL AMPLIFIERS

The push-pull circuit shown in Fig. 5.9 has several advantages over the "single-ended" stage. Because of the symmetry of the circuit, it is clear that any distortion produced in a sinusoidal input signal must

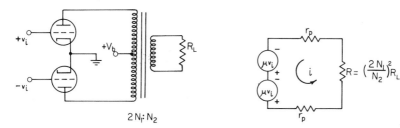

Fig. 5.9 Push-pull amplifier.   Fig. 5.10 Equivalent circuit of a push-pull amplifier.

be the same in positive and negative half cycles. The corresponding Fourier series will contain no even harmonics; in particular, the second harmonic, which otherwise is usually the largest, is eliminated. If the push-pull amplifier is compared with a single-ended one, using the same type of tube, it will deliver twice the power with less distortion or more than twice the power at the same distortion. It is also possible to design the transformer with a higher primary inductance and, therefore, a better low-frequency response. The reason is that there is no magnetization of the core by the d-c plate current, which flows in opposite directions through the two halves of the primary.

Finally, a reasonably linear amplifier with still greater output can be produced by operating in Classes B or AB. It is not surprising that nearly all high-power amplifiers and high-fidelity amplifiers use push-pull output stages.

The behavior of the circuit can be explored further with the help of the linear equivalent circuit in Fig. 5.10. Because the signal on one grid is inverted with respect to the other, the two generators drive current in the same direction. The variational ground at V_b is omitted since no signal current flows to it. The current in the reflected load R is

$$i = \frac{2\mu v_i}{2r_p + R}$$

and the power output is

$$P = i^2 R = \left(\frac{2\mu v_i}{2r_p + R}\right)^2 R$$

The same output would be produced by a single equivalent tube with a plate resistance of $2r_p$ and an amplification factor μ, fed by a signal $2v_i$. Its plate voltage is the difference between the plate voltages of the two actual tubes; similarly, its plate current is the difference between the two plate currents. Its characteristics can be constructed from the individual plate characteristics, and then load lines and dynamic characteristics can be plotted. It would take us too far out of our way to consider the details. For most purposes, the manufacturers' recommendations in a tube manual can be followed and the details ignored.

Sources of Push-pull Signals. If the benefits of push-pull operation are to be fully realized, an accurately balanced input signal is necessary. This can be produced in several ways, most of which have been considered in Chapter 4. Fig. 5.11 shows the most useful of these. The center-tapped transformer shares the defects of any transformer, and is usually reserved for Class B amplifiers, which draw grid current. The split-load cathode follower is very satisfactory; the differential amplifier

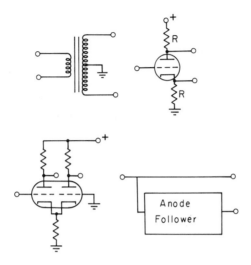

Fig. 5.11 Sources of push-pull input signals.

with one grid grounded is not as good because the two signals are not exactly the same, but it can deliver a larger signal. Finally, a signal can be passed directly to one tube, and inverted by an anode follower for the other.

"Ultralinear" Operation of Beam Tetrodes. As indicated in the previous section, a beam tetrode can deliver more power in Class A than an equivalent triode because of its lower minimum plate voltage. However, the distortion of a push-pull triode amplifier is considerably

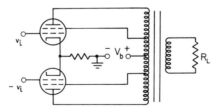

Fig. 5.12 "Ultralinear" amplifier.

less. The so-called *ultralinear* connection combines, in effect, these two advantages in one circuit; in fact, the distortion can be slightly less than that of the triode stage. As shown in Fig. 5.12, the screens are connected to taps on the primary winding of the output transformer, typically about 20 percent of the way from the center tap; the best point is found empirically for a given type of tube. A qualitative understanding of the effect can be had by noticing that the tubes will operate as tetrodes if the screens are transferred to the center tap (that is, to the power supply), and as triodes if the screens are connected to the plate terminals. The actual connection gives an intermediate result that combines the advantages of both. It is widely used for the power stages of high-fidelity amplifiers.

CHAPTER 6

Negative Feedback

6.1 BASIC PRINCIPLES

We have seen that the performance of a power amplifier is limited by the distortion of large signals. Even a voltage amplifier is not what could be called an accurate device; although the distortion may be small, the gain depends on the tube parameters, which vary from tube to tube, and even in the same tube as it ages and as the supply voltages change. It is the principle of negative feedback that allows accurate electronic measuring and amplifying devices to be made. A simple example is the cathode follower, which owes its remarkable properties to the feedback inherent in its circuit.

In principle, any desired accuracy can be obtained by the application of sufficient feedback; in practice, this is made difficult by an increasing tendency to oscillate. To obtain the enormous benefits of feedback without causing oscillation, the designer must understand and work within certain limitations; the emphasis here will be on these limitations.

Definitions. *Feedback* is the process of adding or subtracting part of the output of an amplifier to or from the input. If it is combined in such a way as to increase the input, the feedback is *positive*; the result is an increase in the effective gain if the feedback is small, and oscillation if it is large. Instability of gain and distortion are increased by positive feedback; it is seldom of interest except in oscillators, which are treated in Chapter 14. If the feedback reduces the effective input, it is *negative*;

129

the effective gain is reduced, but so are distortion and instability of gain. Extra gain is easily produced, and can then be traded for these other advantages, which are difficult to get in any other way.

Feedback Theory. Fig. 6.1 shows the block diagram of a feedback amplifier. The *beta circuit* feeds a fraction β of the output voltage back to be added to the input in some way which is not specified at present;

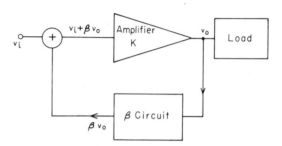

Fig. 6.1 Block diagram of a feedback amplifier.

β can be independent of frequency or not, as the application requires. The net input to the amplifier is seen to be $(v_i + \beta v_0)$; for negative feedback either β or v_0 must be negative. Since the amplifier has a gain K, its output must be

$$v_o = K(v_i + \beta v_0)$$

If we define A as the gain with feedback, we find

$$v_o(1 - K\beta) = Kv_i$$

$$A \equiv \frac{v_0}{v_i} = \frac{K}{1 - K\beta} \tag{1}$$

This is the fundamental feedback equation; it describes both positive and negative feedback, and for negative feedback the product $K\beta$ must be negative. Then the gain with feedback is reduced by the factor $(1 - K\beta)$; as will be shown, the factor of improvement in other properties is the same. The produce $K\beta$ is the gain around the feedback loop and is therefore called the *loop gain*. For our preliminary discussion we assume K and β both real; this restriction is removed in Section 6.3.

A physical understanding of the effects of feedback can be aided by rearranging the circuit as in Fig. 6.2. Let us suppose that the loop gain is very large, so that the difference voltage at the input of the amplifier must always be very small. The amplifier must produce the output

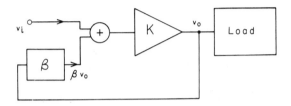

Fig. 6.2 The feedback amplifier rearranged to show it as a null-detector system.

voltage that satisfies this condition; thus, $\beta v_o \doteqdot -v_i$ at all times, and the amplifier serves only as a kind of active null detector. The gain with feedback is approximately

$$A \doteqdot -\frac{1}{\beta}$$

This is the limiting value of (1) when the loop gain is much greater than unity. When this is true, the characteristics of the amplifier are not important and the behavior of the system depends only on the feedback network. The gain will remain close to $-1/\beta$ even for large variations in K. Distortion will be small, because it can be regarded as caused by variation of gain according to the instantaneous value of the signal. If the load changes, the amplifier will act to restore the output to its original value, and will thus appear to have a greatly reduced output impedance.

The principle of feedback is used in many systems besides amplifiers. A common example is a house thermostat, in which the input signal is the desired temperature set on a dial. If the measured temperature is higher, the furnace is shut off; if it is lower, the furnace is started. This is a relatively crude system in which the output is either off or full on. Devices containing mechanical elements in the feedback loop are called *servomechanisms* or *servos*; they are used for a multitude of purposes, such as controlling aircraft, pointing guns, automatically balancing bridges or potentiometers, and so on. In every case the important element is that control is exercised by the difference between the output and the desired value.

6.2 EFFECTS OF FEEDBACK

We now proceed to give a quantitative discussion of the benefits of negative feedback. When the loop gain is large, the gain with feedback is approximately $-1/\beta$; if it is not so large, a useful second approximation can be found by binomial expansion, as follows:

$$A = - \frac{1}{\beta}\left(1 - \frac{1}{K\beta}\right)^{-1} \doteqdot - \frac{1}{\beta}\left(1 + \frac{1}{K\beta}\right)$$

Since $K\beta$ is negative, this is numerically smaller than $-1/\beta$, and the fractional deviation from this ideal value is the reciprocal of the loop gain. This approximation is useful as long as $K\beta$ is at least 10; for smaller values, the original equation (1) must be used.

Gain Stability. Suppose the gain of the amplifier K changes by a small amount ΔK; we wish to compare the fractional change $\Delta K/K$ with the corresponding smaller change $\Delta A/A$ in the gain with feedback. We thus require the ratio

$$\frac{K}{A}\frac{\Delta A}{\Delta K} \quad \text{or} \quad \frac{K}{A}\frac{dA}{dK}$$

Differentiation of (1) gives:

$$\frac{dA}{dK} = \frac{(1 - K\beta) + K\beta}{(1 - K\beta)^2} = \frac{1}{(1 - K\beta)^2}$$

The value of K/A is given directly by (1); we therefore find

$$\frac{K}{A}\frac{dA}{dK} = \frac{1}{(1 - K\beta)}$$

The improvement in gain stability is equal to $(1 - K\beta)$, which is approximately equal to the loop gain.

Distortion. Moderate distortion is caused by the curvature of a dynamic characteristic, as in Figs. 5.3 and 5.4. This can be regarded as a change in gain according to the instantaneous value of the signal.

Negative feedback will therefore straighten the dynamic characteristic and reduce the distortion by the factor $1/(1 - K\beta)$. However, the dynamic characteristic also has sharp bends where the tube cuts off or "bottoms"; the feedback cannot eliminate these and will in fact make them sharper because the rest of the characteristic has been straightened. Thus, very sharp clipping of the peaks of the signal will be produced if it is allowed to overload the amplifier. This type of distortion is particularly unpleasant in sound reproduction and is actually made worse by feedback.

Output Impedance. As an amplifier is loaded by a smaller and smaller load impedance, its output voltage drops; this effect can be represented by a Thévenin output impedance. A feedback amplifier will attempt to raise the output back to its original value; therefore,

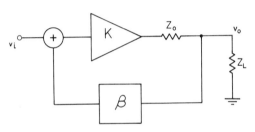

Fig. 6.3 Feedback amplifier with output impedance.

the apparent output impedance will be reduced. Since the loading effect is simply a kind of gain change, the reduction in impedance will be the same as the reduction in gain change, or $1/(1 - K\beta)$. We now proceed to prove this directly, with the aid of Fig. 6.3, in which the output impedance Z_o is shown explicitly, and the gain K is the un-loaded value. The gain with the load is

$$\frac{KZ_L}{Z_L + Z_o}$$

If this is substituted into (1), the result is

$$A = \frac{KZ_L}{Z_L + Z_o - \beta K Z_L} = \frac{K}{1 - K\beta} \frac{Z_L}{Z_L + Z'}$$

where $Z' \equiv Z_o/(1 - K\beta)$. The first part of this expression is the unloaded gain with feedback; therefore, Z' is the effective output impedance with feedback.

This modification of the output impedance does not affect the choice of optimum load discussed in Chapter 5; the output stage must be designed exactly as if feedback were not to be used, and loaded in the same way.

Size of Feedback Loop. It is possible to construct an amplifier in which each stage has its own local negative feedback; we now wish to show that this type of circuit is far inferior to a single feedback loop enclosing the whole amplifier. Unfortunately, there is a serious practical difficulty in applying a large amount of feedback over more than three stages; this will be considered in the next section. However, the feedback should still enclose as many stages as possible. We shall prove

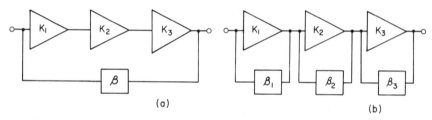

Fig. 6.4 (a) An amplifier with over-all feedback. (b) An amplifier with the same gain, but with the feedback over individual stages.

the theorem by the example of a three-stage amplifier. The two connections to be compared are shown in Fig. 6.4, where the individual βs in Fig. 6.4(b) are chosen to give the same gain as with the overall feedback in Fig. 6.4(a). We compute the effect on the net gain of small changes in individual stage gains as follows. The total gain without feedback is $K = K_1 K_2 K_3$; taking natural logarithms and forming the differential, we find

$$\frac{\Delta K}{K} = \frac{\Delta K_1}{K_1} + \frac{\Delta K_2}{K_2} + \frac{\Delta K_3}{K_3}$$

For overall feedback, $\Delta A/A$ is smaller by the factor $(1 - K\beta)$, or

$$\frac{\Delta A}{A} = \frac{1}{1 - K\beta}\left(\frac{\Delta K_1}{K_1} + \frac{\Delta K_2}{K_2} + \frac{\Delta K_3}{K_3}\right)$$

For individual feedback, a similar equation holds for each stage:

$$\frac{\Delta A_1}{A_1} = \frac{1}{1 - K_1\beta_1}\frac{\Delta K_1}{K_1}$$

and so on. Adding these three together, we get $\Delta A/A$, so that

$$\frac{\Delta A}{A} = \frac{1}{1 - K_1\beta_1}\frac{\Delta K_1}{K_1} + \frac{1}{1 - K_2\beta_2}\frac{\Delta K_2}{K_2} + \frac{1}{1 - K_3\beta_3}\frac{\Delta K_3}{K_3}$$

If the loop gains of the three stages are equal, the improvement in gain stability for overall feedback is approximately equal to the cube of the value for individual feedback. With individual feedback, each stage can only stabilize itself, whereas with overall feedback the whole amplifier acts to stabilize each part of itself.

As already mentioned, if this were the only consideration, feedback should always be applied around a whole amplifier. Because of the danger of oscillation, actual or incipient, it is usually necessary to limit the size of a loop to no more than three stages, unless a great effort to ensure stability can be made.

6.3 FREQUENCY RESPONSE AND STABILITY

It is unfortunate that the word "stability" is used in two different senses when discussing feedback amplifiers. Thus, increasing the amount of negative feedback stabilizes the gain, making it independent of changes in tubes and operating conditions. At the same time, the danger of oscillation is increased, and the amplifier may even become completely unstable against oscillation at the same time that its gain stability is very high. This section is devoted to the consideration of stability against oscillation. A closely associated topic is the effect of feedback on the frequency response, and this will be discussed first. Let us start with an amplifier having the same frequency response as a single R–C coupled stage: a lead at low frequencies and a lag at high, with a region of constant gain in the middle. The mid- and high-frequency gain is given by the expression

$$K = K_0\frac{1}{1 + j\omega\tau}$$

The gain with feedback is therefore

$$A = \frac{K}{1 - K\beta} = \frac{K_0}{1 + j\omega\tau - K_0\beta} = \frac{K_0}{1 - K_0\beta}\frac{1}{1 + j\omega\tau'}$$

where $\tau' \equiv \tau/(1 - K_0\beta)$. Thus, the corner frequency is increased by the same factor that the gain is decreased; this means that the high-frequency asymptote is the same without and with feedback, as illustrated in Fig. 6.5. The effect of feedback on the low-frequency response

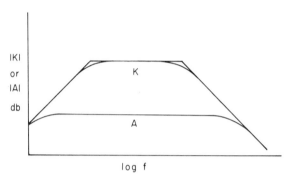

Fig. 6.5 Frequency response of a single-stage amplifier with and without feedback.

can be found in the same way; we will, however, merely note that it follows from the symmetry of the response on the logarithmic frequency scale. This result is also shown in Fig. 6.5.

PROBLEM

Prove the last statement directly.

"Two-stage" Amplifier. Next, we consider an amplifier having the same frequency response as two identical stages: two corners at the same frequency and an asymptotic slope of -40 db$_\text{v}$ per decade. Again, we concentrate on the high-frequency region because the algebra is simpler; the gain without feedback is $K_0/(1 + j\omega\tau)^2$, and with feedback it is

$$A = \frac{K_0}{(1 + j\omega\tau)^2 - K_0\beta} = \frac{K_0}{(1 - K_0\beta - \omega^2\tau^2) + 2j\omega\tau}$$

As with the transformer-coupled amplifier, there is a possibility of a peak in the gain at the frequency where the real part of the denominator is zero. In this case, however, the effect is caused not by resonance but by the phase shift, which may approach 180 degrees, so that the feedback becomes positive instead of negative. To find the approximate excess gain at the peak, we assume that it occurs at the frequency just mentioned:

$$\omega^2 \tau^2 = 1 - K_0\beta \doteq - K_0\beta$$

To the same degree of approximation, the mid-frequency gain with feedback is $A_0 \doteq -1/\beta$. Using the above expression for A, we find

$$\frac{A}{A_0} \doteq \frac{- K_0\beta}{2j\omega\tau} = - \frac{j}{2}\sqrt{- K_0\beta}$$

For example, if $K_0\beta = -100$, the gain at the peak is about five times larger than at mid-frequencies, and the phase shift is -90 degrees. The gain then rapidly drops toward the original asymptote, which is

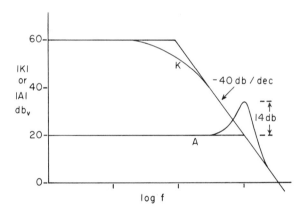

Fig. 6.6 High-frequency gain of a two-stage amplifier, showing the peak that is produced when both stages have the same corner frequency.

given by $A \simeq -K_0/\omega^2\tau^2$. The result is sketched in Fig. 6.6. The peak is at the frequency at which the asymptotes intersect, as shown in the figure.

A peak of this sort is undesirable in almost any amplifier, but especially so if it has to reproduce transients. The rise of a pulse or square wave will have a large overshoot, followed by several cycles of damped oscillations. Moreover, the presence of the peak is a sign that the amplifier is nearly ready to go into oscillation, and a few extra degrees of phase shift may be enough to make the amplifier completely unstable. We therefore conclude that the loop gain must not be allowed to fall off at a rate as high as the 40 db$_v$ per decade assumed here.

PROBLEM

Verify that the frequency given for the gain peak is located where the asymptotes intersect, and that the high-frequency asymptotes for A and K are the same.

Intermediate Case. We now proceed to show that a slope as high as 30 db$_v$ per decade is allowable in most cases, since it produces at most only a small peak. The asymptotic slope of any combination of R-C networks is always a multiple of 20 db$_v$ per decade, but the required slope is readily approached by suitable combinations of phase-retard networks (or phase-advance networks at low frequencies). For mathematical convenience, we assume that the gain in the high-frequency region is given by

$$K = \frac{K_0}{(1 + j\omega\tau)^{3/2}}$$

so that

$$A = \frac{K_0}{(1 + j\omega\tau)^{3/2} - K_0\beta}$$

Since the peak, if present, is well above the corner frequency, the term $(1 + j\omega\tau)^{3/2}$ can be approximated by

$$(j\omega\tau)^{3/2} = \frac{j - 1}{\sqrt{2}}(\omega\tau)^{3/2}$$

The frequency of the peak is given by

$$\omega\tau \doteq 2^{1/3}(-K_0\beta)^{2/3}$$

and the corresponding gain is

$$A \doteq K_0\sqrt{2}/j(\omega\tau)^{3/2} \doteq K_0/j(-K_0\beta) = j/\beta = -jA_0$$

To this rough approximation, there is no peak at all for any value of loop gain. However, the actual example plotted in Fig. 6.7 shows a peak about 2 db_v high for a loop gain of 40 db_v.

Fig. 6.7 shows the gain of an amplifier having an asymptotic slope of -30 db_v per decade, as considered in this section. Loop gains of 0, 20 db, and 40 db were assumed. There is still a small peak, which would probably cause overshoot in a square wave or step function, but for many purposes it could be tolerated.

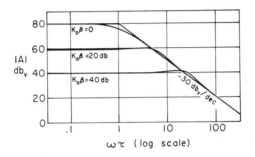

Fig. 6.7 High-frequency gain of an amplifier with an asymptotic slope of -30 db_v decade, for various values of loop gain.

The actual gain at any frequency can readily be found by evaluating the correct expression, but if a large number of values are required, as is usual, the calculations become tedious. Moreover, there are times when the loop gain is known only as an empirical pair of curves giving gain and phase-shift as a function of frequency. A useful calculator for the purpose has been described by Felker*; it was used to produce the data for Fig. 6.7. The device is called a "$\mu\beta$-effect" calculator or, in our notation, a "$K\beta$-effect" calculator.

6.4 CRITERIA FOR STABILITY

In our study of special cases, we have observed that a steep slope in the loop-gain characteristic is accompanied by a peak in the gain with feedback. If the slope is made any steeper than 40 db_v per decade, the peak will in effect become infinitely high, indicating that the amplifier will oscillate. We now wish to examine two criteria that allow one to say whether or not this oscillation will take place. These are

* J. H. Felker. *Proceedings of the IRE*, Vol. 37, October 1949, pp. 1204–1206.

based on either a "gain-phase" plot or a "Nyquist diagram." Let us recall that the gain is given by the fundamental equation

$$A = \frac{K}{1 - K\beta}$$

Ordinarily this is much less than K because $K\beta$ is negative. But in the cutoff regions at low and high frequencies, the phase shift of K can easily surpass 180 degrees; at the point where it is exactly 180 degrees, $K\beta$ is positive. If it is still unity or greater, the amplifier will oscillate. The *gain-phase* plot allows the situation to be visualized by plotting the gain and phase of $K\beta$ against frequency. The scales are superposed with 0 db coinciding with 180 degrees; stability then depends on which curve crosses this line first. Our last two examples are shown in Fig. 6.8; the single stage never has a phase shift larger than 90 degrees and

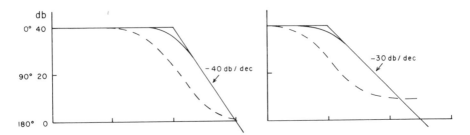

Fig. 6.8 Gain-phase plots for the amplifiers of Figs. 6.6 and 6.7.

is not included. The gain curve for the double stage crosses the 0-db line while the phase curve is still about 10 degrees short of 180 degrees; we say that the *phase margin* is about 10 degrees. This is enough to ensure that the amplifier does not oscillate, but not enough, as we have seen, to prevent a high peak in the gain. The amplifier with the asymptotic slope of 30 db_v per decade has a phase margin of slightly more than 45 degrees; even so, there still may be a small peak.

Fig. 6.9 shows a fairly common type of gain-phase plot in which the phase is held at about 135 degrees while the loop gain goes through 0 db, and then increases rapidly through 180 degrees. Such an amplifier will oscillate if the loop gain is raised; in Fig. 6.9, an increase of less than 20 db_v would be enough.

The *Nyquist diagram* presents the same information on a single polar plot of gain vs. phase. The frequency does not appear explicitly, because it is a parameter along the curve. An example, corresponding to the first

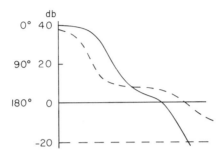

Fig. 6.9 A typical gain-phase plot for an actual amplifier.

diagram in Fig. 6.8, is shown in Fig. 6.10. The whole mid-frequency region is contained in the point on the real axis, and the corner frequency (two coincident corners) is at the intersection with the imaginary axis. If the low-frequency region were also plotted, it would occupy

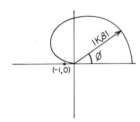

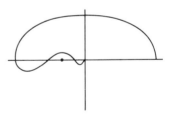

Fig. 6.10 Nyquist diagram for the first amplifier in Fig. 6.8.

Fig. 6.11 Nyquist diagram for the case of conditional stability.

the lower half of the plane. At the critical point $(-1, 0)$ the loop gain is unity while the phase shift is 180 degrees; therefore, the curve must not pass through this point. It must not enclose it either, since if it does the phase shift will be 180 degrees while the loop gain is still greater than unity. If it passes close by, the amplifier will not oscillate, but will have the peaks in its gain curve that we have already studied. The gain-phase and the Nyquist criteria are essentially identical, but the more fundamental basis of the latter allows an additional case known as *conditional stability*, illustrated in Fig. 6.11. This amplifier will not oscillate even though it violates the gain-phase criterion; however, it will oscillate if the loop gain is either increased or decreased, and is hardly to be considered a practical device.

PROBLEMS

1) Plot the Nyquist diagram for a single-stage amplifier.
2) Sketch the gain-phase diagram for the conditionally stable amplifier of Fig. 6.11.

6.5 DESIGN OF A FEEDBACK AMPLIFIER

In this section we consider in detail the design of a two-stage feedback amplifier in order to illustrate the use of phase-advance and phase-retard networks for shaping the cutoff characteristics. First, however, we shall discuss the most useful methods of mixing the feedback and input signals.

Application of Feedback. The first method is *resistive mixing*, shown in Fig. 6.12. This method is used in the anode follower, but its principal

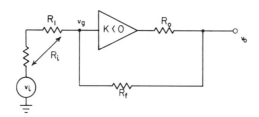

Fig. 6.12 Application of feedback by resistive mixing.

application is with operational amplifiers of the type used in analog computers. These amplifiers have a very high gain and a very low output impedance. To simplify the treatment, we shall therefore assume that K is infinite and R_o is zero, although a complete treatment is not difficult. The voltage v_g may be found by superposition:

$$v_g = v_i \frac{R_f}{R_i + R_f} + v_o \frac{R_i}{R_i + R_f}$$

Because K is very large, v_g is very small compared with v_o and therefore with v_i; it can be set equal to zero, giving

$$\frac{v_o}{v_i} = A \doteq - \frac{R_f}{R_i}$$

As with the anode follower, the two resistors form an electrical "see-saw" with a *virtual ground* at the input of the amplifier. Although the output resistance R_o can usually be neglected, the source resistance must be included in R_i. Because of the virtual ground, the input resistance is equal to R_1 (Fig. 6.12), or usually R_i, since $R_i \doteq R_1$.

An important special case of resistive mixing is *electrometer feedback*, in which the source resistance is infinite. This corresponds to a constant-current source, such as a phototube, a photomultiplier, or an ionization chamber. In any of these, a current is produced by the phenomenon being measured, and the number of electrons collected per second is independent of the plate voltage as long as it is large enough. Because the current is often very small, the amplifier is usually of the electrometer type, with very small input current. The concept of voltage gain is not applicable; what is required is a "transresistance," the ratio of output voltage to input current. The circuit is shown in Fig. 6.13; if the amplifier input draws no current, we can write

$$v_i = v_o + iR = \frac{v_o}{K}$$

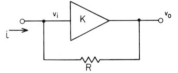

Then

$$v_o = - \frac{K}{K-1} Ri \doteq - Ri$$

Fig. 6.13 Electrometer feedback useful with current sources.

The amplifier simply presents the voltage drop across R at its output, but as usual at a very low impedance level, even though R may be many thousands of megohms.

Cathode feedback is widely used with amplifiers because it permits the usual high input impedance of a grid. It was briefly discussed in Section 4.11 as a kind of differential amplifier. The arrangement is shown in Fig. 6.14, along with the Thévenin equivalent of the cathode circuit. As was shown in Section 4.11, the effective input to the tube is

$$v_i - \frac{1+\mu}{\mu} v_k = v_i - \frac{1+\mu}{\mu} \frac{R_1}{R_1+R_2} v_o$$

The presence of R lowers the gain from both inputs by the same factor and therefore does not affect this expression. The feedback factor β is the coefficient of v_o; thus,

$$\beta = -\frac{1 + \mu}{\mu} \frac{R_1}{R_1 + R_2} \doteq -\frac{R_1}{R_2}$$

The approximation is fairly good, since small amounts have been dropped from both numerator and denominator. It is seen that β depends slightly on the amplification factor of the tube, but the effect

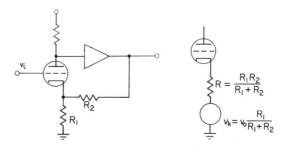

Fig. 6.14 Cathode feedback with an arrangement that is suitable if the cathode input can be attenuated.

is small if μ is large; thus, the tube should be a pentode or a high-μ triode if possible, unless gain stability is not important. Fortunately, μ is the most stable of all the tube parameters. Since β is negative, the amplifier gain must be positive; usually this criterion is satisfied by the use of two stages.

Occasionally it is convenient to use a cathode follower to drive the cathode input; in effect, the first stage is then converted into a differential amplifier. The feedback and signal both encounter a high impedance, and the polarity of feedback can be chosen at will by taking the output from the appropriate plate.

PROBLEM

Derive an exact expression for the gain with resistive mixing (Fig. 6.12) and show that it approximates $-R_f/R_i$ when K is large.

EXAMPLE

We shall now consider the design of the amplifier in Fig. 6.15, showing how the networks in dotted lines can be chosen to shape the cutoffs appropriately. The amplifier has two stages and cathode feed-back; to simplify the discussion, the effects of the screen and cathode bypass condensers of the pentode will not be considered. If the first tube has a μ of 100 and an r_p of 66 K, its mid-frequency gain will be -30; this is much less than μ (in magnitude) because of the resistance in the cathode circuit. For the second stage we assume a gain of -240, so that the total gain without feedback is 7200 or 77 db$_{\rm v}$. The feedback factor is

$$\beta = - \frac{1 + \mu}{\mu}\ \frac{4.7\ K}{4.7K + 470K} = -0.010$$

The loop gain is $K\beta = -72$ or 37 db$_{\rm v}$, and the gain with feedback is very nearly $-1/\beta = +100$.

Let us now consider the high-frequency cutoff, ignoring for the moment the networks in dotted lines. The stray capacitances are shown dotted, and a load of 70 pf on the output is assumed. As shown in Section 4.4, the resistance to be used with these capacitances is the parallel combination of $[r_p + (\mu + 1)R_k]$, the load resistance, and the

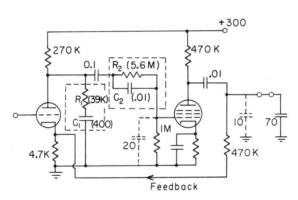

Fig. 6.15 Circuit for the design example.

grid resistance of the next stage; for the pentode in Fig. 6.15, we use the 470 K feedback resistance instead of the grid resistance. The time constants and corner frequencies are shown in the following table:

R, kilohms	C, pf	τ_2, μsec	f_2, kc
147	20	3.0	53
235	80	20	8.0

The corresponding asymptotic characteristic is shown by the dotted line in the upper-right part of Fig. 6.16. The slope is $-20\,\mathrm{db_v}$ per decade from 8 to 53 kc, and then changes to -40. The loop-gain characteristic is the same shape, since β is real, but is 40 $\mathrm{db_v}$ lower. It

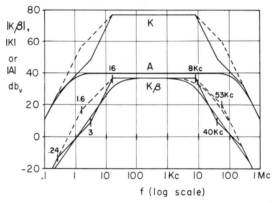

Fig. 6.16 Gain, loop gain, and gain with feedback of Fig. 6.15.

crosses the 0-db level at about 180 kc, and the next step is to estimate the phase shift at this frequency. This is done by adding the values of $\tan^{-1}(f/f_2)$ for each stage, as follows:

STAGE	f_2, kc	f/f_2	$\tan^{-1}(f/f_2)$, degrees
1	53	3.4	74
2	8	22.5	87
			161

This leaves a phase margin of 19 degrees, which is hardly enough. Two possible remedies exist. The first is to arrange the two corner frequencies to have a ratio of about 20; this is called *dominant-lag* stabilization, and can give a satisfactory phase margin of about 40 degrees for the loop gain considered here. The second is to include a phase-retard network. This is more efficient, and we shall proceed to illustrate it by example.

The phase-retard network is composed of R_1 and C_1 in Fig. 6.15. Its action is physically understood as follows: at low frequencies, the reactance of C_1 is large enough that the network has no effect; at high frequencies, R_1 appears in parallel with the 270-K load resistor of the triode, reducing its gain by a factor of 5. The value of C_1 has been chosen so as to place the transition between 8 and 40 kc. At about 800 kc, the plateau runs into the original asymptote and another corner occurs. The effect is to take a "bite" out of the original gain curve, as shown in Fig. 6.17. The new curve for the whole amplifier is shown by

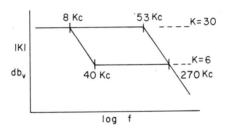

Fig. 6.17 Asymptotes for the phase-retard network.

the solid lines in Fig. 6.16; the loop gain is reduced to 0 db at 120 kc instead of 180 kc as before. We proceed to calculate the phase shift at 120 kc, remembering that the corner at 40 kc contributes a negative angle to the total:

STAGE	f_2, kc	f/f_2	$\tan^{-1}(f/f_2)$, degrees
2	8	15	86
1	8	15	86
1	40	3	−72
1	270	0.44	24
			———
			116

Insertion of the phase-retard network has increased the phase margin from 19 to 64 degrees. Because of this large margin, it may be expected that the gain with feedback will run smoothly into the curve for K, as shown in Fig. 6.16. Notice that, even though K starts to cut off rather sharply at 8 kc, A is constant up to nearly 100 kc.

Let us pause for a moment to discuss the choice of the corner frequencies for the phase-retard network. The usual practice is to carry the gain down at -40 db$_\mathrm{v}$ per decade until the loop gain is a few db$_\mathrm{v}$ (6 in this case), and then turn up to -20 db$_\mathrm{v}$ per decade to go through the critical 0-db level. R_1 is chosen to give the required change in gain, and C_1 to produce the 8-kc corner frequency along with the output resistance of the stage. Since the stray 20 pf gives a corner at 53 kc, $(C_1 + C_p)$ must be 6.6 times larger, or 132 pf. Then C_1 is 112 pf.

The discussion of the low-frequency cutoff follows similar lines. Without the phase-advance network of R_2 and C_2, two corners are formed as follows:

STAGE	R, megohms	C, μf	τ_1, sec	f_1, cps	f_1/f	$\tan^{-1}(f_1/f)$, degrees
1	1.05	0.1	0.1	1.6	3.0	72
2	0.94	0.01	0.01	16	30	88
						160

The resistance is formed from the grid resistor in series with the combination of plate resistance and load resistance, as shown in Fig. 4.14. Loop gain reaches 0 db at about 0.53 cps, giving the phase shifts shown in the table, and a phase margin of 20 degrees. This performance could readily be improved by making the ratio of the corner frequencies larger, but instead let us use the phase-advance network. Because the principles are the same as those just discussed at high frequencies, and because the network itself was considered in Chapter 2, we shall confine ourselves to the results as shown in Fig. 6.16 and the following table:

STAGE	R, megohms	C, μf	τ_1, sec	f_1, cps	f_1/f	$\tan^{-1}(f_1/f)$, degrees
2	0.94	0.01	0.01	16	13	86
1	0.9	0.01	0.01	16	13	86
1	5.6	0.01	0.056	3	2.4	-67
1	6.6	0.1	0.66	0.24	0.19	11
						116

The loop gain crosses the 0-db level at about 1.25 cps, and the phase shift is calculated at this frequency. The phase margin has been increased to 64 degrees, again large enough so that the A characteristic should run smoothly into the K characteristic, as shown in Fig. 6.16. It can be seen that the gain is constant within 3 db$_v$ from about 1 cps to 100 kc, even though no great effort was made to achieve a wide bandwidth.

6.6 SOME APPLICATIONS

We have already studied some special cases of negative feedback. Among these are the cathode follower and the anode follower, and the typical properties of a feedback amplifier are easily recognized in these circuits: reduced gain, substantial independence of gain on tube characteristics, low distortion, and low output impedance.

PROBLEM
Derive the expressions for gain and output impedance by regarding these as ordinary amplifiers with 100 percent negative feedback.

Current Feedback. So far we have studied only *voltage feedback*, in which the feedback signal is derived from the voltage across the load. But it is also possible to derive it from the current through the load, giving *current feedback*. Gain and distortion are reduced in exactly the same way, but the output impedance is increased instead of decreased. This fact is easily seen if we consider the limiting case of infinite loop gain. The load current would then be defined completely by the input voltage and would be totally independent of the load impedance. The amplifier would behave as an ideal current source, which has an infinite source resistance. Quantitative discussion shows that the output impedance is increased by the usual factor, 1 + loop gain.

An example that we have already encountered is the amplifier with resistance in the cathode circuit, discussed in Section 4.5. We noted the loss of gain and the increase in the effective plate resistance to $[r_p + (\mu + 1)R_k]$. Another example is the regulation of current in a power supply, as is required for an electromagnet. Current feedback can also be used to advantage in an amplifier designed to drive a moving-coil meter, as in Fig. 6.18. The feedback voltage V_f is derived by passing the meter current through a resistor R, usually called a *shunt,* and connected to one input of the differential amplifier. If this input draws no current, $V_f = IR$, and

$$V_0 = K(V_i - IR) = I(R + r)$$

where the meter resistance is r. Then

$$I = \frac{K}{r + (K + 1)R} V_i \doteq \frac{V_i}{R}$$

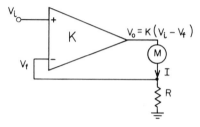

Fig. 6.18 Current-feedback amplifier to drive a milliammeter.

The approximation is excellent if K is large, and it can easily be made several hundred or even several thousand. R can be a precision resistor if desired, and the resistance of the meter need not be known nor constant.

High-fidelity Power Amplifier. Without negative feedback, it is impossible to build a power amplifier with distortion low enough to qualify it for the label "high fidelity." A popular circuit is the *Williamson* type, which is shown, with some simplifications, in Fig. 6.19. To reduce any distortion caused by the output transformer, it is enclosed within the feedback loop. It is therefore necessary to take considerable care to keep the feedback loop stable. First of all, a special transformer of very high quality is needed. The presence of a phase-retard network in the plate circuit of the first stage will be noted, and direct coupling to the second stage eliminates one lead network. The other coupling networks are chosen, in conjunction with the characteristics of the transformer, to give a suitable low-frequency cutoff. The split-load phase inverter is followed by a symmetrical differential amplifier, which ensures that the two output tubes receive identical waveforms and also provides the large voltage swing that they require. In the original Williamson amplifier the output tubes were connected

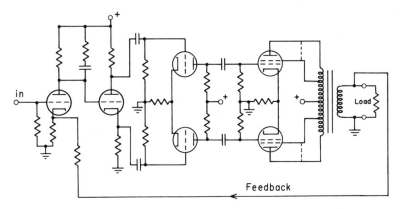

Fig. 6.19 Simplified circuit of the Williamson power amplifier.

as triodes; this is shown by dotted lines. More commonly used, however, is the "ultralinear" connection (Section 5.4), which gives appreciably more power with about the same distortion. The cathode feedback employed is made negative by the correct choice of polarity of the transformer secondary.

REFERENCES

The standard source work is *Network Analysis and Feedback Amplifier Design* by H. W. Bode (Princeton, N.J.: D. Van Nostrand Company, Inc., 1945). Most physicists will find their way about more easily in *Linear Feedback Analysis* by J. G. Thomason (New York: Pergamon Press, Inc., and McGraw-Hill Book Company, Inc., 1955).

CHAPTER 7

Power Supplies

The plate and bias supplies in electronic equipment are usually produced from an a-c source of the appropriate voltage by *rectification* followed by *filtering*; this results in an approximation to direct current with a small superposed a-c component called *ripple*. If the ripple must be very small, or if the d-c voltage must be constant, a *regulator* is also included. In this chapter rectifiers, filters, and regulators will be discussed one at a time, as far as possible.

7.1 RECTIFIERS

A rectifier is a device or a circuit that can convert alternating to direct current, although the latter usually has a large a-c ripple component. The diode vacuum tube, introduced in Chapter 3, and the semiconductor diode, to be discussed in Chapter 8, conduct readily in one direction and very little or not at all in the other. The tube rectifier is much older and is still probably cheaper, but the semiconductor has many advantages and is widely used where reliability is important.

The manufacturer provides each type of rectifier with a set of maximum *ratings*, which should not be exceeded if the device is to have a normal life. The average current and the peak current ratings are mainly controlled by the heating effect; the *peak inverse voltage* is the maximum voltage that the diode can withstand in the nonconducting direction without danger of breaking down. Semiconducting diodes tend to have higher current ratings and lower voltage ratings than tubes; however, the voltage rating can be raised to any desired value with semiconductors by putting the required number of similar diodes in series.

The simplest rectifier circuit is the *half-wave* rectifier, shown in Fig. 7.1; we show the diode as a tube, but it can equally well be a semiconductor. A transformer provides the required a-c voltage (or it may

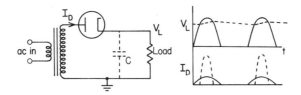

Fig. 7.1 Half-wave rectifier with its voltage and current
waveforms.

be omitted if the line voltage is suitable), and the diode passes the positive half-cycles while blocking the negative. The capacitor C is strictly part of the filter, but it also plays an essential part in the operation of the rectifier by maintaining the load voltage fairly constant between peaks. Current then flows through the diode only when the transformer voltage is higher than the capacitor voltage. A typical waveform is also shown in the figure. The peak diode current can easily be several times larger than the average load current, and this must be taken into account when a rectifier is chosen. The maximum inverse voltage on the diode occurs when the transformer delivers its negative peak, and is equal to the sum of this negative plate voltage and the positive cathode voltage maintained by the capacitor. Because these two are nearly equal, the peak inverse voltage is nearly *twice* the *peak* voltage delivered by the transformer. Transformer voltages are usually given as root-mean-square, rather than peak values, and this must be remembered when the stress on the diode is estimated.

Fig. 7.2 shows a *full-wave* circuit using a transformer with a center tap on the secondary winding. Each half of the winding takes its turn in providing current through the corresponding diode. The remarks already made about the capacitor still apply, but the pulses of current are smaller since they come twice as often. As before, the peak inverse voltage is twice the peak voltage delivered by half the secondary, but this time the result does not depend on the presence of the capacitor, because one diode is always delivering voltage to the cathode of the other. A convenient feature of the circuit is that the cathodes of the two diodes are connected together; they can then be made as a single tube with one cathode and two anodes. It should also be possible to fabricate a similar semiconducting double diode, but this is not normal practice, perhaps because of surface leakage between the anodes.

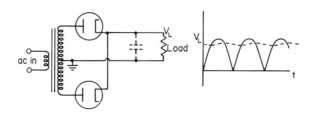

Fig. 7.2 Full-wave rectifier.

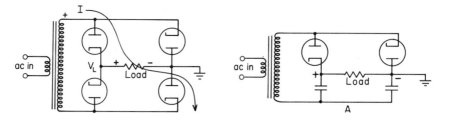

Fig. 7.3 Full-wave bridge rectifier.   Fig. 7.4 Full-wave voltage doubler.

Another kind of full-wave circuit, shown in Fig. 7.3, is called a *bridge* rectifier, because the arrangement is similar to that of a Wheatstone bridge. The waveforms are identical to those of Fig. 7.2. In drawing the circuit, it is convenient to regard it as if each pair of rectifiers were arranged as in Fig. 7.2, but with the second pair reversed to deliver a negative voltage. The center tap, however, is not needed and the output is taken between the pair of cathodes and the pair of anodes. For the same number of turns on the transformer, Fig. 7.3 delivers twice the voltage of Fig. 7.2, but it requires twice as many diodes. It is most useful in high-voltage circuits, where at least two diodes in series are needed in any case because of the high peak inverse voltage. A good example is the power supply for an x-ray tube. With semiconducting diodes, a "high" voltage in this sense may be only a few hundred volts, and the bridge circuit therefore finds considerable use. The current path for one polarity of the transformer winding is shown in Fig. 7.3, and it can be seen that the inverse voltage is divided equally between the two nonconducting diodes.

Fig. 7.4 shows a *full-wave voltage doubler*, so called because the d-c output approaches twice the peak voltage of the transformer secondary. It can be regarded as being made up of two half-wave circuits like the one in Fig. 7.1, but with one of the diodes reversed so that its output is negative. The load is connected between the positive output and the negative output, each of which develops a voltage with respect to the point A equal to the transformer voltage. It makes no difference that the actual ground point is the negative side of the load. The peak inverse voltage on the diodes is equal to the total output voltage; the circuit is thus convenient and economical for use with semiconducting rectifiers with their rather limited inverse ratings. Voltage doublers are also useful in transformerless supplies, since a 115-volt (rms) line voltage produces about a 250-volt d-c output; however, the full-wave doubler is not normally suitable for this purpose because neither side of the output can be grounded. This is only possible if the a-c input and the d-c output have a common terminal, since one side of the a-c line is always grounded.

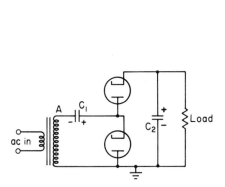

Fig. 7.5 Half-wave voltage doubler.

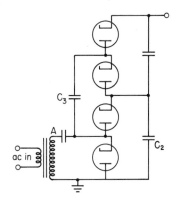

Fig. 7.6 Voltage quadrupler.

The *half-wave voltage doubler*, shown in Fig. 7.5, has this common connection and can therefore be used in a transformerless supply. It is

also suitable for extension by adding more stages into a voltage multiplier, often called a Cockcroft-Walton circuit on the basis of its use in
nuclear physics. When the point A is negative, C_1 is charged with the
polarity shown through the first diode. At the peak of the next half
cycle, when A is positive, the voltage on C_1 adds to the voltage at A, and
the sum is passed by the second diode to C_2. After a few cycles, the
voltage on C_2 will approach twice the peak voltage of the transformer.
Because power is delivered to C_2 only on alternate half cycles, the ripple
is greater than that of the full-wave circuit.

Fig. 7.6 shows the extension of the same principle to form a voltage
quadrupler. The first two stages are unchanged, and the action just
described continues in much the same way. For example, during the
third half cycle, when A is negative again, the bottom end of C_3 is near
ground and it is charged from C_2 through the third diode. Semiconducting rectifiers are especially convenient in this circuit, because
there are no cathodes having power supplies that must be insulated
from the high voltage. The peak inverse voltage on each diode is
twice the peak value of the transformer output, and the d-c voltage on
each capacitor is the same.

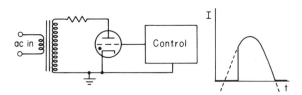

Fig. 7.7 Grid-controlled rectifier with plate-voltage and
plate-current waveforms.

An important class of rectifier, which we shall have to pass over
briefly, is the *grid-controlled* type. For low and medium power, the tube
used is usually a thyratron, that is, a gas-filled tube. For very high
powers, *ignitrons* can be used. A semiconducting equivalent is also
available under the name *silicon controlled rectifier*. Fig. 7.7 illustrates
the principle involved, in a half-wave circuit similar to Fig. 1. A control
circuit keeps the tube cut off until a specific time, when it is allowed to
fire; the grid then loses control and the tube continues to conduct until
the plate goes negative again. A typical current waveform is shown, and

it can be seen that the average current can readily be controlled from a maximum right down to zero by varying the firing time. Many texts on engineering electronics treat these circuits in detail, and the interested reader is referred to them.

Another technique that is useful for high powers, but which we cannot treat in detail, is *polyphase* rectification. Large amounts of electric power are usually transmitted along three or four wires forming three separate circuits, each carrying an a-c wave displaced in phase 120 degrees with respect to the other two. A three-phase full-wave rectifier produces six overlapping peaks per cycle, so that even without filtering the ripple is fairly small. Moreover, the current is shared among six rectifiers. Physicists might encounter such rectifiers in magnet power supplies and in d-c supplies for a building or large laboratory.

7.2 FILTERS

The purpose of a filter is to accept pulsating d-c voltage from a rectifier and reduce the ripple so that the output resembles pure d-c voltage. As we have seen, the rectifier and the filter cannot always be completely separated, but this is not an important difficulty.

In general, filters are made up of series inductance and parallel capacitance; the first opposes the ripple current, and the second shunts it to ground. Alternatively, the elements may be regarded as storing energy during peaks and releasing it during valleys so as to smooth the flow. The energy stored by an inductance is $\frac{1}{2}LI^2$, and by a capacitance is $\frac{1}{2}CV^2$. Inductance is therefore most useful for high currents, since it is not practical to wind a coil with fine enough wire to produce a useful energy storage with currents less than 10 or 20 ma. With electrolytic capacitors, however, it is possible to have a very large capacitance at low voltage, so that the stored energy per unit volume can be large. Therefore, capacitors can be useful at almost any voltage.

It is possible to derive by the methods of circuit analysis approximate equations for the reduction in ripple produced by a filter. The results are approximate for two reasons: the rectifier is inherently a nonlinear circuit, and the ripple is not sinusoidal. We shall consider only the fundamental component of this complex wave, remembering that its frequency is twice the line frequency for a full-wave rectifier.

A filter containing a single inductance, feeding a load R_L, is shown in Fig. 7.8. The ripple at the output of the rectifier is r_1, and past the filter it is r_2. For an angular frequency ω, we can write

$$\frac{r_2}{r_1} = \frac{R_L}{R_L + j\omega L} \doteqdot \frac{R_L}{\omega L}$$

The approximation will be good as long as r_2/r_1 is small, which is the normal case since otherwise the filter is not producing any benefit. We have dropped the j from the approximate expression because

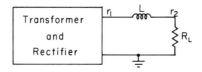

Fig. 7.8 Inductance filter.

only the magnitudes are usually of interest. Since the load current is inversely proportional to R_L, it can be seen that the performance of an inductance as a filter improves in proportion to the current; it has already been noted that this is because it can store more and more energy.

An interesting property of the choke filter is its ability to maintain a flow of current from a full-wave rectifier even when the transformer voltage is less than the load voltage. The self-induction in the choke as the magnetic field collapses provides a potential that keeps the current flowing through the diodes. However, this effect will not continue all the way through the minimum of the wave unless the choke is storing enough energy to carry it through. In other words, for a given choke there is a minimum current below which the rectifier current is no longer continuous; and conversely, for a given current there is a minimum inductance called the *critical inductance*. It can be shown that for 120 cps ripple, its value in henries is approximately $R_L/1000$, with R_L measured in ohms. The advantage of maintaining the inductance greater than this value is that the large peaks of current shown in Fig. 7.1 are smoothed out, and a given diode can deliver more power.

A capacitor filter is shown in Fig. 7.9, along with a waveform diagram illustrating its operation. This has already been discussed briefly, but we now wish to make a quantitative estimate of the ripple. We shall assume full-wave rectification; the result should be doubled for half-wave operation. The part of the ripple between the peaks is formed simply by the discharge of C through R_L, and an estimate of its amplitude can be made by assuming that this decay occupies a complete

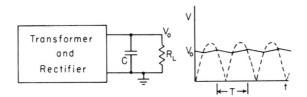

Fig. 7.9 Condenser filter and its output wave.

half cycle T. As shown in Fig. 4.27, the change in voltage is $VT/R_LC = 2\pi V/\omega R_LC$. The actual ripple is less than this value, and we should also reduce it to rms terms; since the wave is not sinusoidal, the factor $2\sqrt{2}$ is not correct, but it can be used as an approximation. As a reasonable estimate of these two factors we can drop the factor π, so that the ripple is given approximately by

$$\frac{r}{V} \doteq \frac{2}{\omega R_L C}$$

In this case the ripple is proportional to the load current; it should be noted that in addition the d-c voltage falls rapidly as the load current increases.

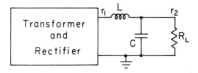
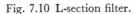

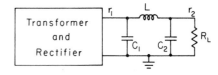

Fig. 7.10 L-section filter.   Fig. 7 11 π-section filter.

Most actual filters contain combinations of inductors and capacitors; the simplest example is the *L-section* or *inductor-input* filter shown in Fig. 7.10. Normally, the shunt impedance of C is much less than that of R_L, and also less than the impedance of L; then we can write

$$\frac{r_2}{r_1} \doteq \frac{1/\omega C}{\omega L} = \frac{1}{\omega^2 L C}$$

The combination gives a ripple independent of the load current. The remarks already made about critical inductance apply equally well to this circuit; if the current is less than the critical value, the circuit behaves like a capacitor-input filter.

If a single L section does not give a low enough ripple, a second can be added; the further reduction in ripple can be calculated by the same equation.

A large number of medium-power applications are served by the *π-section* or *capacitor-input* filter shown in Fig. 7.11. Examples are radio and television receivers, amplifiers, and many kinds of test equipment. The ripple may be estimated from the expressions for the condenser alone, followed by an L section.

$$\frac{r}{V} \doteq \frac{2}{\omega R_L C_1} \frac{1}{\omega^2 L C_2}$$

Since the load current I is equal to V/R_L, we can rewrite this as

$$r \doteq \frac{2I}{\omega^3 L C_1 C_2}$$

As an example, consider the common values $I = 100$ ma, $L = 10$ henries, $C_1 = C_2 = 10$ μf, and a ripple frequency of 120 cps; the ripple should be about 0.5 volt.

Other properties of this circuit resemble those of the single capacitor: the voltage is high, approaching the peak value of the a-c input for light loads and falling rapidly as the load current is increased; and the rectifier current flows in short pulses whose peak value may be several times the average. Despite these disadvantages, the cheapness and low ripple make it very popular.

It has already been mentioned that inductors are of little use when the current is less than about 10 ma. Such low currents are often drawn from the power supplies for cathode-ray tubes, photomultipliers, and nuclear counters. For the lowest currents, a single capacitor, as in Fig. 7.9, may be adequate; if not, it can be followed by an R-C combination, so that the filter resembles the one in Fig. 7.11, but with a resistor instead of the inductor. It is merely necessary to replace ωL by R to find the ripple from the equations already given. The value of R is limited by the permissible voltage drop; rather large values are possible in high-voltage low-current supplies.

PROBLEMS

1) Derive the expression given for the critical inductance of an inductor-input filter.
2) Estimate the ripple from a single capacitor filter under the following conditions: (a) $V = 1000$ volts, $I = 1$ ma, $C = 10 \mu f$; (b) $V = 300$ volts, $I = 50$ ma, $C = 10 \mu f$. (Note that the load resistance $R_L = V/I$.)
3) Verify the estimate of ripple for a π-section filter given in the text.

7.3 VOLTAGE REGULATORS

A voltage regulator is a device that accepts a varying voltage and reduces the variations by an amount that may be large or small, depending on the requirement. As a secondary benefit, it usually reduces the ripple at the same time. The output voltage of an unregulated power supply varies in the same proportion as the line voltage, which commonly changes within a range of about 5 percent above and below normal. Variations as high as 10 percent sometimes occur. Some electronic equipment will not operate properly through such variations, and although other kinds might be designed to operate through them, it may be cheaper to regulate the supplies than to carry out the extra design work. This is frequently the case with experimental equipment which is built for a specific purpose, and after use is torn down or altered. Another convenient feature of some regulated supplies is the ease of adjusting the voltage to a desired value; they are often used for this feature alone, the regulation itself being of secondary interest. Finally, most regulators tend to maintain a constant voltage as the load current changes—a feature that is often useful.

We shall now consider several types of regulator in detail, starting with line-voltage regulators. Strictly speaking, these do not belong in a chapter on d-c power supplies, but they deserve mention and this is a convenient place for it.

The most common line-voltage regulator is the *constant-voltage transformer*. Crudely speaking, this device uses an iron core that is designed to saturate before the a-c wave reaches its peak, and thus clips the peaks at a level that does not depend on the line voltage. The actual embodiment, which is more complex than this brief description would indicate, includes a resonant circuit. The device is very effective and is readily available in a large number of sizes. However, it is well to be aware of its chief limitations, which are as follows:

(1) The waveform is badly distorted by the clipping action; however, special types are available with much smaller distortion if waveform is important.

(2) The output voltage depends on the line frequency, being approximately proportional to it. This is not normally a difficulty, but could give trouble if the power must be generated locally by a motor-generator set.

(3) The short-circuit current is limited to about twice the maximum rated current. More often than not, this is an advantage, since it offers some protection, but it can be annoying if a momentary overload is required, as in starting a motor.

Suitable constant-voltage transformers can be combined with semiconducting rectifiers to give a very simple regulated d-c supply. The square waveform is a definite advantage here, since it gives less ripple. This feature, combined with the limited current, allows the filtering to be done by a very large capacitor without danger to the rectifiers.

Other types of line-voltage regulators can be mentioned only briefly. The first uses an amplifier controlling a saturable reactor (or inductor) in such a way as to preserve a constant line voltage. The distortion is small, and the regulation can be very accurate. Finally, a variable transformer can be driven by a servomechanism to preserve a constant output; this type can deliver very large amounts of power easily, and produces no distortion at all. It does require several tenths of a second to respond to an abrupt change, and these transient changes may affect some types of equipment.

Voltage-regulator Diodes. Gas-filled voltage-regulator tubes were introduced in Section 3.6. It will be recalled that they sustain an approximately constant voltage over a range of currents that is typically 5 to 40 ma. The most useful types develop voltages of 105 and 150 volts; and 75- and 90-volt tubes are also available. Equivalent solid-state devices are also in wide use under the name *breakdown diode* (or *Zener* *diode*); they utilize the sharp avalanche breakdown, analogous to a gas discharge, which takes place in a suitable *p-n* junction at a certain reverse voltage. The voltage is commonly in the range of 4 to 30 volts, but can be made as high as 100; the current is limited only by the permissible power dissipation of the device. Breakdown diodes are superior in almost every respect to voltage-regulator tubes; their chief disadvantage is their greater cost. With minor exceptions, the circuits and design procedures are identical for both.

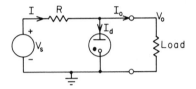

Fig. 7.12 Voltage regulator using a voltage-regulator tube or breakdown diode.

The usual circuit is shown in Fig. 7.12; power is supplied at the potential V_s which will be assumed constant at first. The output voltage V_o is the same as the diode voltage and is therefore also constant; therefore, the drop across R, namely $(V_s - V_o)$, is constant. Thus, the current I through R is constant and equal to

$$I = \frac{V_s - V_o}{R} = I_d + I_o$$

Any variations in the load current must be accompanied by equal and opposite variations in the diode current. The value of R must be chosen so that the minimum diode current is enough to maintain the discharge, and the maximum is within the ratings. If the load current varies too much, this may be impossible and some other type of regulator must be used. The design procedure is best illustrated by an example.

Suppose we are given $V_s = 350$ volts, $V_o = 150$ volts, and I_o between 10 and 25 ma. We arbitrarily choose a total current I of 35 ma, so that the tube current varies between 25 and 10 ma, well within the ratings. The drop across R is 200 volts, and its value must therefore be about 6 K. It must be able to dissipate at least 7 watts. If it is supposed that V_s can vary between 320 and 380 volts, the currents should be recalculated to make sure that they are still within the allowed limits. Finally, for a tube regulator, it is necessary to check that the tube will start, since this requires 185 volts. Suppose that V_s has its standard value, 350 volts, and that the load current is its maximum 25 ma; the voltage across the tube before it begins to conduct is 200, which is enough. But if V_s is 320 volts, only 170 volts will be available. To ensure starting of the tube under these conditions, R would have to be reduced. Alternatively, it might be possible to determine that the load current would never have its maximum value during the starting process. One convenient feature of the semiconducting regulator is that this extra starting voltage is not required.

It is perfectly feasible to put regulating diodes in series to obtain higher voltages or multiple voltages. However, they cannot be operated in parallel to multiply the current capacity, since the one with even a slightly lower voltage will carry all the current.

PROBLEM

Calculate the diode currents for the limiting values of V_s given in the text.

Feedback Regulators. These devices, also known as *degenerative regulators*, are more complicated but have some or all of the following advantages:

(1) Better regulation.
(2) Larger current capacity.
(3) Availability of any voltage or adjustable voltage.

In discussing regulators, it is convenient to specify three performance parameters:

(1) The variational *output impedance* (which is essentially the impedance that would cause the observed drop in output voltage as the load current is increased. A typical value for an unregulated 300-volt supply is 1500 ohms shunted by 10 μf; a change of 10 ma then causes a voltage change of 15 volts. For regulated supplies, a few ohms is a typical value.

(2) The *stabilization factor*, S, which is defined as the ratio of the fractional change in line voltage to the fractional change of output voltage resulting. For example, if a 10 percent change in the line causes a 0.1 per cent change in output, S is 100.

(3) The long-term *stability* at constant line and load. In tube regulators, instability is often caused by changes in cathode emission, which produce an effective fluctuating input to the tube of a few tenths of a volt.

We shall first consider the simple circuit shown in Fig. 7.13, known as a *shunt regulator* because the tube is in parallel with the load. A fraction β of the output is fed to the grid, and a constant voltage V_r (the *reference voltage*) is connected to the cathode. If the output voltage rises

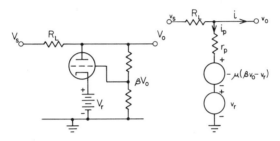

Fig. 7.13 Shunt voltage regulator and its equivalent circuit.

for any reason, the tube conducts more heavily, increases the voltage drop across R_L, and brings the voltage back near its original value. This will be recognized as a typical negative-feedback action, and the regulator can be regarded as a d-c amplifier with gain $1/\beta$ and a constant input V_r, so that the output is V_r/β. For high performance, R_L must be large, and therefore the circuit as it stands is useful only for high-voltage low-current supplies.

The performance can be derived from the equivalent circuit, also shown in Fig. 7.13. The two circuit equations are:

$$v_s - v_o = (i + i_p)R_L$$

$$i_p = \frac{v_o - v_r + \mu(\beta v_o - v_r)}{r_p}$$

$$= \frac{(1 + \mu\beta)v_o - (1 + \mu)v_r}{r_p}$$

We substitute i_p from the second equation into the first, and get:

$$v_s - v_0 = iR_L + \frac{R_L}{r_p}[(1 + \mu\beta)v_0 - (1 + \mu)v_r]$$

$$\doteq iR_L + g_m\beta R_L v_0 - g_m R_L v_r$$

where the approximation is good if $\mu\beta \gg 1$. Finally, if $g_m\beta R_L \gg 1$, the v_0 term on the left can be neglected in comparison with the one on the right, and the equation can be written

$$v_0 \doteq \frac{v_s - iR_L}{g_m\beta R_L} + \frac{v_r}{\beta}$$

The reciprocal of the coefficient of v_s is the stabilization factor S; the coefficient of i is the output resistance, and the third term gives information on the long-term stability. We therefore write

$$S \doteq g_m\beta R_L \qquad \text{and} \qquad r_0 \doteq \frac{1}{g_m\beta} = \frac{r_p}{\mu\beta}$$

As was mentioned earlier, S can be large if R_L is large, but this is only practical if the regulator is to deliver a very small current at a high voltage. Also, the output impedance is relatively high for a regulated supply, but this does not matter if the load current is very small or constant. The shunt regulator is therefore useful with photomultipliers, nuclear counters, and cathode-ray tubes, all of which require power of this type.

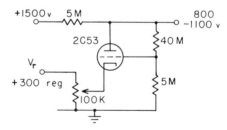

Fig. 7.14 Practical circuit for a shunt regulator.

A practical circuit is shown in Fig. 7.14. The 2C53 triode is an unusual tube designed specifically for this kind of service; its parameters are $\mu = 500$, $r_p = 500$ K, and $g_m = 950\,\mu$mhos. We thus find $S = 530$ and $r_0 = 10$ K.

if   as

The long-term stability depends on the reference voltage through the term v_r/β. Changes in V_r itself will be assumed negligible in the following discussion; for example, the 300 volts shown in Fig. 7.14 may come from a well-regulated B supply. However, an effective change in V_r will be produced by variation of the emission velocity of electrons from the cathode of the tube. It will be recalled that a virtual cathode is formed inside a tube at a potential about one volt lower than the actual cathode, and that the grid voltage should really be measured from here, not from the voltage of the actual cathode. Variations in the emission velocity therefore change the effective bias and have the same effect as changes in the reference voltage. The magnitude of these changes is typically 0.2 volts, or perhaps somewhat more if the line voltage is unstable. This discussion applies generally to any regulator or d-c amplifier having a "single-ended" input stage. An improvement by about a factor of ten is possible by using a well-balanced differential stage in which the two tubes are contained in a single bulb. The variations in the two cathodes tend to cancel in such a circuit, but residual variations of about 25 mv can still be expected.

In Fig. 7.14, then, this effect can be expected to cause random changes in output of $0.2/\beta$ or about 2 volts. With an S of 530, a 10 percent change of line voltage will change the output by only 0.02 percent, or 0.2 volt; and the r_o of 10 K implies a -1-volt change for a current change of 0.1 ma.

PROBLEM

Verify all the performance figures given for this regulator.

Fig. 7.15 shows an elementary *series regulator*. In contrast to the circuit just discussed, this one cannot provide high performance by itself, but it is occasionally useful and it serves as an introduction to the more complicated circuits. It will be noticed that the series regulator is

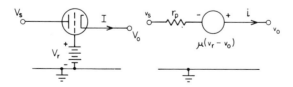

Fig. 7.15 Series regulator and its equivalent circuit.

simply a cathode follower with a constant grid voltage. From the equivalent circuit we can write the equation

$$v_0 = v_s - ir_p + \mu(v_r - v_0)$$

$$v_0 = \frac{v_s - ir_p}{\mu + 1} + \frac{\mu}{\mu + 1}v_r \doteq \frac{v_i}{\mu} - ir_k + v_r$$

in which r_k has been used for $r_p/(\mu + 1) \doteq 1/g_m$ as in Section 4.8. It is thus seen that $S = \mu + 1 \doteq \mu$, $r_0 = r_k$, and changes in V_r are reproduced in the output. The last two results would be expected from the theory of the cathode follower.

S is too small and r_0 is too large for this circuit to be widely useful, particularly since tubes that can carry a large current normally have a low μ. There is no point in using a pentode to get a high μ unless special steps are taken to hold the screen voltage constant with respect to the cathode; otherwise, the triode characteristics apply.

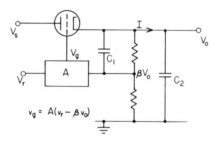

Fig. 7.16 Series regulator with differential amplifier.

An effectively much higher value of μ can be produced by using a separate amplifier to feed the grid, as shown in Fig. 7.16. This form of the series regulator is the one found in nearly all regulated power supplies. The amplifier is a differential one, with the reference voltage on one input and a suitable fraction of the output voltage on the other. The equivalent circuit is identical with the one in Fig. 7.15, except that the grid voltage v_r is replaced by the amplifier output $A(v_r - \beta v_0)$. Then the circuit equation becomes

$$v_0 = v_s - ir_p + \mu[A(v_r - \beta v_0) - v_0]$$

$$v_0[1 + \mu(1 + A\beta)] = v_s - ir_p + \mu A v_r$$

It is convenient to simplify the result by assuming that $A\beta \gg 1$; we then have

$$v_0 \doteq \frac{v_s}{\mu\beta A} - \frac{1}{g_m\beta A}i + \frac{v_r}{\beta}$$

In many regulators an additional complication exists because the last stage of the amplifier must take its plate supply from the source voltage V_s; the regulated voltage is not high enough. The result is that the changes v_s in the source voltage are transmitted to the grid of the series tube with little attenuation through the load resistor of the last stage. This can be taken into account by adding a term μv_s to the circuit equation; when this is followed through, it is found to cancel the μ out of the first term. For this usual case, then, the performance parameters are:

$$S \doteq \beta A \qquad \text{and} \qquad r_o \doteq \frac{1}{g_m\beta A} = \frac{r_k}{\beta A}$$

Subject to the usual difficulties with high loop gain, these figures can be improved to any desired degree by making the gain A large enough. Stabilization factors of a few hundred and output resistances of about one ohm are readily achieved.

PROBLEM
Carry through the development just outlined and verify the results given.

The circuit in Fig. 7.16 contains two capacitors whose purpose has not yet been discussed. C_1 has the effect of making β equal to unity for sufficiently high frequencies, normally chosen to include the ripple frequency. Thus S increases for these frequencies and the regulator can reduce the ripple even more than the other variations in the source voltage. C_2 produces a low output impedance at higher frequencies for which the regulator may start to become ineffective. It also introduces a slope of -20 db$_v$/per decade into the loop-gain characteristic of the regulator, starting at a very low frequency, so that stability against oscillation is usually no problem at all.

A simple and popular example of a practical circuit is shown in Fig. 7.17. The differential amplifier is a single pentode with the reference voltage connected to the cathode, and the gain is about 120.

Since β is $\frac{1}{3}$, the stabilization factor is about 40; and if the r_k of the series tube is 300 ohms, the output resistance is about 8 ohms. The long-term stability will be limited by drifts in the potential of the virtual cathode, as described earlier, but normally this is not an important factor in a low-performance regulator such as this, since a 5 percent change in line voltage will change the output by as much or more.

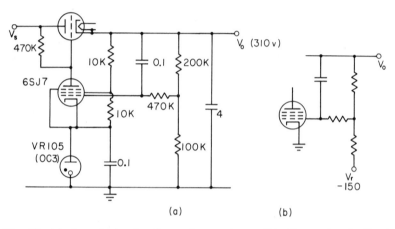

Fig. 17. (a) Actual circuit of a series regulator. (b) Alternative feedback circuit for a negative reference voltage.

In some cases, a regulated negative supply may be available in the same circuit. It may be used as a reference as shown in Fig. 7.17(b), where it is seen that the voltage applied to the grid is $\beta V_o + (1 - \beta) V r$; the regulator maintains this voltage near cathode (ground) potential. If the voltage divider is made variable, the output can be adjusted, and in Fig. 7.17(b) it can be reduced right down to zero.

To make a regulator of higher performance, it is necessary to use a two-stage amplifier and to reduce the long-term drift by making its first stage in the form of a balanced differential pair. Normally it is sufficient to take the output from only one of the plates and amplify it by a second single-ended stage. With high-μ triodes a gain of several thousand is easily attained, so that S will be about 1000 and r_o a few tenths of an ohm. If the differential stage has a long-term drift of 25 mv, the output will typically drift three times as much (for $\beta = \frac{1}{3}$). With this kind of performance, it is worthwhile to pay attention to the stability of the reference voltage itself, and use a special voltage-reference tube such as the 5651 or 0G3.

References

Excellent discussions of tube regulators and their components can be found in *Electronic Instruments*, by I. A. Greenwood, J. V. Holdam, and D. MacRae (New York. McGraw-Hill Book Company, Inc., 1949), and *Electronics*, by W. C. Elmore and M. Sands (New York: McGraw-Hill Book Company, Inc., 1948).

CHAPTER 8

Semiconductors, Diodes, and Transistors

8.1 SEMICONDUCTORS

The electron tubes that we have been studying up to now are based on the control of the motion of electrons in a vacuum or an ionized gas at low pressure. Somewhat analogous devices, diodes and transistors, are based on the control of electron motions in a special class of solids known as *semiconductors*. We shall proceed with an introductory study of these materials before considering the devices made of them.

The most important semiconductors are germanium (Ge) and silicon (Si), which share a column of valence 4 in the periodic table with carbon and have a similar arrangement of valence electrons. That is, they have four electrons outside the last closed shell, and lack four of the next closed subshell. In the pure solid, these electrons participate in *covalent bonds* with neighboring atoms. Each atom has four nearest neighbors, sharing with each of them a pair of electrons. Since each atom has a share of eight electrons, it has a kind of closed shell, and the energy of the arrangement is less than the energy of the free atoms. This binding energy implies a binding force, which is what holds this kind of solid together. The electrons are tied up in the bonds, and none of them are readily available for conduction. However, even at room temperature, the occasional electron can have enough energy to release it from its normal position, so that it can participate in conduction, just as in a metal. The required energy is called the *energy gap* and is 0.75 ev for germanium and 1.1 ev for silicon. The number of conduction electrons increases rapidly with temperature, following an equation similar to Richardson's for thermionic emission, and therefore the conductivity increases in a similar way. The resistivity is thus high, and decreases rapidly with increasing temperature, in contrast to the behavior of a metal with its low resistivity increasing in approximate proportion to the absolute temperature. This behavior was known for many years before the explanation was discovered, and enabled the empirical classification of some elements as semiconductors.

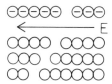

Fig. 8.1 Motion of a hole in an electric field by the jumping of electrons; the hole moves like a positive particle.

When an electron is excited to the conduction *band*, it leaves behind a vacancy known as a *hole*. If an electric field is applied, an electron from a nearby valence bond can easily jump into the hole, creating a new hole in a different place. This behavior is illustrated in Fig. 8.1, which shows that the hole moves in the electric field in precisely the same way that a positive particle would. It can even be regarded as carrying a current, although the actual motion and the actual current are those of electrons jumping the other way. The thermal excitation process should therefore be considered to produce hole-electron *pairs*, and both "particles" participate in conduction. The pure semiconductor we have been discussing is said to exhibit *intrinsic* conductivity, in contrast to the *impurity* conduction we turn to now. Most of the applications of semiconductors involve the latter.

Suppose that the semiconductor crystal is grown with a tiny fraction of impurity atoms, using an impurity element from the fifth column of the periodic table, so that it has five electrons outside the last closed shell; examples are arsenic, phosphorus, and antimony. An impurity atom enters into the crystal lattice by substituting for a germanium atom (using germanium as an example), and four of the electrons enter into valence bonds. The fifth is left over, and is very lightly bound to the site of its parent atom. At room temperature, it is almost certain to have enough thermal energy to escape and become a conduction electron. The result is a concentration of free electrons equal to the concentration of impurity atoms. There is a corresponding decrease in the hole concentration, so that the product of the two is the same as in intrinsic material at the same temperature. This kind of impurity is called a *donor*, and the resulting conductivity is called *n type* (for negative, the sign of the dominant current carriers).

If the crystal contains impurities with a valence of 3, instead of 5, the impurity atoms are able to form only three out of the normal four bonds. There is a strong tendency for the missing electron to be supplied by a nearby atom, forming a free hole. Such material, containing a suitable number of *acceptor* impurities, exhibits *p-type* conductivity, since the effective current carriers are positive. There is a corresponding decrease in the concentration of free electrons.

Finally, if a crystal contains both donors and acceptors, the conductivity is controlled by the difference in their concentrations, and may even resemble the intrinsic type if the difference is very small.

Energy Bands and Fermi Levels. Another useful concept in the discussion of a semiconductor is that of allowed and forbidden energy bands. The former bear some resemblance to the discrete energy levels of an isolated atom or molecule, but differ from them in occupying rather large intervals of energy. The valence electrons bound to the atoms occupy the *valence band*; above this are the forbidden band, having a width equal to the energy gap, and the *conduction band* (Fig. 8.2). Electrons having an energy in the conduction band can move freely.

In Chapter 3 the idea of a Fermi level was used briefly; this is the energy of the highest level that is occupied by electrons at a temperature of absolute zero. In a metal, the Fermi level lies within the conduction band, and a large supply of electrons is available for conduction. In a semiconductor or insulator, the Fermi level lies within the energy gap, and conduction is impossible at low temperatures. The difference between a semiconductor and an insulator appears at higher temperatures, because the former has a smaller energy gap, allowing a few electrons to be thermally excited across it into the conduction band. At the same time, this leaves a few vacant states in the valence band, which are responsible for the hole conductivity. Because the number of holes and the number of electrons is equal in intrinsic material, the Fermi level lies right in the middle of the forbidden band, as Fig. 8.2 shows.

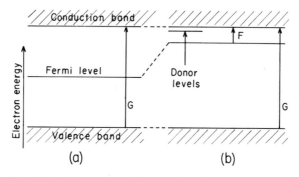

Fig. 8.2 (a) Energy-level diagram for electrons in a pure semiconductor. (b) The same for an *n*-type semiconductor.

If we assume this, we can then calculate the concentration of free electrons and holes, by recalling that for energies well above the Fermi energy, the number of electrons having energy greater than $G/2$ is proportional to a Boltzmann factor:

$$n_e = Ke^{-G/2kT}$$

Since the bottom of the conduction band is $G/2$ above the Fermi energy, this gives the concentration of conduction electrons n_e, and the number of holes n_h is the same. The product of these two is

$$n_e n_h = K^2 e^{-G/kT}$$

It can be shown that this product remains the same even in material with impurity-type conduction.

Let us now locate the Fermi level in *n*-type material. There is a large supply of electrons from donor levels, which are found about 0.01 ev below the bottom of the conduction band, as shown in Fig. 8.2(b). Since kT is about 0.025 ev at room temperature, nearly all the donor states are empty and the electrons are in the conduction band;

the electron concentration is nearly equal to the donor concentration n_d. Correspondingly, the Fermi level rises towards the top of the forbidden band until

$$Ke^{-F/kT} = n_d$$

where F is the energy difference between the Fermi level and the top of the forbidden band; see Fig. 8.2(b).

In p-type material, the acceptor levels are located just above the top of the valence band and are nearly full of electrons, leaving many holes in the valence band; their concentration is nearly equal to n_a, the concentration of acceptors. The concentration of electrons in the conduction band is reduced to keep the product $n_e n_h$ constant:

$$n_e n_a = K^2 e^{-G/kT}$$

But the height of the Fermi level is such that

$$Ke^{-F/kT} = n_e = \frac{K^2}{n_a} e^{-G/kT}$$

and

$$Ke^{-(G-F)/kT} = n_a$$

where $(G - F)$ is the energy difference between the Fermi level and the bottom of the forbidden band. Therefore a given concentration of acceptors lowers the Fermi level by the same amount that an equal concentration of donors raises it.

8.2 p–n JUNCTIONS AND DIODES

We now wish to study the phenomena which arise when a transition from p-type to n-type conduction takes place within a single crystal. It is *not* sufficient to press together two separate pieces of opposite type; the crystal structure is so disturbed near a surface that a connection like this will show none of the characteristic effects. A number of ways are in use to produce *p–n junctions*; among them are the following:

(1) A sharp metal point can be pressed against the suitably prepared surface of an n-type crystal. Although the theory of this arrangement is not well understood, it appears that a small region of the crystal near the point is converted into p type. In some cases, a better junction can be made by discharging a small, controlled amount of

energy through the junction. *Point-contact* diodes made in this way are useful at high frequencies because of the small area of the junction.

(2) Part of a crystal may be grown from liquid containing donor impurities. During the process, a larger concentration of acceptors may be added, so that the rest of the crystal is *n* type.

(3) Germanium of *n* type may be changed to *p* type by "soldering" to the surface with indium. At the joint, an alloy is formed, but a thin layer of recrystallized *p*-type germanium is also produced. Some "point-contact" diodes may belong in this category if the junction is *formed* by discharging a capacitor through it.

(4) Impurities can be made to diffuse into a crystal from the surface by holding it at a suitable high temperature. Also, further layers of crystal can be grown on the surface by thermal decomposition of a suitable vapor (epitaxial growth). These techniques are highly versatile and can be expected to find more and more use in the future.

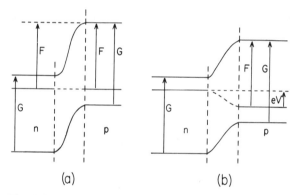

Fig. 8.3 (a) Energy-level diagram for electrons near a *p–n* junction in equilibrium. (b) The same, but with an applied forward potential V, displacing the Fermi levels by an energy eV.

The energy-level diagram near a *p–n* junction is shown in Fig. 8.3(a), where the system is in equilibrium, with the Fermi levels aligned. We shall first prove that this is the equilibrium situation by writing the currents of electrons diffusing to the right and to the left and showing them equal. The same argument is true for holes. F, the height of the conduction band above the Fermi level, is taken at its value on the *p* side.

The current of electrons moving to the left is composed of minority carriers which diffuse to the junction and then rapidly cross it because of the aiding potential difference. This current is proportional to the electron concentration on the p side,

$$Ke^{-F/kT}$$

The current of electrons moving to the right is composed of the tail of the Fermi distribution having energy high enough to surmount the potential barrier. This energy, measured from the Fermi level on the n side, is just the F shown in Fig. 8.3(a). The current is proportional to

$$Ke^{-F/kT}$$

Since the two currents are equal, the junction is indeed at equilibrium.

PROBLEM
Show that a similar equilibrium is true for holes.

Current-voltage Characteristic of a Junction. Fig. 8.3(b) shows the junction with a forward bias applied; that is, the p region is made positive with respect to the n. The applied potential V is of the order of a few tenths of a volt and displaces the Fermi levels by an energy eV. The situation in the junction is far from equilibrium and the Fermi level is no longer defined there, but the currents in the p and n regions do not appreciably disturb the energy distributions, and Fermi levels are still meaningful. The application of the potential does not change the flow of minority carriers across the junction, since they are still able to diffuse to it and fall across the energy step. However, the barrier to the flow of majority carriers is reduced and many more carriers now have sufficient energy to cross it. For electrons, this current is proportional to

$$Ke^{-(F-eV)/kT}$$

Subtracting the unchanged current of minority electrons in the other direction gives a net current proportional to

$$Ke^{-(F-eV)/kT} - Ke^{-F/kT} = Ke^{-F/kT}(e^{eV/kT} - 1)$$

A similar expression is found for holes. Adding both together and calling the coefficient I_0, we find for the total current

$$I = I_0(e^{eV/kT} - 1)$$

Although we assumed a positive potential V in deriving this characteristic, a negative value can be substituted without changing anything essential, and thus the equation is true for the complete range of V. However, V is merely the potential across the junction itself; if I is large, there may be additional voltage drops in the bulk of the semiconductor and at the connections to the external circuit.

For negative values of V, the current rapidly approaches $-I_o$, independent of voltage over a wide range. Its value depends on the area of the junction and the conductivity of the crystal, but even more on the size of the energy gap. The larger gap of silicon results in back currents only one thousandth as large as in germanium; however, the forward voltage required for the same current is also larger: typically 0.5 instead of 0.3 volt. Additional components of back current may be caused by surface leakage and by breakdown at high voltages.

Although this breakdown limits the back voltage that can be applied to a diode, it also has valuable applications in *breakdown diodes*, which are specifically designed to be used in this way. *Zener* breakdown occurs in junctions between material of very high impurity content; the thickness of the junction itself is very small, and electrons can cross it by the quantum-mechanical tunnel effect. The corresponding breakdown voltage ranges from 3 to 6 volts. Junctions between material of lower conductivity are thicker and can sustain much larger voltages; breakdown then appears to take place by the *avalanche* process, which is exactly like the process in a gas discharge. Here, electrons or holes are accelerated by the strong electric field until they are fast enough to create hole-electron pairs by collision; the new carriers repeat the process and a very large current can flow. Breakdown diodes are used in voltage regulators, as discussed in Chapters 7 and 9.

PROBLEMS

1) Plot the current-voltage characteristic of a junction with $I_o = 1.0\,\mu\text{a}$, remembering that kT/e is 0.025 ev at room temperature. It is advisable to use different scales for the positive and negative parts of the curve.

2) Calculate the variational resistance (dV/dI) of a junction as a function of the bias V. Sketch a circuit by which the attenuation of a small signal can be controlled by another signal.

We now wish to examine briefly one or two processes that take place during the operation of a diode. When it is back-biased, a rather large electric field is present in the region of the junction, and it is essentially swept free of charge carriers; it is therefore called a *depletion layer*. The charges that must be present to produce the change of potential are furnished by the ionized impurity atoms; as already mentioned, their concentration controls the magnitude of the electric field and thus the thickness of the depletion layer for a given applied potential difference. As this potential difference is increased, the thickness of the depletion layer must increase proportionally. The junction acts in the same way as the dielectric in a capacitor, and since its thickness can be varied by the applied bias, a voltage-variable capacitor can be produced. As with the variational resistance in Problem 2 above, it is useful only for very small signals.

The flow of current during conduction in the forward direction is also worth closer examination. The majority carriers that cross the junction immediately become minority carriers. They continue to carry the current for some distance, but eventually they recombine with carriers of the opposite sign, and the current is taken over once more by majority carriers. This process is referred to as *injection* of minority carriers. If the *p*-type region, for example, has a much higher conductivity than the *n*-type region, most of the injected carriers will be holes in the latter. This asymmetry is essential to the operation of the emitter of a transistor.

So far, we have assumed that *ohmic*, or nonrectifying, connections could be made between each region and the external circuit. If this were not possible, another rectifying junction would be formed, and the device would lose its asymmetry. Fortunately, ohmic contacts are not difficult to make. They often are made by simple soldering to the semiconductor in such a way that hole-electron recombination is very rapid at the joint. This implies that generation of hole-electron pairs is equally rapid; thus, plenty of carriers are available at every point for conduction in either direction. The same sort of effect can be obtained by grading the junction very slowly from one type to the other.

An obvious application of a *p–n* junction is in rectification, both of signals and of power. It is customary to call the device a diode if it is primarily intended for use with signals, and a rectifier if it is for use with power, but there is no sharp division between the two. Diodes typically have a very small capacitance, produced by keeping the area of the junction small; the point-contact construction is common. The small area makes them unsuitable for carrying large currents. Rectifiers therefore have a large-area junction and a relatively large capacitance, which is still negligible at power frequencies. Both germanium and silicon are used for diodes, but most rectifiers are made with silicon. Silicon junctions with peak inverse voltage ratings of 600 can be made; higher ratings are readily produced by putting several junctions in series. No special precautions are required; the small inverse current of minority carriers distributes the voltage automatically across all the junctions.

It is worth mentioning one effect that limits the use of diodes with fast pulses or high frequencies. Suppose that the diode is conducting heavily, and the applied voltage suddenly reverses. A current is found to flow for a short time before the diode stops conducting; the time may be around a microsecond for ordinary diodes. The reason is that during conduction carriers are injected across the junction, becoming minority carriers. When the voltage reverses, these carriers remain for a short time and are able to carry a large reverse current, until they either cross the junction again or recombine. Special fast-responding diodes can be made, for example by using material with very fast recombination, but as a result their inverse voltage rating is small.

8.3 TRANSISTORS

The principle of the transistor was discovered in 1948 by J. Bardeen and W. H. Brattain. Their device used two point contacts very close together on a germanium surface. Not long after, W. Shockley realized that a *junction transistor* should be possible, and it was found to work as predicted. It has entirely superseded the point-contact type and is the only type we shall consider. Typical arrangements are shown in Fig. 8.4; the first represents a grown-junction type, the second an alloy type, and the third a diffused type. In all cases the essential thing is to have two *p–n* junctions with the *base* region in the middle very thin. Also, the conductivity of the *emitter* region should be much higher than that of the base; the conductivity of the *collector* region is not so important, but a high value is desirable. Both *p–n–p* and *n–p–n* transistors are in use; we shall concentrate on the *p–n–p* type, since the alloy construction which is most commonly used for low-priced transistors normally produces a *p–n–p* transistor.

Fig. 8.5 shows the symbols that are normally used for *p–n–p* and *n–p–n* transistors; the arrow on the emitter shows the direction of easy current flow from emitter to base. The symbols actually represent the physical configuration of a point-contact transistor, but have been retained even though the junction type has superseded it. As with a tube symbol,

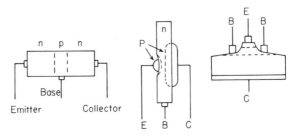

Fig. 8.4   Typical configurations of transistors. Left to right: grown-junction, alloy, and diffused types.

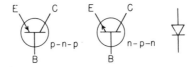

Fig. 8.5   Transistor and diode symbols. Left to right: *p–n–p* transistor, *n–p–n* transistor, and diode.

the circle around the symbol is not really necessary. A strong argument for keeping it is that the tube or the transistor is the focus of attention in an electronic circuit; the circle helps the understanding by drawing the eye to the important points.

We shall now consider the operation of an *n–p–n* transistor. A simple circuit is shown in Fig. 8.6(a), and the energy-level diagram for electrons in Fig. 8.6(b). The emitter-base junction is biased in the forward direction, and conducts the current supplied by the external circuit with a voltage drop of a few tenths of a volt typical of a junction. The collector junction is reverse-biased by several volts, and in the absence of emitter current, the collector current would be nearly zero.

Since the emitter has a much higher conductivity than the base, the emitter current is nearly all carried by electrons injected into the base; the supply of holes from base to emitter is negligible by comparison. This is the reason for the name given to the emitter. Once in the base, the emitted electrons are minority carriers, having the energy of the arrow in Fig. 8.6(b), and they wander around under the influence

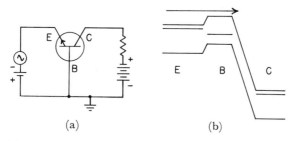

(a)   (b)

Fig. 8.6 (a) Elementary transistor amplifier in the grounded-base connection. (b) Energy-level diagram for the bias voltages shown in (a).

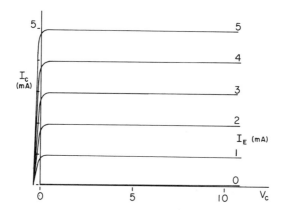

Fig. 8.7 Collector characteristics of a transistor with emitter current as the parameter.

of diffusion forces only. They are therefore much more likely to encounter the collector junction than the base lead, and at the collector junction the large potential step collects them immediately. The result is that nearly all the emitter current flows out at the collector terminal, and only a tiny fraction at the base. The collection does not depend on collector voltage over a wide range; therefore, a large load resistor can be used without impairing the collecting action. As a result, a current injected from a low resistance can be made to flow in a high resistance, and a large voltage gain is possible.

Fig. 8.7 shows the collector characteristics for this *grounded-base* connection. The collector action works right down to a collector potential of zero, as a study of Fig. 8.6(b) will suggest; reversed voltages of the same order as the emitter voltage are required to stop the collector current. For normal collector voltages, the collector current is slightly less than the emitter current and nearly independent of voltage. The ratio of collector to emitter current is called the *current-amplification factor* (or sometimes *current gain* for short) and given the symbol α. Its value ranges as low as 0.95, but more often is between 0.97 and 0.99. It is less than 1 for two reasons: (1) Not all the emitter current is carried by injection from emitter into base; this effect is usually negligible. (2) Some carriers may recombine in the base or flow out the base lead. The usual remedy is to make the base region very thin, so that carriers are more likely to encounter the collector before something else happens to them. This remedy has the further advantage of improving the high-frequency response.

The emitter characteristic is not shown here, since it is almost identical with a diode characteristic; the only difference is a slight dependence on the collector voltage. However, of great importance are the collector characteristics for the grounded-emitter connection, in which transistors are most commonly used. The base current is the difference between the collector and emitter currents, and is therefore much smaller than either of them. If it is used to control the transistor, there will be a large current gain in addition to the large voltage gain already available. If the collector current is less than the emitter current by the factor α, their difference, the base current, must be less by $(1 - \alpha)$, and the ratio of collector to base current is $\alpha/(1 - \alpha)$. This quantity is called the grounded-emitter current amplification factor and represented by β; its common range is from 30 to 100. Transformation of the collector characteristics of Fig. 8.7 gives Fig. 8.8 in which the increments of input current are greatly reduced, and the slope of the curves is similarly increased. Also, since the voltage is now measured from the emitter, the current goes to zero at the same point as the voltage.

So far, we have been using an *n–p–n* transistor in our examples, with a positive collector and a negative emitter. The characteristics and behavior of *p–n–p* units are exactly similar; it is merely necessary to reverse all voltages and currents.

The high-frequency response of a transistor may be seriously limited by transit-time effects, since the carriers wander across the base under the influence of diffusion only. In a tube, these effects become

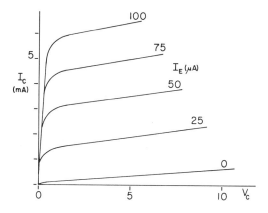

Fig. 8.8 Collector characteristics of a transistor in the grounded-emitter connection, with base current as the parameter.

appreciable at several hundred megacycles, but in a low-priced alloy transistor, the corresponding frequency is typically only 1 mc; in other words, the transit time is of the order of a microsecond. Unfortunately, this limit is reduced by a factor $1/\beta$ in a grounded-emitter amplifier, and may then be just above the audio-frequency range. However, there are special transistors available in which the limitation is much less serious, and even grounded-emitter amplifiers may be used at frequencies in the tens and hundreds of megacycles. One remedy is to make the base region very thin, usually by diffusion or epitaxial techniques, so that the time for diffusion is less. Or the conductivity of the base region may be graded to produce an electric field in it, so that the carriers will move much faster. Such transistors are usually called *drift* types.

REFERENCES

An excellent discussion of the physics of semiconductors and junctions at an intermediate level is given in *Modern Physics*, by R. L. Sproull (New York:

John Wiley & Sons, Inc., 1956). More detail about the specific application to transistors will be found in *Physical Principles and Applications of Junction Transistors* by J. H. Simpson and R. S. Richards (New York: Oxford University Press, 1962).

CHAPTER 9

Transistor Circuits

9.1 EQUIVALENT CIRCUITS

Just as with tubes, the quantitative analysis of most transistor circuits is based on the use of a small-signal linear equivalent circuit. This circuit is a little more complicated, because the current drawn by the input of a transistor cannot be ignored; and the analysis is more complicated, because the reaction of the load on the input cannot be ignored.

As our explanation of transistor action shows, the important input variable is the current, not the voltage, and it is therefore chosen as the independent variable. At the output, the choice is not clear-cut, and systems are in use in which either current or voltage is taken as independent. For the present we shall use current. By convention, currents flowing into the transistor are taken as positive (Fig. 9.1), no matter what their actual direction. The transistor characteristics can then be described by two empirical functions:

$$V_1 = f(I_1, I_2)$$
$$V_2 = g(I_1, I_2)$$

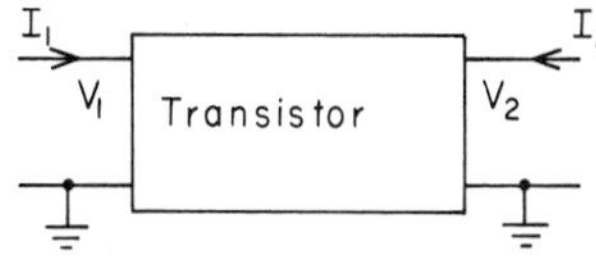

Fig. 9.1 Illustration of transistor input and output voltages and currents.

In practice, these functions are described by sets of curves, such as Figs. 8.7 or 8.8. We now make a Taylor expansion of the equations, as in Section 4.3, with the result

187

$$v_1 = r_{11}i_1 + r_{12}i_2$$
$$v_2 = r_{21}i_1 + r_{22}i_2$$

where the rs represent partial derivatives, and the vs and is are variational quantities. The rs are transistor parameters, and are sometimes called "r parameters." An equivalent circuit is readily written down to represent this pair of equations, but since we shall have no further use for it, it is not given here. Instead, we transform the second equation by adding $r_{12}i_1$ to both sides and then transposing $r_{21}i_1$ to the left:

$$v_1 = r_{11}i_1 + r_{12}i_2$$
$$v_2 + (r_{12} - r_{21})i_1 = r_{12}i_1 + r_{22}i_2$$

This can be represented by the network shown in Fig. 9.2, known as the

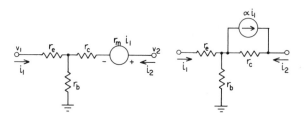

Fig. 9.2 T-Equivalent circuit of a transistor in voltage-generator and current-generator forms.

T equivalent circuit of a transistor. Two forms are shown, one containing a voltage generator and the other a current source. The mesh equations are:

$$v_1 = (r_e + r_b)i_1 + r_b i_2$$
$$v_2 - r_m i_1 = r_b i_1 + (r_b + r_c)i_2$$

from which the correspondences can be written down immediately. From the transformation of voltage source to current source, it can be seen that $\alpha = r_m/r_c$. This variational current gain is not really the same as the total current gain defined in Chapter 8, but in practice they are closely equal. The names of the parameters and their typical magnitudes are given below:

r_e	emitter resistance	40 ohms
r_b	base resistance	400 ohms
r_c	collector resistance	1.0 M

α	current gain	0.98
r_m	mutual resistance	0.98 M
β	grounded-emitter current gain	49

The last is given for future reference.

The collector resistance r_c is found from the slope of the curves in Fig. 8.7, and α from their spacing. They are reasonably constant whatever the operating point. But r_e varies strongly with emitter current, being to a fair approximation inversely proportional; the value given is for 1 ma.

Another set of parameters is widely used in the literature, and will be briefly mentioned. These are the *hybrid* or *h* parameters, so-called because one is a resistance, one a conductance, and two are dimensionless.   The linear equations are defined with input current and output voltage as independent variables:

$$v_1 = h_{11}i_1 + h_{12}v_2$$

$$i_2 = h_{21}i_1 + h_{22}v_2$$

The relations between these and the *r* parameters can be found by manipulating one set of equations into the same form as the others and comparing the terms. With some simplifying approximations, it is found that $h_{11} \doteq r_e$, $h_{12} \doteq r_b/r_c$, $h_{21} \doteq -\alpha$, and $h_{22} \doteq 1/r_c$.

PROBLEM

Show this.

9.2 THE GROUNDED-EMITTER AMPLIFIER

We shall now proceed to discuss this most important configuration of the transistor in some detail. Although it is possible to use the grounded-base T circuit directly in this discussion, it is more convenient to derive still another equivalent circuit; this is the one we shall be using exclusively from now on.

The T equivalent circuit of Fig. 9.2 is redrawn in Fig. 9.3(a) with the emitter grounded and input to the base. A change in notation has been necessary: the input current is still called i_1, but the generator is controlled by the *emitter* current, now denoted by i_e. However, it is more convenient to transform the circuit so that the generator is once more controlled by the input current i_1. To do this we note that, by Kirchhoff's second law, $i_e = -(i_1 + i_2)$; therefore, the generator voltage can be written $r_m(i_1 + i_2)$ with the polarity reversed, as in Fig. 9.3(b). However, the second term in this expression, $r_m i_2$, can be represented by a resistance $-r_m$ with the current i_2 flowing through

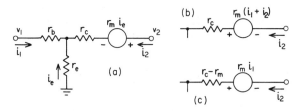

Fig. 9.3 Transformation to the grounded-emitter equivalent circuit.

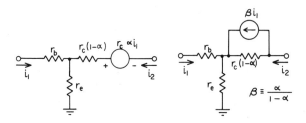

Fig. 9.4 Grounded-emitter equivalent circuits.

it; when this is combined with r_c, the result appears in Fig. 9.3(c). Finally, the complete equivalent circuit is shown in Fig. 9.4, where r_m has been replaced by its equivalent $r_c \alpha$. For the form with a current generator, the current gain is greatly increased because the resistance is much less; its value is $\alpha/(1 - \alpha)$, which we shall denote by β. As α varies in the range from 0.95 to 0.99 for different transistors, β changes from 19 to 99; for our typical transistor, it is 49. The effective collector resistance $r_c(1 - \alpha)$ is 20 K.

A numerical example may help to illustrate the reason for the high current gain of the grounded-emitter configuration. Fig. 9.5 shows a p–n–p transistor with an emitter current of 1.0 ma. If α is 0.98, the collector current is 0.98 ma and the remaining 0.02 ma must flow out the base connection. However, this 0.02 ma is actually controlling the collector current of 0.98 ma; the current gain is the ratio of these, or 49. To be strictly correct, this argument should be carried out with current changes rather than total currents, but the result would be identical.

We are now ready to analyze an actual amplifier such as the typical one shown in Fig. 9.6. The two resistors R_1 and R_2 set the bias voltage and current of the base, aided by the emitter resistor R_e. Their functions are discussed later. R_e does not appear in the a-c equivalent circuit because it is bypassed by a capacitor. It will be assumed that R_1 and R_2 are large enough that they do not load the generator appreciably; if this is not so, their effect may readily be taken into account with the help of Thévenin's theorem. The re-

Fig. 9.5 Currents in a transistor with emitter grounded.

actance of the coupling capacitor will also be neglected. The load resistor R_L serves exactly the same function as in a tube amplifier.

When the transistor is replaced by its equivalent circuit, and the approximations just mentioned are made, the result is as shown in Fig. 9.6(b). Although the circuit is simple, the equations are complicated enough to hide the important factors unless some terms are

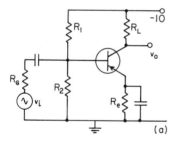
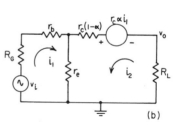

Fig. 9.6 A grounded-emitter amplifier and its equivalent circuit.

neglected. A study of the list of parameters shows that r_e and r_b are much smaller than $r_c(1 - \alpha)$, and r_e is only 10 percent of r_b. Moreover, R_L is seldom more than one or two thousand ohms, and can be neglected in comparison to $r_c(1 - \alpha)$ without a large error. Keeping these in mind, we write the circuit equations:

$$(R_G + r_b + r_e)i_1 + r_e i_2 = v_i$$
$$r_e i_1 + [r_e + r_c(1 - \alpha) + R_L]i_2 = r_c \alpha i_1$$

The determinant of the coefficients is

$$\Delta = \begin{vmatrix} R_G + r_b + r_e & r_e \\ r_e - r_c\alpha & r_e + r_c(1 - \alpha) + R_L \end{vmatrix}$$

$$= (R_G + r_b + r_e)[r_e + r_c(1 - \alpha) + R_L] - r_e(r_e - r_c\alpha)$$

Ignoring R_L and all the r_es except the one multiplying $r_c\alpha$, we find

$$\Delta \doteq (R_G + r_b)r_c(1 - \alpha) + r_e r_c\alpha$$
$$\doteq r_c(1 - \alpha)(R_G + r_b + \beta r_e)$$

since $\beta \equiv \alpha/(1 - \alpha)$. This expression is accurate enough for most purposes, but the complete one can always be used if desired.

To find i_2, we set up the substituted determinant Δ_2:

$$\Delta_2 = \begin{vmatrix} R_G + r_b + r_e & v_i \\ r_e - r_c\alpha & 0 \end{vmatrix} = v_i(r_c\alpha - r_e) \doteq v_i r_c\alpha$$

This is a very good approximation. The output current i_2 is equal to the ratio Δ_2/Δ, or

$$i_2 \doteq v_i\frac{\beta}{R_G + r_b + \beta r_e}$$

The output voltage v_0 is equal to $-i_2 R_L$, so that the voltage gain is

$$K \doteq -\frac{\beta R_L}{R_G + r_b + \beta r_e}$$

It should be remembered that this expression is restricted to the small values of R_L that are normally used, and that it includes the loss of gain in the generator resistance R_G.

Because a transistor is a current-driven device, the current gain is even more important than the voltage gain. It is simply i_2/i_1 or Δ_2/Δ_1. We have

$$\Delta_1 = \begin{vmatrix} v_i & r_e \\ 0 & r_e + r_c(1 - \alpha) + R_L \end{vmatrix} \doteq v_i[r_c(1 - \alpha) + R_L]$$

and so

$$\frac{i_2}{i_1} = K_i \doteq \frac{r_c\alpha}{r_c(1 - \alpha) + R_L} \doteq \beta$$

The final approximation is as usual fairly good for normal values of R_L; however, it is easy to take the better equation into account by regarding the current amplification factor β as being split between R_L and $r_c(1 - \alpha)$, effectively in parallel.

For many purposes it is useful to know the input impedance, although its effect on the gain has already been taken into account. Inspection of the equation for the voltage gain suggests that the input resistance is the quantity appearing after the generator resistance, or $(r_b + \beta r_e)$; we shall now prove this. The input resistance plus the generator resistance should be equal to the ratio v_i/i_1; thus,

$$R_i = \frac{v_i}{i_1} - R_G = \frac{v_i\Delta}{\Delta_1} - R_G$$

$$\doteq \frac{r_c(1 - \alpha)(R_G + r_b + \beta r_e)}{r_c(1 - \alpha) + R_L} - R_G$$

We have already dropped an amount R_L from Δ in a place very similar to its position in the denominator; it is therefore a good approximation to drop it again, cancel the factors, and find $R_i \doteq r_b + \beta r_e$, as expected. For our typical transistor this value amounts to $400 + 1960 \doteq 2400$ ohms.

Most transistor stages have another similar stage as their load; this value of 2400 ohms is therefore a typical load resistance, which must be considered to be in parallel with the resistor R_L of Fig. 9.6(a). Under these conditions the voltage and current gains are essentially equal and somewhat less than β; either may be used in design, but usually the current gain is more useful. As we have seen, this may be found readily by dividing a current gain of β among several impedances in parallel: the effective collector resistance $r_c(1 - \alpha)$, the load resistor R_L, the bias resistors R_1 and R_2 of the next stage, and finally the useful load, the input of the next transistor. This process is illustrated in Fig. 9.7.

As an example, consider the circuit of Fig. 9.8(a) to be loaded by an exactly similar stage. The various resistors involved are shown in Fig. 9.8(b), where the input resistance of the next transistor has been

taken as 2500 ohms to simplify the calculations. If the current gain of
49 is distributed among the various resistances in proportion to their
conductance, it is found that of the total, 6 percent goes to $r_c(1 - \alpha)$,

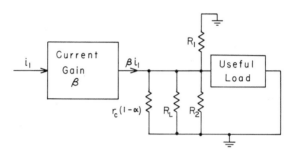

Fig. 9.7 Distribution of the current gain among the
different components of the effective load.

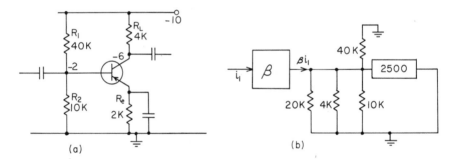

Fig. 9.8 Example for the calculation of current gain.

30 percent to R_L, 15 percent to the bias resistors, and 48.5 percent to
the transistor. Therefore the actual current gain is 48.5 percent of
49, or 24.

PROBLEM
    Verify these statements.

Bias Stabilization. We shall now discuss the methods used to define
and maintain the operating point of a transistor in the grounded-
emitter connection. It is necessary to be careful because the high
current gain is obtained essentially by a large amount of positive feed-

back, and this condition is inherently unstable. Fig. 9.9 illustrates the instability of the simplest possible circuit, the *fixed bias* circuit. Reference to the grounded-emitter characteristics and the load line

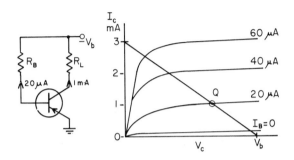

Fig. 9.9 Fixed bias circuit and the corresponding load line.

shows that the desired operating point can be maintained by a base current of 20 μa. Since the emitter is grounded, the base is only a few tenths of a volt below ground, and the current through R_B is nearly V_B/R_B. R_B is then chosen to give the required current. This circuit can be used for low-power stages, but even there it has a serious disadvantage. The current gains of different transistors of the same type vary over a wide range. If one happens to have a β of 30 instead of 50, the collector current will be only 0.6 ma and the operating point will no longer be at the desired place. It is almost necessary to select an individual value of R_B for each individual transistor.

If the transistor is dissipating an appreciable amount of power, a more serious danger exists. It will be noted that the lowest curve in the characteristics of Fig. 9.9 gives an appreciable collector current even when the base current is zero. This is the so-called *cutoff* current, which results mainly from backward flow of minority carriers at the collector junction, amplified by the high current gain of the grounded-emitter connection. The cutoff current rises sharply with temperature according to an exponential law, and is *not* under the control of the base. It is easily possible to reach a condition of "thermal runaway," in which the collector current heats the transistor, increasing the cutoff current, and thus generating more heat, and so on. If this happens, the transistor is usually destroyed in a very short time.

Since the cutoff current is not controlled by the base, it is necessary to have some control of the emitter current as well. If a simple constant-current device were available, it would be ideal for the purpose; since it is not, an approximation to it is produced by a voltage source in series with a resistance. In Fig. 9.6(a), the voltage is produced by the two bias resistors R_1 and R_2, which hold the base, and therefore the emitter, away from ground; the resistor is R_e. The emitter current is forced to be approximately the ratio (base voltage)/R_e. Elaborate procedures are available to predict the behavior with a given value of R_e, but for most designs a value of 1000 ohms or more is found to be satisfactory. Also, R_2 should not be too large, or the circuit will revert essentially to fixed bias; usually it does not exceed 10 K. Fig. 9.8 shows a circuit that will maintain the operating point of Fig. 9.9. With a supply voltage of -10 volts, a base voltage of -2 volts is a reasonable choice; then, for an emitter (and collector) current of 1 ma, R_e must be 2 K. The collector can swing between -10 and -2 volts, and a suitable operating point is halfway between, at -6 volts; therefore the load resistor should be 4 K. Note that it is not even necessary to use the transistor characteristics to design this circuit. Thus we can see that the circuit is stable against changes in current amplification factor.

The emitter resistor reduces the gain in a manner that is exactly analogous to the behavior of the cathode resistor in a tube amplifier. It is therefore usually bypassed by an electrolytic capacitor of several microfarads. Suitable capacitors with a very low voltage rating are available in a size comparable to that of the transistors. It is necessary to use them also for coupling, because the resistances in the coupling network are small. Quantitative treatment of these matters is possible but is beyond our scope. The treatment is similar to that of tube amplifiers in Chapter 4.

PROBLEM

Estimate the corner frequency when a 4-μf coupling capacitor is used in Fig. 9.6.

9.3 THE GROUNDED-COLLECTOR AMPLIFIER

This circuit is exactly analogous to a cathode follower, and a natural and common name for it is *emitter follower*. The circuit is shown in Fig. 9.10, along with the equivalent circuit. The version shown is provided with bias resistors to hold the base at a suitable average potential, but these may often be omitted and the base connected

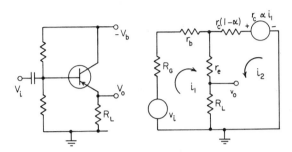

Fig. 9.10 Emitter follower and its equivalent circuit.

directly to the source, if its operating point is in the right range. The mesh equations are readily written as follows:

$$i_1(R_G + r_b + r_e + R_L) + i_2(r_e + R_L) = v_i$$

$$i_1(r_e + R_L) + i_2[r_c(1 - \alpha) + r_e + R_L] = r_c\alpha i_1$$

and the determinant is

$$\Delta \doteq \begin{vmatrix} R_G + R_L & R_L \\ R_L - r_c\alpha & r_c(1 - \alpha) + R_L \end{vmatrix}$$

where, as usual, we have dropped the small quantities r_b and r_e. Before expanding, we subtract the first row from the second; we then have

$$\Delta \doteq r_c(1 - \alpha)(R_G + R_L) + R_L(R_G + r_c\alpha)$$

$$\doteq r_c(1 - \alpha)[R_G + R_L(1 + \beta)]$$

For the last line, we have made the usually good approximation that $R_G \ll r_c\alpha$.

The substituted determinants are:

$$\Delta_1 \doteq v_i[r_c(1 - \alpha) + R_L]$$

$$\Delta_2 \doteq v_i(r_c\alpha - R_L)$$

Now the output voltage is $(i_1 + i_2)R_L$, and the voltage gain is

$(\Delta_1 + \Delta_2)R_L/\Delta$, or

$$K \doteq \frac{r_c(1 - \alpha) + R_L + r_c\alpha - R_L}{r_c(1 - \alpha)[R_G + R_L(1 + \beta)]}R_L$$

$$\doteq \frac{R_L(1 + \beta)}{R_G + R_L(1 + \beta)}$$

In the last line, $1/(1 - \alpha)$ has been replaced by $(1 + \beta)$. It is seen that the gain is close to unity unless the generator resistance is appreciable compared to $R_L(1 + \beta)$, which is easily made large.

The current gain is $(i_1 + i_2)/i_1$, or $(\Delta_1 + \Delta_2)/\Delta_1$:

$$K_i \doteq \frac{r_c}{r_c(1 - \alpha) + R_L} = (1 + \beta)\frac{r_c}{r_c + R_L(1 + \beta)}$$

If R_L is small, this approaches $(1 + \beta)$, and it drops to half this value when R_L is 20 K for our typical transistor. The emitter follower thus has essentially the same current gain as the grounded-base amplifier, and in situations in which current gain is the only important thing, the choice between them can be made on the basis of other considerations, such as input impedance.

The transistor input resistance is

$$R_i = \frac{v_i}{i_1} - R_G$$

$$\doteq \frac{r_c(1 - \alpha)[R_G + R_L(1 + \beta)]}{r_c(1 - \alpha) + R_L} - R_G$$

$$\doteq \frac{r_c R_L - R_G R_L}{r_c(1 - \alpha) + R_L}$$

in which we have made use of the fact that $(1 - \alpha)(1 + \beta) = 1$. In the numerator, R_G can normally be neglected with respect to r_c, and we have finally

$$R_i \doteq \frac{r_c R_L}{r_c(1 - \alpha) + R_L} = \frac{r_c R_L(1 + \beta)}{r_c + R_L(1 + \beta)}$$

The result is simply the parallel resistance of $R_L(1 + \beta)$ and r_c. With a large value of R_L the input resistance is essentially r_c, or about 1 megohm, a very large value for a transistor circuit. If bias resistors are used, as in Fig. 9.10, they appear in parallel.

As with the cathode follower, one of the important properties is the low output impedance. Just as the input impedance depends on the load resistance, so the output impedance depends on the generator resistance. As usual, some terms will be omitted to simplify the discussion. The output resistance is given by the ratio of open-circuit voltage to short-circuit current. The gain is unity if the load resistance is infinite; therefore, the open-circuit output voltage is equal to v_i. The short-circuit current is $(\Delta_1 + \Delta_2)/\Delta$ with $R_L = 0$, or $v_i r_c / r_c R_G (1 - \alpha)$; then the output resistance is $R_o \doteq R_G (1 - \alpha)$. This resistance can be extremely small if R_G is small, and under these conditions some terms that we have neglected become important. These are r_b and r_e in the original expression for Δ. If they are included, the output resistance is found to be

$$R_o \doteq r_e + (R_G + r_b)(1 - \alpha)$$

In deriving this, we have omitted one term in r_e, since it is much less than $r_c(1 - \alpha)$.

PROBLEM

Go back to the mesh equations, set up the complete expression for Δ, and derive the above expression.

A study of the expressions for the gain and the input and output resistances reveals a curious fact. The amount by which the gain falls below unity is to be regarded simultaneously as caused by (1) the loading of the generator resistance by the input resistance and (2) the loading of the output resistance by the load resistance. (For the latter viewpoint, the gain should be put in the form $R_L / [R_G(1 - \alpha) + R_L]$.)

Long-tailed Pair. The transistor version of this circuit is shown in Fig. 9.11; it is clearly analogous to the tube form discussed in Chapter 4, and similarly has a variety of applications. An input v_1 is emitter-coupled to the second transistor, and if R_e is large very nearly half the signal appears on each transistor. The differential output v_o depends to a close approximation on the difference $v_1 - v_2$, and not on the actual value of the inputs. The amplifier may therefore be used to subtract two voltages or to cancel unwanted signals, including many sources of drift in d-c amplifiers. This last application is discussed in Chapter 12. As with tubes, the individual collector voltages also depend primarily on the difference between the inputs, and a single-ended output may be taken if accurate differential action is not of prime importance. Used this way, the circuit is useful for mixing the feedback with the signal in a feedback amplifier. With only one input, the circuit may be used as a phase splitter.

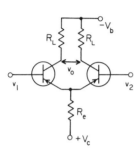

Fig. 9.11 Long-tailed pair differential amplifier.

For good differential action, the emitter resistor R_e should be moderately large, and it is useful to connect it to a positive supply as shown (negative for n–p–n transistors). Otherwise, the base-biasing networks should be chosen to give an emitter bias of several volts. We shall not analyze the circuit, since it is much easier to depend on the analogy with the tube version.

9.4 POWER AMPLIFIERS

Although Class A transistor power amplifiers are built, the majority of applications are better satisfied by Class B operation, which therefore will be stressed here. In any case, the problems of Class A operation are very similar to those encountered with tubes. As stated in Chapter 5, the advantage of Class B is its high efficiency, and this may be important for two reasons. First, many transistors are used in portable applications where minimum power consumption is necessary; second, high-power transistors may not be available with the required characteristics, and a given pair of transistors can deliver more power in Class B than in Class A operation.

A basic push-pull amplifier is shown in Fig. 9.12(a). For strict Class B operation, the base-bias resistors R_1 and R_2 are omitted and the base circuit is returned to ground. However, the result is serious *crossover distortion*, as shown in Fig. 9.12(b). Neither transistor conducts until the signal on its base reaches a value of a few tenths of a volt, and therefore the collector-current pulses are not perfect half sine waves as they should be for a sine-wave input. A small amount of forward bias moves the amplifier slightly into the Class AB region, as shown in Fig. 9.12(c); the correct choice of bias gives a very smooth crossover. Because the required bias varies with temperature, it is sometimes useful to replace R_2 by a conducting diode, whose voltage drop varies in a similar way. This type of amplifier is strictly Class AB, but it is probably more useful to regard it as a modified Class B.

Although a properly biased Class B amplifier may have very low harmonic distortion, it can probably never be regarded as a high-fidelity device. Crossover distortion causes intermodulation, considered

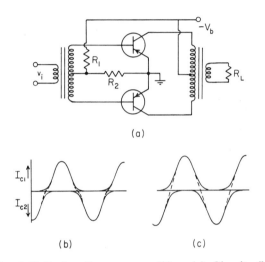

Fig. 9.12 Push-pull power amplifier. (a) Circuit. (b) Crossover distortion in strict class B operation, and (c) its reduction by a small forward bias.

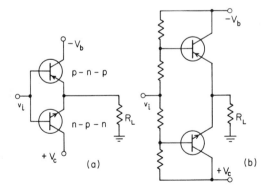

Fig. 9.13 Push-pull amplifier using complementary transistors. (a) Basic circuit. (b) Bias arrangement to eliminate crossover distortion or to give class A or AB operation.

in Chapter 13, and in a manner very different from the smooth nonlinearities that are usually discussed. Moreover, the output transformer can cause difficulty by developing transients when the current switches from one transistor to the other.

The use of a *complementary* pair of transistors (one p–n–p and one n–p–n) permits a simple push-pull circuit with single-ended input and output, as in Fig. 9.13. Both positive and negative power supplies are required if the load is to be directly connected to the emitters as shown; if it can be connected through a capacitor, a single supply of twice the voltage can be used, with a suitable shift of ground point. The circuit is most simply regarded as a pair of emitter followers in parallel, and therefore gives current gain but no voltage gain. For some purposes this may be a disadvantage, but for many it is not serious.

The simple circuit of Fig. 9.13(a) is pure Class B and gives the usual crossover distortion, since neither transistor conducts when the input is at ground. The required forward bias can be developed by the voltage dividers shown in Fig. 9.13(b), and if a high enough bias is allowed, the operation can even be Class A. The complementary amplifier has seen less use than would be expected, because suitable pairs of transistors have not been available or have been very expensive. This difficulty will almost certainly disappear as methods of manufacturing transistors improve.

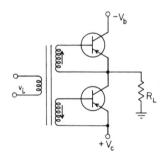

Fig. 9.14 Push-pull amplifier with single-ended output using similar transistors.

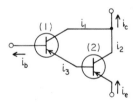

Fig. 9.15 Compound connection of transistors.

A similar amplifier using two transistors of the same type is shown in Fig. 9.14; it is also possible with tubes and has been called a "single-ended push-pull" circuit. As with the complementary amplifier, this circuit would normally use a single power supply and a blocking capacitor in series with the load. The use of two separate transformer secondary windings allows input voltages to be fed between base and emitter of each transistor, so that the circuit is effectively of the grounded-emitter type. The driving voltages can be generated by a complementary pair of low-power transistors, which are easier to obtain, but we shall omit the details because the operation of the circuit is not very easy to grasp. This version is often called a "quasi-complementary" amplifier.

When a high current gain is needed in an amplifier, the *compound* or *Darlington* connection shown in Fig. 9.15 may be useful. If the second transistor is connected as an emitter follower, the first is simply another emitter follower connected directly to the base. However, the pair can be regarded as a single "supertransistor" and connected in any desired configuration. We shall now derive an expression for the current gain of the pair. The first transistor has current gain β_1 to the collector, and $(1 + \beta_1)$ to the emitter; therefore,

$$i_1 = \beta_1 i_b, \qquad i_3 = (1 + \beta_1)i_b$$

The latter current is the input to the second transistor, giving outputs

$$i_2 = \beta_2(1 + \beta_1)i_b, \qquad i_e = (1 + \beta_2)(1 + \beta_1)i_b$$

If β is the effective current gain of the combination, we have

$$i_c = \beta i_b, \qquad i_e = (1 + \beta)i_b$$

Comparison of the expressions for i_e shows that

$$1 + \beta = (1 + \beta_1)(1 + \beta_2)$$

The same result can be found by comparing i_c with $i_1 + i_2$. Since $1 + \beta = 1/(1 - \alpha)$, we also have

$$1 - \alpha = (1 - \alpha_1)(1 - \alpha_2)$$

Thus, for transistors with $\alpha = 0.98$ and $\beta = 49$, the combination has the corresponding values 0.9996 and 2499.

When this circuit is used, it is necessary to pay some attention to bias conditions and the flow of leakage currents. Also, in low-power circuits the base current of the second transistor may not provide enough emitter current for the first; this problem can be remedied by feeding in the extra current required to the junction through a resistor.

9.5 HIGH-FREQUENCY RESPONSE

As with tubes, the high-frequency response of a transistor amplifier is affected by two main factors: output capacitance and transit-time lags. However, the latter effect is negligible in a tube at frequencies at which the capacitive effects are already very large, and need be taken into account only in tuned amplifiers operating at frequencies in hundreds of megacycles. In a transistor, as we have seen, the transit time may be of the order of a microsecond, because the carriers move across the base by diffusion only. And in the grounded-emitter configuration, this can affect the response at frequencies as low as 20 kc, because β depends on the reciprocal of $(1 - \alpha)$.

One type of transistor, known as a *drift* type, is arranged to have an electric field in the base region, by grading the conductivity from a high value near the emitter to a low value near the collector. This can raise the high-frequency cutoff by a factor of the order of 10.

Typically, the capacitive effects may come into play in the same region of frequencies. Anything approaching a complete treatment would be far beyond our scope, and we shall have to be content with some rough first approximations, which are adequate as long as the loss of gain does not exceed a few decibels.

The most important capacitance is that across the collector-base junction, and to a first approximation it may be placed in parallel with r_c in the equivalent circuit of Fig. 9.2. For an alloy transistor, a typical value is 35 pf; much smaller values may be attained by special constructions, especially the "mesa" design sketched in Fig. 8.4 at the right. During the transformation to the grounded-emitter equivalent circuit illustrated in Figs. 9.3 and 9.4, the impedance of r_c is multiplied by $(1 - \alpha)$. If this impedance consists of the resistance r_c in parallel with C_c, the final result is $r_c(1 - \alpha)$ in parallel with $C_c/(1 - \alpha)$, or approximately βC_c. Thus, the capacitance of 35 pf behaves like 1750 pf in the grounded-emitter connection.

For an estimate of its effect on the gain, this capacitance can be assumed to be in parallel with the output. If the transistor is feeding a large load resistance such as 10 K, including all the components shown in Fig. 9.8(b), a time constant of 18 μsec is formed, and the corner frequency is only 9 kc. With a more normal load, such as the 1200 ohms actually shown in Fig. 9.8(b), the time constant is 2.1 μsec and the corner frequency 75 kc. Special high-frequency transistors can go very much higher.

The transit-time effects are normally represented by a variation of α with frequency. The actual variation is rather complicated, but for convenience we shall represent it by the frequency response of a single R-C lag network:

$$\alpha \doteq \frac{\alpha_0}{1 + j\omega\tau_\alpha}$$

The corner frequency of this expression, f_α, is called the α-*cutoff frequency*. The relationship between the true and approximate expressions is sketched in Fig. 9.16. For typical alloy transistors, the α-cutoff frequency is around 1 mc.

Fig. 9.16 Variation of α with frequency, and approximation to it (shown dotted).

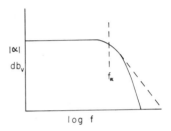

Let us now investigate the form of the β cutoff. This is found simply by substituting the expression for α into the definition of β:

$$\beta \equiv \frac{\alpha}{1 - \alpha} \doteq \frac{\alpha_0}{1 + j\omega\tau_\alpha - \alpha_0} = \frac{\alpha_0}{1 - \alpha_0} \frac{1}{1 + j\omega\tau_\alpha/(1 - \alpha_0)}$$

$$= \frac{\beta_0}{1 + j\omega\tau_\beta}$$

Thus, the β-cutoff frequency is less than the α-cutoff frequency by a factor $(1 - \alpha_0)$ or $1/(1 + \beta_0)$. Our typical example has a β-cutoff frequency of 20 kc. Therefore, β cutoff will dominate the high-frequency response for normal loads, but collector capacitance may be more important with unusually large load resistances. Preferably, both effects should be taken into account simultaneously. For accurate design, and for work above the cutoff or corner frequencies, more complete descriptions are required, but our approximations will serve for many purposes and also to indicate the magnitude of the effects to be expected.

9.6 POWER SUPPLIES AND REGULATORS

Most of the material in Chapter 7 applies to transistor power supplies as well as to tube supplies. Some of the advantages of junction rectifiers and regulating diodes were pointed out there. Transistor power supplies normally provide much lower voltage and perhaps greater current, but this does not affect any principles. Here we shall be principally concerned with transistor regulators. These regulators are normally used when a regulated power supply is required by a transistor circuit, but they have less obvious applications as well. A requirement often arises for regulated power at low voltage and high current—tens or hundreds of amperes. The commonest example is the power supply for an electromagnet, which is most economically wound with few turns of heavy wire. Tube regulators are almost useless for this purpose, because the voltage drop across the tube may be many times larger than the drop across the load, and the power dissipation is prohibitive. Transistors can carry such currents with a drop of 1 volt or even less, and have opened up a wide range of new possibilities.

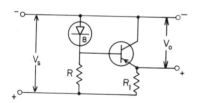

Fig. 9.17 Shunt voltage regulator.

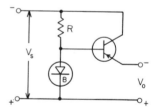

Fig. 9.18 Series voltage regulator.

Very good performance at low and medium power can be provided by a breakdown diode in the circuit of Fig. 7.12. These diodes behave as a constant potential in series with a resistance of a few ohms, the exact value depending on the particular diode. The output resistance of this regulator, by Thévenin's theorem, is this resistance in parallel with R, the series dropping resistance; normally the diode resistance is so much smaller that it completely controls the result. For heavy currents, this output resistance may be too large, and it may be difficult to obtain a diode with a large enough power rating. It can then be supplemented by a transistor, or several in parallel, using either the shunt connection as in Fig. 7.13, or the series connection as in Fig. 7.15. A shunt regulator is shown in Fig. 9.17; the transistor is connected as an emitter follower with a constant base-to-collector voltage. The output resistance is therefore reduced by a factor nearly equal to the β of the transistor. Since the diode is still exposed to the changes of source voltage, the stabilization factor is unchanged. The performance may be improved enormously by adding a differential amplifier to amplify the difference between the reference voltage and a fraction of the output. It is then possible to feed the breakdown diode from the regulated voltage and get a stable reference voltage. The biggest disadvantage of shunt regulators is that they are very inefficient at light loads, because any power that does not go to the load must be absorbed by the transistor. On the other hand, they have the advantage of being automatically immune to destruction by a short circuit, which simply reduces the power dissipated by the transistor to zero.

The simplest series regulator is shown in Fig. 9.18. Again, the transistor is connected as an emitter follower, but this time all the load current passes through it instead of through R_1 as in Fig. 9.17. The output resistance is that of an emitter follower with negligible generator

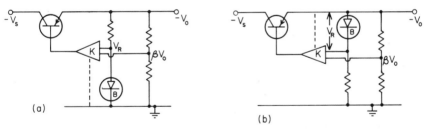

Fig. 9.19 High-performance series regulators with differential amplifier to drive the control transistor. (a) Emitter-follower output. (b) Grounded-emitter output.

resistance, or approximately $(r_e + r_b)/\beta$. The emitter resistance becomes very small at high currents, and the second term of this expression may then dominate. A value of 1 ohm at a load of 1 ampere is typical. As with the simple shunt regulator, the stabilization factor is essentially that of the diode.

Series regulators of higher performance are shown in Fig. 9.19. The circuit in Fig. 9.19(a) is the exact analog of the tube regulator in Fig. 7.16, with the series transistor connected as an emitter follower. However, if the voltage is to be varied over a wide range, it may be difficult for the amplifier to develop the large change in voltage required by the base. Then the circuit in Fig. 9.19(b) may be preferable; the reference point for the amplifier is at the negative output instead of ground, as suggested by the dotted lines. The series transistor acts as a grounded-emitter stage with considerable voltage amplification. The performance of the two circuits is the same; the additional gain is compensated by the fact that the impedance to be reduced by the feedback is greater by the same factor.

Any series transistor regulator must be carefully protected against the effects of an accidental short circuit of the output terminals. The series transistor can be destroyed in milliseconds, as may some of the others, depending on the circuit. Tubes will withstand a momentary overload and are therefore able to survive many accidents that will ruin a transistor. Protection schemes usually take the form of arrangements to limit the short-circuit current to a safe value, and may be as simple as arranging to limit the base current of the series transistor to a value just greater than that needed to permit the maximum allowed collector current to be passed. In general, fuses are not effective, since the reaction time of the fuse is greater than the time needed to burn out a transistor.

As with tubes, a current regulator is made by developing the feedback from a "shunt" in series with the load, instead of from a voltage divider in parallel with it. Otherwise, the circuits closely resemble the ones in Fig. 9.19.

9.7 POWER INVERTERS

By convention, the term *inverter* means the exact opposite of a rectifier: a device for converting direct current to alternating current. Many applications exist for an efficient inverter, especially in battery-operated equipment, because otherwise it is impossible to make a "d-c transformer." An inverter can be followed by a transformer to give an alternating voltage of any desired value. If direct current is required, a rectifier and filter can be added. There had never been a fully satisfactory solution to this requirement until the advent of transistors. The devices that were used were *dynamotors* and *vibrators*. The former is a dynamo and motor sharing the same field structure and armature; it works well, but is heavy and expensive, and produces considerable radio interference unless carefully shielded. Moreover, it is unsuitable for transforming very small amounts of power. The vibrator uses an arrangement similar to a buzzer or doorbell to make a contact arm oscillate, and the contacts on the arm are used to "chop" the direct current into alternating current. Since the transistor inverter is closely equivalent to this device, it will be discussed in some detail. Again its main disadvantages are production of radio noise, and limited life of the contacts.

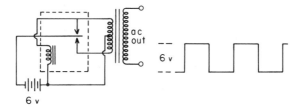

Fig. 9.20 Power inverter using a mechanical vibrator.

A typical vibrator circuit is shown in Fig. 9.20. One of the contacts is used to break current to the coil, so that the reed vibrates approximately at its natural frequency. As it vibrates, it connects the negative battery terminal alternately to each end of the transformer primary winding. As far as the transformer is concerned, it is just as if the battery polarity were being reversed rapidly across half of the primary winding, and so an alternating flux is produced in the core. The same effect could be produced by actually reversing the battery connections across a single winding, but this would require four contacts on the vibrator instead of two. (Compare the full-wave rectifier of Fig. 7.2, which saves two diodes by using a center-tapped secondary.)

Since a power transistor can carry many amperes with a potential drop of only a few tenths of a volt, the vibrator contacts can be replaced by transistors connected in a suitable oscillating circuit. The generation of radio noise is negligible, and a well-designed circuit has an almost indefinite life. The transistor inverter can handle several hundred watts, or can be designed for satisfactory efficiency with a load of a fraction of a watt. This is another example of an application that can be handled very well by transistors and not at all by tubes.

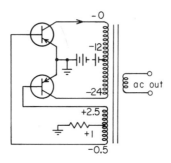

Fig. 9.21 Transistor oscillator for power inversion.

A typical oscillator is shown in Fig. 9.21. The transformer is specially designed so that the core can saturate without the dissipation of too much energy. This characteristic normally requires the use of a material with a square hysteresis loop. The saturation is used to switch the current from one transistor to the other; if the switching is done in some other way, an ordinary transformer can be used. As an example, the bases might be driven from a separate oscillator.

If the upper transistor is conducting, it holds its end of the primary winding almost at ground, and a steadily increasing flux is generated in the core. The collector of the other transistor is held at −24 volts, but there is no conduction because there is no base current. The base winding generates a voltage that holds the lower transistor off and provides enough base current to the upper transistor to keep it conducting hard. The battery voltage, transformed by the turns ratio, appears across the load winding. This situation can remain only until the flux builds up in the core to the saturation value. The flux can then no longer increase appreciably, and the induced voltages in the secondary windings disappear; therefore, there is no longer any driving current for the base of the upper transistor. Its collector current is suddenly reduced, and the resulting small induced voltage in the base winding turns it off completely and turns on the lower transistor. As soon as this happens, base voltages are generated which hold the upper transistor off and the lower one on. The flux steadily reduces to zero, and then increases to saturation in the other direction. Thus the circuit oscillates at a frequency determined by the time it takes the flux to go from positive to negative saturation.

The output is a square wave which can be used directly, or rectified and filtered. A rectified square wave is almost pure d-c voltage without any filtering, and a simple capacitor is usually sufficient to reduce the ripple; this is especially true since the a-c frequency is relatively high, 400 cps being typical.

Calculation of the period of the oscillation helps to illustrate the operating principle. We use Faraday's law of magnetic induction, which can be written:

$$V = 10^{-8} \frac{d\Phi}{dt} \text{ volts}$$

where Φ is the magnetic flux in maxwells or gauss-cm^2. For N turns of wire the voltage is N times larger, and if the cross-sectional area of the core is A cm^2 the flux is AB, where B is the induction in gauss:

$$V = 10^{-8} A N \frac{dB}{dt}$$

In the inverter, this equation gives the rate of change of the induction for a given voltage applied to a given number of turns. We now find the time taken for B to change from saturation one way to saturation the other way, and set this time equal to half the period of oscillation: $\Delta t = 1/2f$. If the saturation induction is B_m, the change in half a cycle is $2B_m$, and $dB/dt = 2B_m/\Delta t = 4fB_m$; thus,

$$V = 10^{-8} NA \cdot 4fB_m \qquad \text{or} \qquad f = 10^8 \frac{V}{4NAB_m}$$

In practice, a core and a frequency would be chosen, and this relation would be used to find the required number of turns for a given voltage.

A few practical points are worth mentioning. The "off" transistor must be able to withstand a voltage of twice the supply voltage plus an extra allowance for a "spike," which is generated when the transformer saturates. The circuit shown will not start itself, since no base current is provided unless a transistor is already conducting. A common remedy is to insert a voltage divider to deliver enough base current to ensure starting, but other methods are in use. Finally, it is desirable to modify the circuit of Fig. 9.21 so that the collectors are at ground potential,

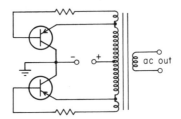

Fig. 9.22 Arrangement of the power inverter with collectors grounded.

because the collector of a power transistor is normally connected to the case, and the heat is most easily dissipated if the case can be electrically connected to a metal chassis. A suitable rearrangement of the circuit is shown in Fig. 9.22.

REFERENCES

An excellent introduction to the physics of transistors and to transistor circuits is *Physical Principles and Applications of Junction Transistors* by J. H. Simpson and R. S. Richards (New York: Oxford University Press, 1962). For the application of transistors it is useful to have a compilation of tested circuits to choose from and if necessary modify; this purpose is served very well by *Selected Semiconductor Circuits Handbook* edited by S. Schwartz (New York: John Wiley & Sons, Inc., 1960).

CHAPTER 10

Trigger Circuits

In nearly all the applications we have considered so far, the tubes and transistors have been used as linear (or nearly linear) amplifying elements. In this chapter we turn to an entirely different class of circuits, those in which the tubes and transistors are used as switches. Normally they are either cut off completely or conducting as hard as possible, and in many cases they are caused to change states by a *trigger*, usually a short pulse. Thus, the name *trigger circuit* is a convenient one for the whole class. The description will be carried out in terms of transistors wherever possible, since transistor trigger circuits have the advantages of small size, low power consumption, and reliability, all of which are important in pulse systems.

As just described, most trigger circuits have two discrete states. A stable state can maintain itself indefinitely unless disturbed by a violent trigger. A quasi-stable state is stable for a certain period of time, but then spontaneously becomes unstable, and the circuit changes to its other state. A convenient classification is by whether both, one, or neither of the states is stable. Since a stable state is simpler than a quasi-stable one, we start with the circuits having two stable states. This is the opposite of the common practice of starting with the circuits having no stable state. Although the latter look simpler in many cases, since they may contain fewer components, they are actually more complicated.

213

10.1 CIRCUITS HAVING TWO STABLE STATES

The simplest of all trigger circuits is the *thyratron* switch; a close relative among semiconducting devices uses the *silicon controlled rectifier*. In the "off" condition the grid is biased sufficiently negative to keep the tube cut off. A short positive pulse on the grid is sufficient to allow the tube to fire, after which it remains on until the plate voltage is removed or goes negative. The circuit may be used in a device that is to be actuated only once by the first of a series of events. In such an application the tube would usually be reset manually by opening the plate circuit, but it can be done automatically if desired.

Flip-flop. The *flip-flop* circuit uses a pair of tubes or transistors and goes by a confusing variety of names, such as *bistable multivibrator*, *Eccles-Jordan trigger circuit*, and *toggle*. Although we shall use the name "flip-flop," the reader should be warned that some writers use it for the

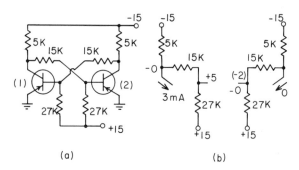

(a)   (b)

Fig. 10.1 (a) Flip-flop circuit. (b) Voltages on the coupling networks.

device we call a *univibrator*. A typical circuit is shown in Fig. 10.1; it is symmetrical and the stable states each have one transistor on and one off. Because of the symmetry the two states are mirror images, and only one need be discussed. A symmetrical state with both transistors conducting is conceivable, but it is highly unstable and any small deviation from perfect symmetry will be amplified and cause a rapid transition to one of the unsymmetrical states.

Let us suppose that transistor 1 is conducting and transistor 2 is cut off; the voltages at each point are shown in Fig. 10.1(b). The conducting transistor holds its collector just below ground and is therefore carrying about 3 ma. Fig. 10.1(b) then shows that the base of transistor 2 is about 5 volts positive, and it is therefore thoroughly cut off. Since this is so, Fig. 10.1(b) shows that the base of transistor 1 would be 2 volts negative, except that it then draws current and holds itself only slightly negative. Thus, transistor 1 is conducting heavily as was originally assumed. The state will be maintained in the face of slow variations of resistances, supply voltages, and transistor characteristics over a considerable range, and is thus truly stable.

However, a number of ways exist of inducing a rapid transition to the other stable state; the details will be discussed shortly. Suppose base 1 is raised a few tenths of a volt, thus reducing the collector current and allowing the collector voltage to fall towards the supply voltage. Most of this change will appear at base 2, and if the change is large enough transistor 2 will start to conduct. Its collector voltage will rise towards ground and this change will be coupled back to base 1, reinforcing the action which started everything. The result is a very rapid transition to the other stable state.

The transition can also be induced by a negative trigger on base 2, but a larger signal is required since it must overcome the 5-volt cutoff bias before anything happens. During the transition, the flip-flop can be regarded as a two-stage amplifier with the output coupled back to the input. The speed of the transition is limited by the same factors that limit the rise time and high-frequency response of an amplifier. For switching times below a microsecond, it is necessary to use special high-speed transistors. Some increase in speed is also possible by connecting small capacitors in parallel with the collector-to-emitter resistors. Their effect is to increase the loop gain during the transition, but they also tend to produce overshoots and to paralyze the circuit for a short time after the transition. These capacitors are normally used with tubes, and if high speed is necessary, the tubes must have high transconductance and small load resistors, as in a video amplifier.

Triggering Methods. The triggering methods discussed here apply to almost all trigger circuits, especially those based on the flip-flop; it is therefore convenient to have them considered in one place.

The simplest and least satisfactory method is to couple a pulse to the appropriate point by a small capacitor. For example, in Fig. 10.1 a positive pulse would be coupled to the base of transistor 1, either directly or by way of the collector of transistor 2. The latter method is preferable because it interferes less with the operation of the circuit. Similarly, a negative pulse could be coupled to base 2 or collector 1. One difficulty with capacitor coupling is that it works both ways; the large pulses generated by the flip-flop are transmitted back to the source of the trigger, which is often another trigger circuit, and may affect its operation.

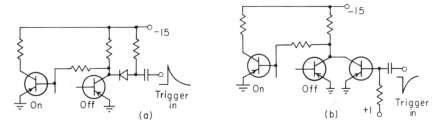

Fig. 10.2 Triggering methods. (a) Diode coupling. (b) Parallel transistor triggering.

A much better coupling element is a diode, as shown in Fig. 10.2(a). The positive trigger is freely transmitted by the diode to collector 2, and coupled by the resistor to base 1 as before. As soon as the transition gets under way, collector 2 rises towards ground and the diode cuts off, isolating the trigger source completely. If the available trigger is negative, a parallel transistor may be used instead; see Fig. 10.2(b). This transistor normally is cut off by a small bias and has no effect on the circuit, but the trigger brings it into conduction and it effectively initiates a transition; as soon as the trigger is over, it cuts off again.

Another way to consider the flip-flop is as a pair of logic circuits coupled together. The details are considered in Section 15.4, and the "logic" method of triggering is illustrated in Fig. 15.27.

Applications. Sometimes it is desired to generate a square pulse having a starting point that coincides with one trigger and an end that is controlled by another (Fig. 10.3). The resulting waveform is often called a *gate* because it can be used to control the passage of some other signal by means of a *gate circuit* (Chapter 15). The gate is readily generated by a flip-flop triggered on by one pulse and off by the other.

The commonest application of all is in counting pulses that occur at a rate too rapid to be followed by a mechanical device. The pulses may be from a nuclear counter, from small objects passing along a production line, or from the cycles of a wave whose frequency is being measured. An apparent difficulty is that in this case both the "start" and "stop" pulses reach the flip-flop along the same wire; instead of

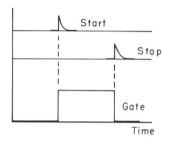

Fig. 10.3 Generation of a square pulse from short start and stop pulses.

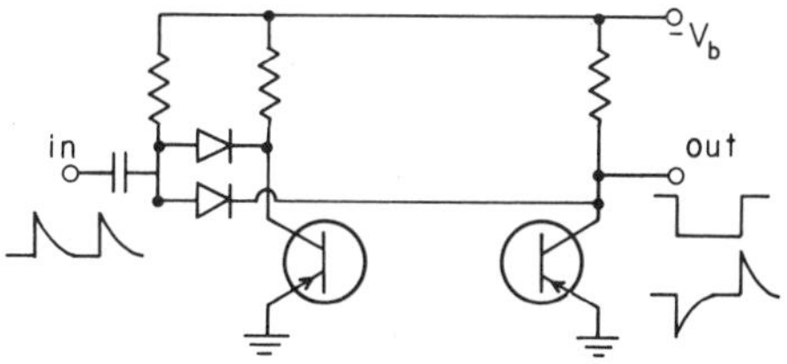

Fig. 10.4 Scale-of-two circuit.

separate wires as in Fig. 10.3. However, diode coupling, as in Fig. 10.4, automatically "steers" the trigger to the collector of the "off" transistor, since the other collector is at a low potential and its diode cannot conduct. The circuit is called a *scale-of-two*, since it delivers one pulse out for each two coming in. The collector waveform is a series of steps; this waveform is usually differentiated, by coupling with a short time constant, into a train of short positive and negative pulses. Note that the negative pulses in the output will be ignored by a similar stage following the one shown, because of the coupling diodes. A chain of n stages like this forms a scale of 2^n, and the number can be as large as desired.

In effect, such scalers count on the binary number system; however, if the numbers are to be recorded and used by a human observer, this system is very inconvenient. It is common practice to make decimal scalers by converting a scale of 16 into a scale of 10. This conversion is accomplished by means of internal feedback paths, which effectively introduce 6 extra counts while 10 external ones are received.

Other Flip-flops. Fig. 10.5 shows a typical tube flip-flop, which works on exactly the same principle as the transistor version of Fig. 10.1. However, this circuit has been drawn with a single power supply to show that the cathodes (or emitters) can be held away from ground by the current through R_k, which is the same in both states. A small bypass capacitor is sufficient to hold the voltage constant during the transitions. Note that in order to keep the drawing neat, connections have been made to both ends of the grids.

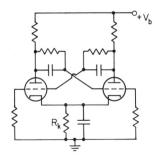
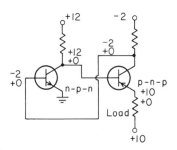

Fig. 10.5 A tube flip-flop, shown with cathode bias.

Fig. 10.6 Complementary transistor flip-flop.

The availability of both p–n–p and n–p–n transistors makes possible an interesting class of circuits based on the use of *complementary pairs*. An example is shown in Fig. 10.6. The collector of each transistor is connected directly to the base of the other. In the "off" condition, both transistors are cut off; the collector voltages are nearly equal to the supply voltages, which in both cases have the correct polarity to back-bias the emitter of the other transistor. No current can flow through the load resistor. In the "on" condition, both transistors conduct heavily, and the collector and emitter voltages are nearly equal. The circuit can be turned on by lowering the emitter of the n–p–n transistor below -2 volts; to permit this, a diode is connected between emitter and ground, and a negative pulse is used. To turn it off, the base of the other transistor is pulled above $+10$ volts, the value of its emitter supply, so that it can no longer conduct. This is most easily done by means of a third transistor, a p–n–p, in a connection similar to Fig. 10.2(b), with a negative pulse input.

Diode Catching. The *diode-catching* technique, sometimes called *clamping*, is used for two purposes. The first is to define accurately the voltage at which a terminal will rest during a stable state; the second is to raise the effective speed of a transition. Fig. 10.7 shows a transistor with an input voltage V_i, which either cuts it off or makes it conduct heavily. If it is cut off, the collector falls towards -40 volts, but when it reaches -10 volts the upper diode conducts and it can fall no lower; it is then *caught* at -10 volts, or slightly lower when the diode voltage drop is included. The value of this voltage depends only on the 10-volt power supply and the diode, and can therefore be accurately specified. Moreover, since the collector was starting off towards -40 volts, the rise time of the output is considerably shortened by the clipping off of the last 30 volts. When the transistor is turned on, its collector tries to rise to nearly $+2$ volts, but again is caught just above ground potential by the lower diode. This technique can be applied to almost any trigger circuit of the flip-flop class; for example, the complete version of Fig. 10.6 may include three catching diodes. In many cases, only one of the two voltage limits is defined in this way.

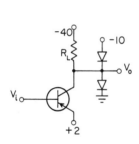

Fig. 10.7 Diode catching.

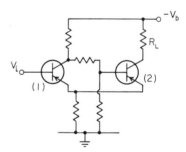

Fig. 10.8 Schmitt trigger circuit.

Schmitt Trigger Circuit. The flip-flop of Fig. 10.1 can be regarded as a direct-coupled amplifier with the output connected regeneratively back to the input. One of the couplings can be replaced by an emitter coupling, as in the long-tailed-pair amplifier, giving the circuit of Fig. 10.8, called an emitter-coupled flip-flop or Schmitt trigger circuit. The properties are now rather different, since the state depends primarily on the value of the d-c emitter voltage V_i. Its main use is as a voltage *discriminator*: to flip if the magnitude of V_i exceeds a certain threshold value, even momentarily. It can be used for sorting pulses by their amplitude, or to ring an alarm if a signal becomes dangerously large.

To understand the action, let us examine it as V_i starts at ground potential and is slowly made negative. Initially, transistor 1 is cut off; the voltage divider sets a certain voltage, say -5 volts, on the base of transistor 2, and by emitter-follower action, the emitters will be at nearly the same potential. This is what keeps transistor 1 cut off, and will continue to do so as V_i goes negative, until it approaches -5 volts. At that point transistor 1 starts to conduct, its collector rises towards ground, and so does base 2 and therefore the emitters as well. But this action turns transistor 1 fully on, and since the emitter voltage is kept from changing more than a few tenths of a volt, transistor 2 is turned fully off. Further change in V_i will cause changes in the emitter and collector voltages of transistor 1, but the state will remain essentially the same until the magnitude of V_i is less than some value near 2 or 3 volts negative. At this point, which depends on the ratio of the voltage divider, transistor 2 will start to conduct again, and a rapid reverse transition will take place. Thus, the circuit exhibits *hysteresis*, which is desirable for many applications and irrelevant for others. The output can be taken from R_L in the collector circuit of transistor 2; its magnitude can be chosen freely since it does not participate in the action of the circuit. For alarm purposes, R_L could be the coil of a relay.

PROBLEM

Design an actual circuit, specifying the resistors in Fig. 10.8, and estimate the voltages at which it will trigger.

10.2 CIRCUITS HAVING ONE STABLE STATE

Again, we start off with a *thyratron* circuit. Under the right conditions, a thyratron has only one stable state, namely, the cutoff state. When it is triggered, it conducts briefly and then goes out again. A suitable circuit is shown in Fig. 10.9; a tetrode thyratron, as shown, is appropriate since it requires only a small bias to hold it off. In the stable state, the capacitor C is charged to the full value of the supply voltage and no currents are flowing. A positive pulse on the grid will fire the thyratron, and C will discharge through it and the series resistor

R_k; a short and very large output pulse can be taken from R_k. If the plate resistor is greater than about 20 K, it does not pass enough current to keep the thyratron conducting, which goes out. Possibly this is aided by stray inductance in the circuit, which would cause the plate voltage to oscillate, carrying it very near zero. The capacitor then charges up again through the plate resistor and, after a few time constants, is ready to deliver another pulse of essentially the same size.

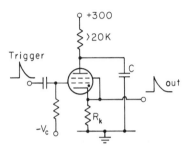

Fig. 10.9 Triggered thyratron pulse generator.

The resistor R_k is necessary to prevent the tube from carrying too much current and damaging itself. The voltage drop across the tube is only about 15 volts, and the initial current is therefore nearly equal to the supply voltage divided by R_k. This current must be kept within the tube rating, typically 10 amp, but less for some tubes. If a negative pulse is required, the resistor can be placed between the capacitor and ground instead.

Sometimes the output pulse is required to have a square shape instead of the sharp rise and exponential decay given by the capacitor. This is possible by replacing the capacitor with a *delay line* or artificial transmission line (Chapter 17). When R_k is made equal to its characteristic impedance, it acts in the same way as a capacitor except that it delivers its stored energy at a steady rate until it is suddenly exhausted, thus producing the desired square pulse. Its amplitude is half the supply voltage and its length twice the delay of the line. Lengths up to a few microseconds are practical; beyond that, a univibrator can be used instead.

Univibrator. The *univibrator*, a relative of the flip-flop, also has a variety of other names; in fact, it is itself sometimes called a *flip-flop*.

Another popular name is *monostable multivibrator*. A suitable pulse can trigger it into its quasi-stable state; after a certain time, it spontaneously reverts back to the stable state. It thus produces a standard square pulse, or gate, in response to each trigger; the length of the pulse ranges upward from a few microseconds and can be made to exceed a second.

To change a flip-flop into a univibrator, we replace one of the two direct couplings by a capacitor coupling to give the result shown in Fig. 10.10. As with the flip-flop, emitter bias is possible if only one

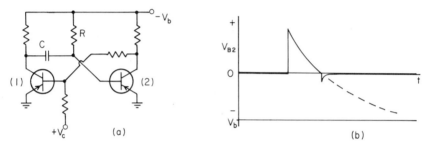

Fig. 10.10 Univibrator. (a) Circuit. (b) Timing wave during the quasi-stable state.

supply voltage is available. The capacitor coupling is from collector 1 to emitter 2, and the resistor is normally returned to V_b as shown. It therefore draws current from base 2 and keeps transistor 2 in conduction, thereby producing a cutoff voltage at base 1 and keeping transistor 1 out of conduction. This stable state of the system will last indefinitely unless a trigger arrives to cause a transition to the quasi-stable state. Any of the methods of triggering discussed in the preceding section may be used; normally, a positive pulse will be delivered to collector 1 and therefore base 2. The transition takes place by the familiar regenerative process, which turns on transistor 1 and turns off transistor 2 by carrying its base many volts positive. However, the voltage of base 2 does not remain constant, since C must discharge through R, generating an exponential *timing wave* as shown in Fig. 10.10(b). When this wave becomes negative, transistor 2 starts to conduct and the reverse transition takes place; base 2 goes negative briefly until C charges up again. Notice that the timing wave crosses the axis at a fairly large angle, since it is only about halfway to its asymptotic voltage; therefore, the length of the quasi-stable state is well defined and reproducible. In tube univibrators it is possible to return R to ground instead of to the supply voltage. The result is a longer delay, but the length of delay is subject to large variations since the timing wave crosses the cutoff level at a very small angle.

Output in the form of a square pulse can be taken from either collector, depending on the polarity desired. Alternatively, a short delayed pulse can be produced by differentiating one of these square pulses with a short time constant.

PROBLEM

Show that the length of the quasi-stable state is approximately $RC \ln 2$.

An *emitter-coupled univibrator* is also possible, as shown in Fig. 10.11. It is derived from the Schmitt trigger circuit in the same way that the collector-coupled circuit is derived from the flip-flop, and the action

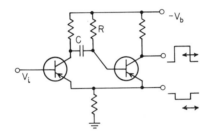

Fig. 10.11 Emitter-coupled univibrator.

may be understood from the previous descriptions. The length of the quasi-stable state depends on the d-c base voltage V_i, and can therefore be readily changed over a wide range. Moreover, the delay time is a linear function of V_i to rather good accuracy over much of the range.

PROBLEM

Analyze the action of the circuit when triggered.

Phantastrons and Sanatrons. Circuits known as *phantastrons* and *sanatrons* are useful when it is desired to generate delays with high accuracy and closely linear variation with control voltage. They use a linear timing wave, generated by an integrating process, instead of the exponential of the univibrator. We shall not describe them, merely pointing out that they exist and can be studied in the references if such a requirement should arise.

Blocking Oscillator. The blocking oscillator, which has no bistable analog, can be either monostable or astable. Its applications are similar to those of the thyratron pulse generator; the pulse shape is a little better for some purposes, and the pulse repetition rate can be higher. As Fig. 10.12 shows, the circuit is a transformer-coupled amplifier with

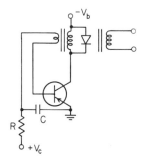

Fig. 10.12 Blocking oscillator.

the secondary winding connected to the input; we shall consider the grounded-emitter version, but the grounded-base type is also useful, since the transformer ratio can be chosen to match the low input impedance. Even with the emitter grounded, the transformer has a voltage step-down, with a ratio of $2 : 1$ to $5 : 1$.

The normal state of the circuit is with the transistor cut off. It can be brought into conduction by a negative pulse connected to the base, or by a parallel transistor as in Fig. 10.2(b), driving the base negative through the transformer. As soon as the transistor starts to conduct, it provides its own base current through the transformer. Essentially all the supply voltage appears across the transformer primary, and the flux in the core builds up until it starts to saturate. When this happens, the base current can no longer be maintained, the transistor stops conducting, and the transformer drives the base rapidly into cutoff. The diode in parallel with the primary absorbs the stored energy, which might otherwise damage the transistor. A similar action occurs in the power inverters discussed in Section 9.6. The output is a square pulse whose length depends mainly on the characteristics of the transformer. For some purposes it is convenient to take it from a tertiary winding as shown.

The base current which flows during the pulse is taken mainly from C, since R is relatively large. After the pulse, the voltage left on C keeps the transistor biased off even without the help of the voltage V_c. This action of charging a capacitor, which then holds the circuit off, is known as *blocking* and gives the circuit its name. Power is actually supplied to the bias source. The transformer is a special *pulse* type usually designed specifically for a blocking oscillator. Its frequency range is from a few tenths of a megacycle to several megacycles, attained by windings of only a few turns very closely coupled, and by the use of high-frequency core materials. Very thin iron laminations have been used, but ferrites, which are insulators, are more common.

10.3 CIRCUITS HAVING NO STABLE STATE

Both states in this class are quasi-stable; each one relaxes into the other after its own characteristic time. Devices of this kind are often called *relaxation oscillators*; they oscillate, but no resonant circuit is present to define the frequency. A common mechanical system of this kind is the squeaking of chalk on a blackboard or of a rusty hinge. (The same principle, when associated with resonant systems, gives as musical a sound as that of a violin.)

Thyratron Oscillator. If the bias in Fig. 10.9 is reduced, so that it is not enough to hold off the full supply voltage, the tube will fire again when the plate voltage rises high enough, and will continue to do so at a frequency that depends on the time constant with which the voltage rises. The circuit of Fig. 10.13 is the same, except that a triode thyratron is used instead of the tetrode, because the plate voltage at which it fires is more reproducible. The sawtooth waveform is useful for the sweep in an oscilloscope, especially if it is nearly linear. The rise is actually part of an exponential, as shown in Fig. 10.13, but will be linear to about 1 percent if its magnitude is restricted to 10 percent of the supply voltage. In most oscilloscopes, a nearly linear wave of small amplitude is generated in this way, and then amplified enough to drive the cathode-ray tube. Methods of obtaining even better linearity are discussed in Chapter 15.

Usually the sweep frequency is required to be a simple fraction of the frequency of the wave to be displayed, so that an integral number of cycles will be shown on the screen. This can be achieved by *synchronizing* the sweep oscillator to it. The "sync" signal is applied to the grid of the thyratron, as Fig. 10.13 shows, and the frequency of the sweep oscillator is adjusted to be near, but slightly lower than, the

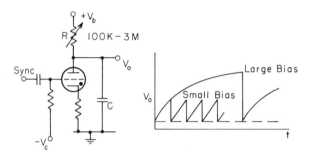

Fig. 10.13 Sawtooth oscillator using a thyratron.

desired value. The thyratron will tend to fire at those times when the grid is less negative than average—that is, near the positive peaks of the synchronizing signal. Under the conditions just mentioned, it will therefore "lock in" at the desired frequency. The process works especially well if the synchronizing signal contains a sharp peak, and oscilloscopes often contain circuits to distort it into such a shape before it is applied to the sweep oscillator.

Occasionally the desired output is a train of short pulses instead of the sawtooth wave. This output is readily available at the cathode of the thyratron. In this case, there is no need to restrict the amplitude of the sawtooth, and the amplitude of the pulses can be a large fraction of the supply potential.

PROBLEM

If the peak-to-peak amplitude of the sawtooth is V, show that the frequency is approximately V_b/RCV for small values of V.

Multivibrator. The *multivibrator* is the astable member of the flip-flop family and, as we have seen, some writers name the whole family after it and call this member the *astable multivibrator*. The name was given because the square-wave output of this circuit contains a large number of harmonics, so that it can be considered as an oscillator that vibrates simultaneously at a number of different frequencies. One important application is the generation of a series of standard frequencies by a multivibrator that is locked to a stable oscillator, usually crystal controlled. At the same time, it often operates as a frequency divider.

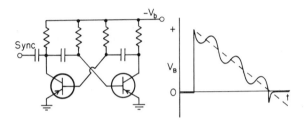

Fig. 10.14 Multivibrator and its timing wave when a synchronizing voltage is present.

The circuit, shown in Fig. 10.14, is derived from that of the flip-flop by using R-C coupling from both collectors to the corresponding bases. Two timing waves are generated; they may be of equal length or not, as required, but seldom differ by more than a factor of 10. Each state is exactly like the quasi-stable state of the univibrator, and the timing waves at the bases are as shown in Fig. 10.10(b). During a transition the base of one transistor is carried positive, cutting it off, and the capacitor then discharges towards V_b. When the base becomes slightly negative, the transistor starts to conduct and another transition takes place; the same action then occurs at the other base. The length of a quasi-stable state may be estimated by noting in Fig. 10.10(b) that the base voltage goes approximately halfway from its initial to its asymptotic voltage; for a time constant τ this requires a time T such that

$$e^{-T/\tau} = \tfrac{1}{2}$$

$$T = \tau \ln 2 \doteq 0.69\tau$$

If a multivibrator has timing networks with time-constants τ_1 and τ_2, the period is approximately $0.7(\tau_1 + \tau_2)$ and the frequency is the reciprocal of this quantity.

The symmetrical multivibrator is the most common, and is the one used for frequency division and harmonic generation. Fig. 10.14 shows a timing wave at the right-hand base with a synchronizing signal superposed. The latter carries the base through cutoff a little sooner than it would go by itself, and therefore shortens the half period to a length of exactly four of its own cycles; the multivibrator thus synchronizes at $\frac{1}{8}$ of the input frequency. Division ratios of $\frac{1}{10}$ can be used with good stability.

Fig. 10.15 shows the block diagram of a frequency standard in which multivibrators are used to divide the original frequency to give a whole series of useful fractions. A very stable oscillator, controlled by a quartz

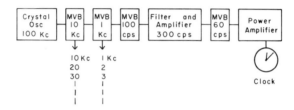

Fig. 10.15 Primary frequency standard using a crystal oscillator and a series of multivibrator frequency dividers.

crystal (Chapter 14), operates at 100 kc; this frequency can be multiplied to give higher harmonics if desired. Three successive multivibrators divide the frequency to 100 cps; the third harmonic of this frequency is used to control a fourth unit at 60 cps. The 60-cps signal is amplified and used to run an electric clock. The reading of the clock can be compared with time signals to standardize the frequency directly in terms of time; for example, an error of 0.1 sec in a day (86,400 sec) gives an error just over 1 part in a million. If the time signals are derived from astronomical observations, the frequency standard is a primary one. A well-made standard of this type is accurate to about 1 part in 10^8 or $\frac{1}{3}$ sec per year, if it is compared only with star observations. If the drifts in frequency are corrected by comparison with an atomic clock, the performance can be improved by another factor of 100 or better. (An atomic oscillator is synchronized to a characteristic frequency of an atom, such as cesium, which happens to fall in the high radio-frequency range.)

Blocking Oscillator. The free-running, or astable, blocking oscillator has the same circuit as the monostable version in Fig. 10.12, except that the bias is negative instead of positive. During a pulse a cutoff bias is developed on the capacitor C, and after the pulse this voltage leaks off through R. With the negative bias supply, the transistor base will eventually be taken negative again; as soon as the transistor starts to conduct, the positive feedback through the transformer will initiate another pulse. The result is a continuous train of short pulses at the collector, as well as a sawtooth wave at the capacitor. This circuit offers a transistor equivalent to the thyratron oscillator, with a further advantage of a better pulse shape and the ability to work at a higher frequency. Like other relaxation oscillators, it is readily synchronized. The tube version finds wide application in the sweep circuits of television receivers, where the oscillators are synchronized to pulses broadcast by the transmitter.

10.4 EXAMPLES OF PULSE SYSTEMS

The circuits just described can be regarded as basic "building blocks," which can be combined in a large number of ways to produce pulse systems that are sometimes very complicated. In designing and analysing pulse systems this way of thinking should always be adopted; the basic diagram is the block diagram. Many applications also require

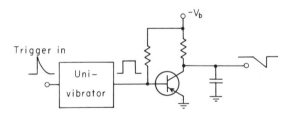

Fig. 10.16 A simple triggered sweep circuit.

the use of auxiliary circuits, such as gate and logic circuits. Although the latter will not be described until Chapter 15, we can give a few illustrations here that do not depend on them.

Fig. 10.16 shows a *triggered sweep circuit*, whose function is to deliver a single sawtooth each time it is triggered by an incoming pulse. It is used to display infrequent or randomly occurring signals on an oscillo-scope. The trigger actuates a univibrator, which generates a negative pulse with a length equal to that of the desired sweep. This gate cuts off a transistor which has been conducting and holding its collector voltage near ground; the *R-C* circuit then proceeds to generate an exponential fall, which (as in Fig. 10.13) is a good approximation to a linear fall if its amplitude is kept small. As soon as the gate ends, the transistor discharges the capacitor and the output returns to its quiescent value.

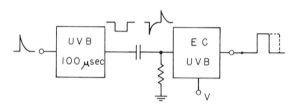

Fig. 10.17 A circuit to generate a delayed pulse of variable width.

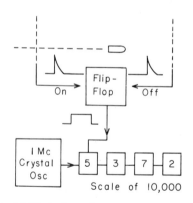

Fig. 10.18 A timer for very short intervals.

Fig. 10.17 shows a circuit that responds to a trigger by generating a delayed pulse of variable width, starting 100 μsec after the trigger. The trigger actuates a univibrator with a fixed pulse length of 100 μsec, and its output is differentiated to produce a delayed trigger. This trigger fires a second univibrator of the emitter-coupled type, whose pulse length can be controlled by varying the voltage *V*.

Fig. 10.18 shows a device that can measure very short time intervals, such as the time taken for a bullet to travel a known distance. As the bullet passes two stations, it generates short pulses, for example by interrupting a light beam or breaking a wire. These pulses trigger a flip-flop on and off, thus generating a gate having a length equal to the desired time. The gate controls the first stage of a scale of 10,000 in such a way that it counts only when the gate is present. The counter counts the cycles of a 1-mc crystal oscillator. Thus, if it is initially set to zero, its final count will give the required time interval directly in microseconds.

References

An excellent reference text for tube trigger circuits, and some using transistors, is *Pulse and Digital Circuits* by J. Millman and H. Taub (New York: McGraw-Hill Book Company, Inc., 1956). Two others, covering tube circuits only and written less in textbook style are *Waveforms* by B. Chance, V. Hughes, E. F. MacNichol, D. Sayre, and F. C. Williams (New York: McGraw-Hill Book Company, Inc., 1956) and *Electronics* by W. C. Elmore and M. Sands (New York: McGraw-Hill Book Company, Inc., 1949).

CHAPTER 11

Tuned Amplifiers

A tuned amplifier is one that is designed to pass only a relatively narrow band of frequencies, rejecting all others to at least some degree. Vast numbers are used at radio frequencies, since the heart of a receiver of any kind is a high gain tuned amplifier, which selects the signal from a particular transmitter and amplifies it to a level of the order of a volt. At these frequencies, the tuned amplifier is nearly always based on an *L-C* resonant circuit (or tuned circuit). We shall consider this type briefly, in both voltage-amplifier and power-amplifier forms. At audio frequencies, and especially at still lower frequencies, tuned circuits have several disadvantages, and tuned amplifiers not based on them are useful. Since this type is frequently used in research, and is not so easily purchased, we shall spend more space on it.

11.1 L-C TUNED VOLTAGE AMPLIFIERS

The simplest tuned amplifier is the *single-tuned* type, shown in two versions in Fig. 11.1. A capacitor-coupled type with the resonant circuit forming the load impedance is shown in Fig. 11.1(a). This arrangement is convenient for individually constructed amplifiers, since the coil can readily be wound to the required inductance. Fig. 11.1(b) shows a transformer-coupled type in which the secondary is tuned. It is used in radios produced in quantity, since it is cheaper to wind another coil on the form than to add an extra capacitor and resistor. Also, it can be wound to give an additional voltage gain if desired. Otherwise, the two circuits behave the same, and we shall analyze only the simpler version shown in Fig. 11.1(a).

At radio frequencies the tube is always a pentode, in order to minimize the feedback through the grid-plate capacitance. The gain is

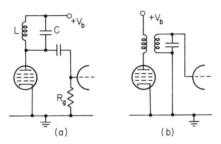

Fig. 11.1 Two versions of a single-tuned amplifier.

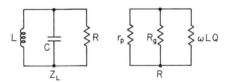

Fig. 11.2 The load impedance in Fig. 11.1, and the equivalent circuit of the resistance R.

given by $K = -g_m Z_L$, where Z_L is the impedance shown in Fig. 11.2; this expression is accurate when the plate resistance is included in the resistance R as shown. The other components of R are the grid resistance of the next stage and the loss resistance of the coil. It was shown in Section 2.5 that when this is represented by a parallel resistance, its value is $\omega L Q$, with Q representing the quality factor of the coil. A typical value is 100 K, so that the other two resistances are normally much greater, except in special cases when R_g is made small to reduce the Q of the system.

To express Z_L in a convenient form, we first define two auxiliary quantities:

$$\omega_0 \equiv \frac{1}{\sqrt{LC}}, \text{ the resonant angular frequency}$$

$$\gamma \equiv \frac{\omega}{\omega_0} - \frac{\omega_0}{\omega}, \text{ a new frequency variable}$$

Since Z_L is a parallel combination, it is convenient to work with its reciprocal Y_L, the load admittance; from Fig. 11.2 we see that

$$Y_L = \frac{1}{R} + j\omega C - j\frac{1}{\omega L}$$

$$= \frac{1}{R} + j\left(\omega C - \frac{\omega_0^2}{\omega}C\right)$$

$$= \frac{1}{R}(1 + j\omega_0\gamma RC),$$

in which we have successively substituted $\omega_0^2 C$ for $1/L$, and γ for the appropriate combination. We thus find

$$Z_L = \frac{R}{1 + j\omega_0\gamma RC} \quad \text{and} \quad K = -\frac{g_m R}{1 + j\omega_0\gamma RC}$$

This band-pass amplifier can be compared with an equivalent *low-pass* amplifier; this name is used for the amplifiers which were considered in Chapter 4, in which the stray capacitance limits the high-frequency response only. Although most low-pass amplifiers have a low-frequency cutoff as well, this is only for convenience and is not inherent in the principle, as it is in band-pass amplifiers. The equivalent low-pass amplifier has the same effective load resistance R and the same shunt capacitance C; its gain is

$$K = -\frac{g_m R}{1 + j\omega RC}$$

and these two amplifiers are analogous in the sense that the substitution $\omega \rightarrow \omega_0\gamma$ takes us from the latter to the former. All the familiar results for the low-pass amplifier may thus be readily adapted to the band-pass case.

Before proceeding, let us examine the significance of the new frequency variable γ. This is most easily done by restricting the frequency to a small range about ω_0. By definition,

$$\gamma = \frac{\omega^2 - \omega_0^2}{\omega\omega_0} = \frac{(\omega + \omega_0)(\omega - \omega_0)}{\omega\omega_0} \doteq 2\frac{\Delta\omega}{\omega_0}$$

where $\Delta\omega \equiv (\omega - \omega_0)$. Thus, over this small frequency range, γ is essentially twice the fractional deviation of the frequency from f_0.

When this deviation becomes large, the approximation is no longer valid; we shall next show that γ has geometric symmetry about ω_0, or in other words has the same numerical value for equal frequency *ratios* above and below ω_0. We take two numerically equal values of γ, so that $\gamma_1 = -\gamma_2$;

$$\frac{\omega_1}{\omega_0} - \frac{\omega_0}{\omega_1} = -\frac{\omega_2}{\omega_0} + \frac{\omega_0}{\omega_2}$$

$$\frac{\omega_1 + \omega_2}{\omega_0} = \omega_0\left(\frac{1}{\omega_1} + \frac{1}{\omega_2}\right) = \frac{\omega_0}{\omega_1\omega_2}(\omega_1 + \omega_2)$$

$$\omega_1\omega_2 = \omega_0^2$$

This is the desired relation. In particular, the expression for the gain has two 3-db points or corner frequencies related in this way and given by the expression

$$\omega_0\gamma RC = \pm 1$$

The difference in frequency between these points is called the *bandwidth* and represented by B. Thus,

$$B = \frac{1}{2\pi}(\omega_b - \omega_a) = \frac{1}{2\pi}\left(\omega_b - \frac{\omega_0^2}{\omega_b}\right) = \frac{\omega_0\gamma_b}{2\pi} = \frac{1}{2\pi RC}$$

where ω_a and ω_b are the two "corner" angular frequencies. This expression is identical with that for the angular frequency of the upper

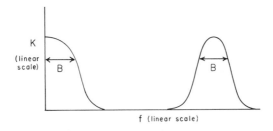

Fig. 11.3 Frequency responses of equivalent low-pass and band-pass amplifiers. Note the linear scales.

corner of the analogous low-pass amplifier. We see that if the low-pass amplifier is converted to a band-pass amplifier by tuning its shunt capacitance with the appropriate coil, it will have the same maximum gain and the same bandwidth, as shown in Fig. 11.3. The conversion must allow for the contribution to R of the loss resistance of the coil. Thus, if a wide band is required, R and C must be kept small, and a large transconductance is needed if the gain is not to be very small. Therefore, the same figure of merit applies to tubes for wide-band service, whether the band be at low or high frequencies. As shown in Section 4.7, this figure is g_m/C_p.

A wide band is required when a video signal is modulated on a radio-frequency carrier for broadcasting; as shown in Chapter 13, normally the modulated signal occupies twice the bandwidth of the corresponding video wave. Thus, a television signal ideally requires a band 9 to 10 mc wide; in practice, only about half of this bandwidth is allowed in order to conserve space in the radio spectrum, but at some sacrifice of quality. In terms of transient response, the relationship is sketched in Fig. 11.4. When a pulse is applied to a single low-pass stage,

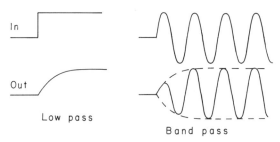

Fig. 11.4 Transient responses of low-pass and band-pass amplifiers.

the output rises exponentially with time constant RC_p. If a burst of oscillations at ω_0 is applied to a band-pass stage, the output again rises slowly, its envelope also following an exponential. If it is to have the same time constant, the bandwidth must be twice as great.

In our study of the load impedance of Fig. 11.2, we have found a special case of the low-pass to band-pass transformation. The general case is shown in Fig. 11.5. A capacitor in the low-pass circuit is to have a coil connected in parallel, with its inductance chosen to resonate at the required center angular frequency ω_0. The admittance of C_1 is $j\omega C_1$; the admittance of the parallel combination is $j\omega C_1 + 1/j\omega L_1$, which we have already shown is equal to $j\omega_0\gamma C_1$. A coil in the low-pass circuit is to have a capacitor placed in series, again chosen for resonance. The impedance of L_2 is $j\omega L_2$; the impedance of the series combination is $j\omega L_2 + 1/j\omega C_2$, which by its form is obviously equal to $j\omega_0\gamma L_2$. Thus, the impedance of the low-pass circuit is converted into that of the band-pass circuit by changing ω to $\omega_0\gamma$.

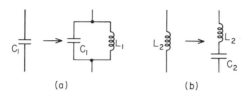

(a)   (b)

Fig. 11.5 Low-pass to band-pass transformation.

In our studies of the video amplifier, we found that shunt peaking could give a large improvement in bandwidth. The band-pass analog of the shunt-peaked amplifier of Fig. 4.28 is shown in Fig. 11.6. The version in Fig. 11.6(b) is not practical because there is no route for direct current from V_b to the plate, and if there were it would be short-

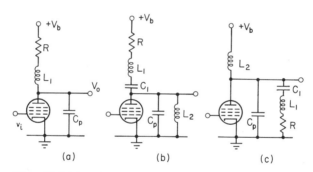

(a)   (b)   (c)

Fig. 11.6 Transformation of a shunt-peaked video amplifier to an equivalent band-pass amplifier.

circuited to ground by L_2. However, a simple rearrangement, as in Fig. 11.6(c), takes care of both troubles without altering the a-c equivalent circuit.

Although any low-pass circuit has a band-pass analog, the converse is certainly not true. To see this, it is merely necessary to note that any band-pass circuit produced in this way contains only resonant circuits tuned to the same frequency. If one of them is tuned to a different frequency, or if an untuned capacitor or coil is present, no low-pass analog exists.

1) Show that the bandwidth of the amplifier of Fig. 11.1(a) is related to the Q of the load circuit by $Q_0 = f_0/B$, where $Q_0 \equiv R/\omega_0 L$. This is sometimes taken as a definition of Q. Also, show that Q is 2π times the ratio of energy stored to energy dissipated per cycle, remembering that the energy is dissipated in R.

2) A shunt-peaked low-pass amplifier was considered in Problem 1 at the end of Section 4.7. Convert it to its analog, shown in Fig. 11.6(c), for a center frequency of 30 mc.

Double-tuned Amplifiers. Fig. 11.7 shows an amplifier stage similar to Fig. 11.1(b), but with both primary and secondary windings tuned to ω_0. Although, as we shall see, its resonance curve may show two

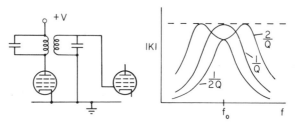

Fig. 11.7 Double-tuned amplifier and frequency response curves.

peaks, this is *not* because the two windings are tuned to different frequencies. The analysis of the circuit is complicated and not particularly enlightening; we shall therefore merely quote the results and discuss a mechanical analogy.

The character of the results depends on the *coefficient of coupling*, or k, defined as

$$k \equiv \frac{M}{\sqrt{L_1 L_2}}$$

In which L_1 and L_2 are the primary and secondary inductances, and M is the mutual inductance between them. The maximum possible value of k is 1, achieved if all the magnetic flux produced by the primary threads the secondary; this condition is closely approached in iron-core transformers for power and audio frequencies, but for a double-tuned amplifier k is normally much less. The *critical* coupling coefficient is $k_c = 1/Q$ if the primary and secondary windings have the same Q; if not, the geometric mean is used. The resonance curves for three values of k are shown in Fig. 11.7; the values are $k_c/2$, k_c and $2k_c$. For coupling less than critical, the curve resembles that of a single-tuned circuit; at critical coupling, it has a flat top, and for *overcoupling*, it splits into a double peak, the splitting increasing slowly and becoming more marked as the coupling increases still further.

The perturbation of a pair of resonances by coupling between them is a phenomenon that is met in many branches of physics. Consider a pair of simple pendulums coupled by a weak spring, as in Fig. 11.8;

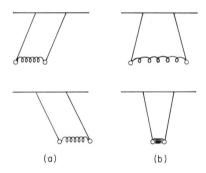

(a)   (b)

Fig. 11.8 Mechanical analogy to a double-tuned circuit.

we shall neglect the mass of the spring. The motion of the system has two normal modes, as illustrated; in one, they swing together, the spring does not expand or contract, and the frequency is the same as the un-perturbed value. In the other, the pendulums swing in opposite direc-tions, stretching and contracting the spring, and this additional restor-ing force increases the frequency. If the system is set swinging in any other way, the motion will be some superposition of these two, and will show beats in which at times one pendulum is at rest, and at others it has all the energy. The coupled system has its two natural frequencies, one being in this case equal to the unperturbed frequency, and the other higher. If the coupling is very weak, the effect on the motion is so slight that the pendulums behave almost as if they were independent.

The analogy with the double-tuned amplifier is almost perfect; the main difference is that in the amplifier the splitting is symmetrical (geometrically) about the original frequency.

The advantage of the double-tuned amplifier is that a number of stages can be cascaded without as large a reduction in bandwidth as is found with single-tuned stages. However, they are extremely difficult to adjust, since there is no simple way of knowing when the separate circuits of an overcoupled system are in tune. For this reason, nearly all double-tuned amplifiers are, in practice, undercoupled. The flat-topped passband can also be achieved by *stagger tuning*, in which separate single-tuned stages are tuned above and below the center frequency. This practice is normal when such a characteristic is required.

11.2 TUNED POWER AMPLIFIERS

Widely used in radio transmitters, tuned power amplifiers also find use in generating power for a multitude of technical purposes, such as high-frequency heating, medical diathermy, and excitation of gas discharges. Because powers of many kilowatts are often involved, high efficiency is important, and the Class C arrangement is normally used; for certain purposes, the less efficient Class B is required, but we shall restrict ourselves to Class C. The distinguishing characteristic of the class is that plate current flows in a tube for less than half the cycle, $\frac{1}{4}$ to $\frac{1}{5}$ being typical. Therefore, even a push-pull amplifier cannot be linear and must generate strong harmonics in its plate current. However, the load always includes a resonant circuit, which stores energy between current pulses and delivers it to the load at a fairly uniform rate; to put it another way, the harmonics are filtered out so that the voltage waveform is nearly sinusoidal. If it is tuned to one of the harmonics, the circuit becomes a frequency multiplier, and can deliver substantial power at the second or third harmonic of the input wave.

The operation of push-pull and single-ended circuits is much the same; for simplicity we restrict ourselves to the latter, as in Fig. 11.9. Class C amplifiers always draw grid current; the input must therefore come from a previous power stage, which is likely to be of the same type. The transformer secondary is coupled to the grid by a capacitor and *grid-leak* resistor, which automatically provide bias, since the grid draws pulses of current at the positive peaks of the input wave, charging the capacitor. During the rest of the cycle some voltage leaks away, but not a significant amount. A bias voltage is therefore built up with a value slightly less than the peak voltage of the input. Since this is a

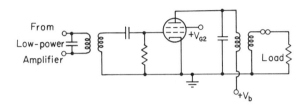

Fig. 11.9 Class C tuned power amplifier.

Class C stage, the bias is well below cutoff. The output is coupled to the load by a transformer, the primary of which is tuned to provide the required energy storage. Because of this storage function, it is often called the *tank circuit*.

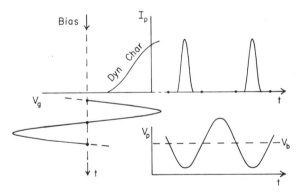

Fig. 11.10 Grid wave, dynamic characteristic, and plate current and voltage waves in a Class C amplifier.

To understand the operation of the circuit, we shall use an assumed dynamic characteristic, which, it will be recalled, is the load line replotted on the transfer plane. Actual design is not carried out in this way, and we shall refer later to the method used in practice. Such a dynamic characteristic is shown in Fig. 11.10. The grid signal is shown on an auxiliary time axis; it remains below cutoff for about $\frac{3}{4}$ of the cycle, and the tube conducts for the other $\frac{1}{4}$ cycle, as shown by the plate-current waveform on the right. The plate-voltage waveform, kept sinusoidal by the resonant circuit, is also shown. It is seen that it is near a minimum whenever the tube is conducting, and that when it is high the tube is cut off. Therefore the tube dissipates only a small part of the power coming from the plate supply, the rest appearing as useful output. An efficiency of 70 percent is normally obtained.

It has been pointed out several times that the tuned circuit must store a substantial amount of energy. This requires that its Q should be moderately large, even with the heavy damping imposed by the load; a value of at least 10 is considered good practice. If the load resistance

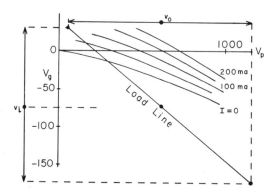

Fig. 11.11 Design of Class C amplifier from the constant-current characteristics.

is reflected back in parallel with the tank circuit, the equivalent circuit is the same as Fig. 11.2, except that the value of R is essentially determined by the load. The Q of this circuit is $R/\omega L$; since R is fixed, L must be kept small (and C correspondingly large) to maintain the required Q. This may be seen in another way by considering energy storage, remembering that $Q/2\pi$ = stored energy divided by the energy lost per cycle. The denominator of this expression is fixed by the required power output; the numerator must therefore be made large. The stored energy is all in C at the peaks of the voltage wave, and can therefore be written $CV^2/2$, where V is the peak a-c voltage. But Fig. 11.10 shows that V is almost equal to V_b, which is fixed. Therefore, the stored energy is proportional to C, and so is the loaded Q. In the design of a Class C amplifier, use is made of the constant-current characteristics of the tube, in which plate voltage is plotted against grid voltage, with plate current as the parameter. A set of these curves for a triode is shown in Fig. 11.11. The lines have nearly a constant slope, equal to the amplification factor. The advantage of this plot for the present purpose is that the load line is straight, always a great convenience. This condition exists because both the grid voltage and the plate voltage are nearly sinusoidal, with the maximum of the former coinciding with the minimum of the latter. Once the limits of their variation have been decided, they can be entered on the diagram, as shown by arrows in Fig. 11.11. Combination of two sine waves with this phase relation gives a straight line, shown as the load line. The instantaneous operating point oscillates sinusoidally along this line, and the plate-current waveform can therefore be readily plotted. It has already been shown in Fig. 11.10 as if it had been derived from a dynamic characteristic. Once the waveforms of plate voltage and current are known, the power output and efficiency can be derived by numerical integration.

PROBLEM

Carry out on Fig. 11.11 the operation just described and plot a plate-current pulse along with the sinusoidal plate-voltage wave.

11.3 LOW-FREQUENCY TUNED AMPLIFIERS USING FEEDBACK

At audio and lower frequencies, coils of high Q are expensive and may be bulky and heavy; the size and weight are inversely proportional to the frequency, to a good approximation. There is thus a need for tuned amplifiers that use either low-Q coils or none at all. This need is met by the circuits to be discussed in this section.

The principle of these circuits is shown in Fig. 11.12. An amplifier, shown as differential for convenience, has in its feedback loop a β circuit (called a T circuit), which produces a null at some frequency f_0. At this frequency the gain is just the gain without feedback, K. At higher and lower frequencies the feedback approaches 100 percent and the gain approaches unity; the gain curve is just the inverse of the β curve except near f_0, where it goes to K instead of to infinity. A detailed analysis shows that the shape of the peak is the same for this and an *L-C* tuned amplifier, but the curves deviate in the tails, one going to unity and the other to zero. We shall now consider the T

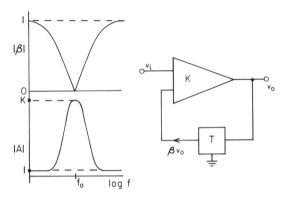

Fig. 11.12 Tuned amplifier using a feedback network that produces a null at one frequency. Frequency responses of the network and the amplifier are shown.

circuits themselves, deriving the conditions for a null at a specified frequency.

Twin T. The *twin-T circuit*, shown in Fig. 11.13, consists of two T circuits in parallel, one containing two resistors and a capacitor, the other two capacitors and a resistor. With six components, there are so many

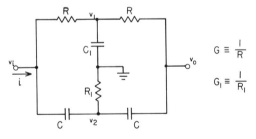

Fig. 11.13 Twin T.

degrees of freedom that there is no loss of generality in making the circuit symmetrical with respect to input and output. Since the object of the analysis is to find the output *voltage*, it is convenient to use the nodal scheme. Therefore, we assume an input current i and solve for v_0, then setting it to zero. The nodal equations are:

$$(G + j\omega C) v_i - G v_1 - j\omega C v_2 - 0 = i$$
$$- G v_i + (2G + j\omega C_1) v_1 - 0 - G v_0 = 0$$
$$-j\omega C v_i - 0 + (G_1 + 2j\omega C) v_2 - j\omega C v_0 = 0$$
$$0 - G v_1 - j\omega C v_2 + (G + j\omega C) v_0 = 0$$

The determinant is

$$\Delta = \begin{vmatrix} G + j\omega C & - G & -j\omega C & 0 \\ - G & 2G + j\omega C_1 & 0 & - G \\ -j\omega C & 0 & G_1 + 2j\omega C & -j\omega C \\ 0 & - G & -j\omega C & G + j\omega C \end{vmatrix}$$

To find the condition for a null, $v_0 = 0$, we need only form the substituted determinant Δ_0 and set it equal to zero:

$$\Delta_0 = \begin{vmatrix} - G & 2G + j\omega C_1 & 0 \\ -j\omega C & 0 & G_1 + 2j\omega C \\ 0 & - G & -j\omega C \end{vmatrix} i = 0$$

$$- G^2 (G_1 + 2j\omega C) + \omega^2 C^2 (2G + j\omega C_1) = 0$$

Since this is a complex equation, both real and imaginary parts must be separately zero:

Real: $G^2 G_1 = 2 G \omega^2 C^2$ Imaginary: $2\omega C G^2 = \omega^3 C^2 C_1$

$$\omega^2 = \frac{G G_1}{2 C^2} = \frac{1}{2 R R_1 C^2} \qquad \omega^2 = \frac{2 G^2}{C C_1} = \frac{2}{R^2 C C_1}$$

These conditions must be satisfied at the same frequency ω_0; hence we must have

$$\frac{1}{2 R R_1 C^2} = \frac{2}{R^2 C C_1}$$

$$\frac{R}{2 R_1} = \frac{2 C}{C_1} \equiv n \qquad\qquad (1)$$

Substitution of this into either expression for ω_0^2 gives

$$\omega_0^2 = \frac{n}{R^2 C^2} \tag{2}$$

Once a value of n has been chosen, the two relations (1) and the single relation (2) provide three restrictions on the choice of components. Once any one component has been specified, the values of the rest follow. In low-impedance circuits, the resistances will be chosen small and the capacitors large; in high-impedance circuits, they will be chosen the opposite way. Since large capacitors are bulky and expensive, they are usually made as small as the circuit impedance permits.

The optimum value of n can be found by a detailed circuit analysis which we shall outline later. It turns out that the sharpest null is produced when $n = 1$, but that values of $\frac{1}{2}$ and 2 are not seriously worse. Therefore, the value 1 is normally used unless it is desired to have all three capacitors equal ($n = 2$) or all three resistors equal ($n = \frac{1}{2}$). When $n = 1$, $R_1 = R/2$, $C_1 = 2C$, and $\omega RC = 1$ at the null.

A complete expression for β follows by the use of some tedious but straightforward algebra. Evaluation of the fourth-order determinant Δ can be avoided, since $v_o/v_i = \Delta_0/\Delta_i$. The equations are simplified by using (1) to express R_1 and C_1 in terms of R, C, and n, and eliminating R (or G) by means of (2); finally, the frequency ratio $\rho \equiv \omega/\omega_0$ is used instead of ω. It is then found that

$$\beta = \frac{1}{1 - 2j(n^{1/2} + n^{-1/2})\rho/(\rho^2 - 1)} = \frac{1}{1 - (2j/\gamma)(n^{1/2} + n^{-1/2})}$$

The second form uses the frequency variable γ defined in Section 11.1, equal to $\rho - (1/\rho)$ or $(\rho^2 - 1)/\rho$. We shall return to this expression later, when we compare the twin-T and the bridged-T circuits.

Bridged T. Considerably simpler than the twin T, the *bridged-T* circuit is shown in Fig. 11.14. It contains a single T bridged by a coil of which the losses are represented by a series resistance r; for this representation, $Q = \omega L/r$ (Section 2.5). Again, the circuit is made symmetrical, and it is convenient to use nodal analysis; to simplify the writing, we shall use the symbol Y for the admittance of the coil, $1/(r + j\omega L)$.

Then the node equations are

$$(Y + j\omega C)v_i - j\omega C v_1 - Y v_0 = i$$

$$-j\omega C v_i + \left(\frac{1}{R} + j2\omega C\right)v_1 - j\omega C v_0 = 0$$

$$- Y v_i - j\omega C v_1 + (Y + j\omega C)v_0 = 0$$

and the determinant is

$$\Delta = \begin{vmatrix} Y + j\omega C & -j\omega C & -Y \\ -j\omega C & \dfrac{1}{R} + j2\omega C & -j\omega C \\ -Y & -j\omega C & Y + j\omega C \end{vmatrix}$$

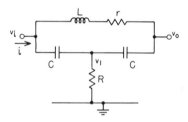

Fig. 11.14 Bridged T.

The condition for zero output is $\Delta_0 = 0$, or

$$\begin{vmatrix} -j\omega C & \dfrac{1}{R} + j2\omega C \\ -Y & -j\omega C \end{vmatrix} = 0$$

$$- \omega^2 C^2 + Y\left(\frac{1}{R} + j2\omega C\right) = 0$$

Replacing Y by its value and clearing all fractions, we have

$$\omega^2 C^2 R(r + j\omega L) = 1 + j2\omega RC$$

Real: $\omega^2 C^2 Rr = 1$ Imaginary: $\omega^2 LC = 2$

The second of these is simply the condition for resonance of L with the resultant of the two Cs in series; the first gives the required value of R, but it can be put in a more convenient form involving the Q of the coil. We note that

$$r = \frac{\omega L}{Q} = \frac{2}{Q \omega C}$$

Then, substituting this value of r, and ωC from the second equation, we find

$$R = \frac{\omega L Q}{4}$$

This is just one quarter of the loss resistance of the coil in the parallel representation.

The complete expression for the transmission can be found in the same way as for the twin T. Again the design equations are used to eliminate two of the parameters, say R and L; it is then found that

$$\beta = \frac{1}{1 - \dfrac{2j}{Q} \dfrac{\rho}{\rho^2 - 1}} = \frac{1}{1 - \dfrac{2j}{\gamma Q}}$$

This has the same form as the expression for the twin T, which can be considered equivalent to a bridged T with a certain value of Q, given by

$$Q = \frac{1}{n^{1/2} + n^{-1/2}} = \frac{n^{1/2}}{n + 1}$$

This has a maximum value for $n = 1$, as already mentioned, of $Q = \frac{1}{2}$; for $n = \frac{1}{2}$ or 2, it is found that $Q = \sqrt{\frac{2}{3}} \doteq 0.472$. For any value of Q, the transmission has the form shown in Fig. 11.12, but as Q is taken larger the frequency scale must be expanded in proportion, since it is the product γQ that controls the expression.

An idea of the width of the "notch" can be gained by considering the value of β when $\gamma Q = 2$; this is seen to be $1/\sqrt{2}$. Two examples are:

Twin T with $n = 1$: $Q = \frac{1}{2}$ $\gamma = 4$ $\omega = 4.24\omega_0$
Bridged T: $Q = 10$ $\gamma = 0.2$ $\omega = 1.22\omega_0$

Especially for the twin T, the attenuation is appreciable over a wide frequency range, of the order of four octaves. Despite this broad region of attenuation, the twin T is used far more than the bridged T, since it can be adjusted by varying only resistances and requires no inductance. The twin T can be balanced at a specified frequency by adjusting each of the three resistors in turn, so as to satisfy the three equations (1) and (2). Adjustment of the bridged T requires the variation of R and at least one of the two Cs. The small departures from symmetry caused by these adjustments have no noticeable effect on the characteristics.

Amplifiers. The equivalent circuit of the tuned amplifier itself has been given in Fig. 11.12, and its behavior has been discussed. At f_0, the gain is K, since there is no feedback; at high and low frequencies, it is nearly unity. The width of the passband depends on the Q of the T and also on the loop gain. It is most easily discussed in terms of the apparent Q of the amplifier, Q_A, defined as follows:

$$Q_A \equiv \frac{f_0}{B}$$

where B is the 3-db bandwidth as used in Section 11.1. If the expression for β is substituted into the feedback equation, an approximate value for Q_A is readily found:

$$\beta = \frac{1}{1 - (2j/\gamma Q)} \doteq j\frac{\gamma Q}{2}$$

for frequencies very near f_0.

$$A = \frac{K}{1 - K\beta} \doteq \frac{K}{1 - Kj(\gamma Q/2)}$$

This is 3 db less than K when the imaginary part of the denominator is equal to 1:

$$\frac{K\gamma Q}{2} = \pm 1 \qquad \text{and} \qquad \gamma = \pm \frac{2}{KQ}$$

Remembering that $\gamma \doteq 2\Delta f/f_0$, we see that

$$Q_A \doteq KQ/2$$

A more careful analysis gives the value $(K + 1)Q/2$, but the difference is usually negligible. The important case of the twin-T circuit can be represented by $Q = \frac{1}{2}$, so that

$$Q_A \doteq \frac{K + 1}{4} \doteq \frac{K}{4} \qquad \text{(twin T)}$$

It is not difficult to obtain a bandwidth of a fraction of a cycle at low audio frequencies by using a high enough gain. However, it should be remembered that performance under these conditions requires careful adjustment of the T and the use of stable components.

If the β of the amplifier is to equal that of the T, as we have assumed, certain conditions must be satisfied. Ideally, the T should be fed from a source (the amplifier output) of zero impedance; in practice, a value of less than $R/10$ is satisfactory. Similarly, the output of the T should not be loaded; it is often fed to an open grid in a differential amplifier, but it is almost as satisfactory if it is loaded by an impedance greater than $10R$. (The grid return should be made on the source side of the T; this is possible because both types have a d-c connection between input and output terminals.) If these effects are appreciable, they reduce the feedback away from resonance and therefore broaden the band.

PROBLEMS

1) Carry out the analysis and substitutions to derive the expression for β of the bridged-T circuit.

2) If you are still interested, repeat for the twin-T circuit.

REFERENCES

The primary reference for Sections 1 and 3 is *Vacuum Tube Amplifiers*, edited by G. E. Valley and H. Wallman (New York: McGraw-Hill Book Company, Inc., 1948); in particular, Section 3 has drawn heavily on its Chapter 10, by H. Fleisher. Class C power amplifiers are treated in many texts and handbooks on radio techniques.

CHAPTER 12

Direct-current Amplifiers

12.1 INTRODUCTION

The term *d-c amplifier* can be considered to stand for either "direct current" or "directly coupled"; in any case, the amplifier responds right down to zero frequency. Because d-c amplifiers are not used in radio work, they are neglected in many texts and handbooks. Therefore, they will be treated in some detail, since many important measuring instruments contain or consist of a d-c amplifier. If the output of the instrument is to a meter or recorder, a d-c amplifier is needed; examples are vacuum-tube voltmeters, photometers, and ionization chambers for x-rays. Many oscilloscopes respond right down to zero frequency so that they can show a wave and its d-c bias together; in this case, good high-frequency response is required, but in the other examples, response need extend only up to a few cycles per second. Another important application is in the operational amplifiers used in analog computers, as discussed in Chapter 15.

It is convenient to classify d-c amplifiers into two groups, which we may loosely call *current amplifiers* and *voltage amplifiers*. The problems are entirely different in the two classes. A low input current is essential in amplifiers of the first class, which are usually called *electrometers*. In the second, the main difficulty is with zero drift—that is, a slow variation of the output even when the input is zero. In principle, this drift can be allowed for by occasionally interrupting the measurement, short-circuiting the input, and adjusting the zero. In practice, however, this operation is annoying at best and impossible at worst, especially in automatic instruments. Finally, an occasional application requires both current and voltage gain at the same time. Satisfactory solutions exist for all these problems, and they will be discussed in turn.

First, however, we shall consider methods of *coupling* between stages. At first sight, this problem looks difficult because the plate of one stage is at a high positive potential, and the grid of the next is near ground. One obvious but poor solution is to use a small battery of the required potential to join the two. Another possibility is to arrange the plate or grid potential so that no difference exists; this is done in the regulated power supply of Fig. 7.17, and is fairly common when the second stage is a cathode follower. However, this arrangement is seldom satisfactory for more than two stages, or occasionally three.

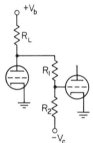
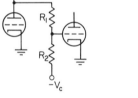

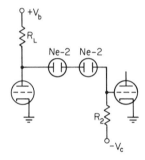

Fig. 12.1 Resistor coupling.   Fig. 12.2 Coupling with a
                                    constant-voltage device.

The most commonly used method is *resistor coupling*, shown in Fig. 12.1. The plate is joined to the grid by a voltage divider, the other end of which goes to a large, regulated negative voltage, usually -150 or -300 volts. There is a loss of gain, typically by a factor of $\frac{1}{2}$ or $\frac{2}{3}$, but it is easily made up by adding another stage if necessary. Clearly, the loss is smaller for larger bias voltages, but it is not important enough to justify the expense of providing a really large voltage. The coupling resistors load the first stage appreciably and reduce its effective supply voltage; these effects are readily taken into account with the help of Thévenin's theorem.

The loss of gain may be eliminated by using a constant-voltage device instead of R_1; for example, a pair of neon bulbs, as shown in Fig. 12.2, or a silicon breakdown diode, can be used. With neon bulbs, the advantage is normally cancelled by the small values of R_L and R_2 required to pass the minimum of 0.2 ma needed by the bulbs. However, they do permit transmission of a large voltage swing, which may be useful for driving an output stage. The breakdown diode does not have this limitation, but is rather expensive.

Transistors can be coupled in the same manner, and offer several additional possibilities. In some cases, the change of voltage from base to collector is so small that two or three stages can be cascaded directly. Emitter followers may be cascaded even more easily, if current gain rather than voltage gain is needed. One of the most useful techniques is to alternate n–p–n and p–n–p transistors, so that a voltage rise in one stage is followed by a voltage fall in the next. Both positive and negative power supplies are needed, but this is nearly always true in any case for a d-c amplifier.

PROBLEM

Design a coupling network, as in Fig. 12.1, for $V_b = 300$ volts, $V_c = -150$ volts. Apply Thévenin's theorem to find the effective load and supply voltages, and calculate the loss of gain in the coupling network.

12.2 CURRENT AMPLIFIERS

In this section, we discuss amplifiers suitable for use with constant-current signal sources. These sources include several important detecting devices: ionization chambers, phototubes, and photomultipliers. In each of these there is a supply of electrons liberated by the radiation being measured, and as long as the anode voltage is high enough to collect them all, the current is independent of its exact value. Because the current can be passed through a large resistor to generate a voltage much larger than the amount typical of amplifier drift, the latter causes no trouble at all. It is merely necessary to have an amplifier whose input grid current is much less than the current that is to be measured. For many years this kind of measurement was made by means of sensitive and temperamental electrostatic voltmeters known as *electrometers*, and the name has been transferred to the tubes and amplifiers that perform the same function.

Until now we have usually assumed that the grid current of a tube was essentially zero, although it has been pointed out that it is not usually good practice to use grid resistors larger than 1 M, or perhaps

10 M for low-power tubes. The reason is that the grid current is actually far from zero, being in the range 10^{-7} to 10^{-9} amp in most tubes. As we have seen, there is no fundamental reason for the grid to draw any current at all, but a number of reasons exist nevertheless. These sources of current were first brought out in a classic investigation by Metcalf and Thompson in 1930. They are:

(1) Positive ions from the cathode
(2) Ionization of residual gas
(3) Photoelectrons released from the grid by
    (a) external light
    (b) light from the cathode
    (c) soft x-rays produced at the plate
(4) Unusually fast electrons able to overcome the bias
(5) Poor insulation.

The first three sources give a current to the grid, and the fourth gives a current away from it; in most tubes the net current is zero at a bias of around -1 or -2 volts.

Most cathodes emit ions of alkali metals, especially sodium, in addition to the intended electrons. They can be eliminated by means of an extra grid, maintained a few volts positive, between the control grid and the cathode. Modern electrometer tubes usually omit this grid, the positive ions presumably having been eliminated by careful purification of the cathode material and by keeping the temperature low. This low temperature is necessary in any case to reduce the number of fast electrons (4) and the intensity of the light (3b). A very low plate voltage greatly reduces the production of x-rays (3c) and the ionization of gas (2); the latter can be eliminated completely by operating below the ionization potential, but this is not necessary, especially in modern tubes, which contain very little gas. Values around 15 volts are typical. External light is kept out by a suitable enclosure, and leakage is reduced to negligible amounts by careful construction and the use of a water-repellent silicone coating on the glass around the leads. In humid climates, it may be worthwhile to desiccate the enclosure. If the sensitivity is very high, the circuit may detect ionization currents produced in the enclosure by cosmic rays and radioactive contamination. These currents are kept down by having a small volume, and perhaps by evacuating the enclosure or filling it with insulating wax.

Modern electrometer tubes are made very small, with filaments that can operate from a single dry cell, since they are often used in portable equipment. Their grid current is around 10^{-15} amp, or 6000 electrons per second. For currents down to 10^{-11} amp, it is possible to use an ordinary tube, preferably an all-glass low-μ triode such as the 6C4. A low μ is desirable so that the grid can be more than 1 volt negative, even with the low plate voltage used. A heater potential of 4 volts is suitable.

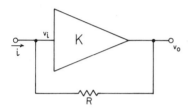

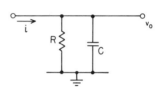

Fig. 12.3 Electrometer feedback amplifier.

Fig. 12.4 Circuit for studying transient response of a current amplifier.

The usual circuit of a current amplifier is shown in Fig. 12.3, which is a reproduction of Fig. 6.13. The amplifier typically contains several stages, the first being an electrometer tube, and has a gain K that may be in the range -50 to $-10,000$, depending on the application. It was shown in Section 6.5 that the output voltage is

$$v_0 = -\frac{K}{K-1}Ri \doteq -Ri$$

This is just the voltage drop across R; the amplifier serves to produce this voltage at a very low impedance level, and its own characteristics are not important. Other effects that are often important are the speeding up of the transient response and the fact that the voltage (v_i) at the output of the source of current is held essentially constant.

The importance of transient response can be illustrated by an example. In an alternative method for developing the voltage v_0, shown in Fig. 12.4, the resistor R is simply connected to ground and the current passed through it. It could then be used to drive an electrometer tube connected as a cathode follower. However, stray capacitance C must be present, and any changes in current will be followed sluggishly by the corresponding change in v_0, with a time constant RC. Typical values may be 10^{12} ohms and 20 pf, giving a product of 20 sec. An instrument that responds this sluggishly is useless for many purposes. The feedback circuit speeds up the response by the factor $(1 + \text{loop gain})$ or $(1 - K)$, giving an effective time constant $RC/(1 - K)$, which can in principle be made as small as desired.

With very large loop gains, stability against oscillation is usually a serious problem, as we have seen in Chapter 6. Fortunately, this circuit is an exception, since the time constant RC just discussed appears as a lag in the feedback loop. For the example with $RC = 20$ sec, the loop gain will slope at -20 db per decade from a frequency of only 0.008 cps. The gain is therefore sure to be less than unity long before any other lags in the circuit become appreciable.

EXAMPLE

Fig. 12.5 shows a simple electrometer amplifier of wide utility; it is particularly suitable for use with photomultipliers, which produce output currents seldom less than 10^{-11} amp. The first stage is a cathode

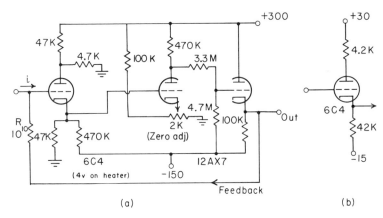

Fig. 12.5 (a) Circuit of a simple electrometer using an ordinary receiving tube. (b) Equivalent circuit of the first stage.

follower using a 6C4 operated with low heater and plate voltages as already discussed. The second stage is a high-μ triode amplifier having an adjustable cathode voltage so that the output zero can be set. The third stage is another cathode follower using the other half of the twin triode. The loop gain, therefore, is simply the gain of the middle stage, allowing for the coupling network, or about 50. With a 10^{10}-ohm resistor as shown, the output will be 1 volt for a current of 10^{-10} amp, and the time constant about $0.2/50 = 0.004$ sec for a capacitance of 20 pf.

The circuit of the first stage can be simplified by application of Thévenin's theorem, as shown in Fig. 12.5(b). It is a cathode follower with supplies of $+30$ and -15 volts. The voltage dividers allow it to be operated from the high-voltage supplies required for later stages.

The feedback resistor should be chosen to give an output of several volts for the largest signal expected, since the zero drift would be expected to be one or two tenths of a volt. If the resistor is less than 10^8 ohms, the first stage may be omitted. The output can supply several milliamperes to a load such as a recorder; if a millivolt recorder is used, the output should be attenuated (and the zero drift along with it).

For higher performance, a true electrometer tube should be used, and the loop gain made larger.* The zero drift of such a circuit, using well-stabilized power supplies for the electrometer tube, may be as low as a few millivolts.

The zero drift of these current amplifiers is necessarily referred to the output, because an input voltage drift has little meaning. Because of the 100 percent voltage feedback, the output drift is essentially equal to the input drift of the same amplifier used as a voltage amplifier. For the voltage amplifiers discussed next, the input drift is used directly.

PROBLEM

Show that a current step applied to the network of Fig. 12.4 produces a voltage that rises exponentially with time constant RC. Repeat for Fig. 12.3 and show that the time constant is now $RC/(1 - K)$, as expected from general feedback theory.

12.3 VOLTAGE AMPLIFIERS

The all-important problem with voltage amplifiers is zero drift. In terms of a signal that would cause the same change at the output, single-ended amplifiers drift 100 to 200 mv; differential amplifiers, 25 mv; and as we have just seen, well-stabilized electrometers may

---

* An excellent example of this kind of circuit is given by R. H. Weitbrecht, *Review of Scientific Instruments* **28**, 883 (1957).

drift as little as a few millivolts. Transistor amplifiers offer comparable performance. If the full-scale deflection of the instrument is at least a large fraction of a volt, these may be satisfactory, but they are useless for millivolt and microvolt signals. We shall return briefly to them at the end of this section.

Fortunately, another technique is possible, giving drifts in the microvolt region, or even less with special precautions. This technique is to *chop* the d-c signal to produce an a-c wave, which can then be amplified and rectified without difficulty. An amplifier can be made to produce almost no spurious a-c signal, and the only important zero drift is that contributed by the chopper itself. This device is normally a mechanical switch driven by a magnetic coil at a frequency of 60 cps, although frequencies up to about 600 cps are possible. Coupling of the driving voltage into the signal circuit limits choppers to a drift of about 1 μv. This effect can be eliminated by driving the chopper contacts from a rotating shaft, with the motor at a distance. Usually, the frequency is chosen to be incommensurable with the line frequency. The chopper then has practically no drift of its own, but it is limited to perhaps 10^{-9} volt by thermoelectric voltages developed in the connections. Chopping is a form of modulation (Chapter 13), and the chopping frequency is often called the *carrier frequency*.

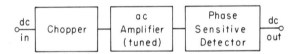

Fig. 12.6 Block diagram of a chopper-type amplifier.

The block diagram of a chopper amplifier is shown in Fig. 12.6. The chopper is followed by an a-c amplifier, which is often tuned to the carrier frequency so as to pass only frequencies near it. Finally, there is a *phase-sensitive detector*, abbreviated ϕSD, which is essentially a chopper in reverse, and which converts the amplified a-c signal back into a d-c signal. This important class of circuits will be discussed in Section 13.2.

Although we shall concentrate mainly on the mechanical chopper, a number of other types are also important. Mechanical choppers are expensive and short-lived, and are limited to low carrier frequencies. Clearly, the highest component of frequency in the amplified signal must be only a fraction of the carrier frequency, seldom more than one tenth. Electronic choppers are readily designed, but most of them produce drift in the same way as electronic d-c amplifiers. Silicon diodes and transistors are fairly good, with drift or about a millivolt. Semiconducting photocells can be used for drifts in the microvolt region, but at present are just as slow as mechanical choppers

In certain cases, chopping can be carried out on a physical signal before it is converted to an electrical form. An important example is sketched in Fig. 12.7. Here the signal is some kind of light or other

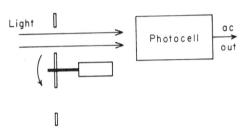

Fig. 12.7 Light chopping in an optical system.

radiation that can be interrupted by a rotating disk with several holes around it. Any "dark currents" in the photocell are not modulated and therefore not amplified; a "tag" that has been put on the light allows the corresponding electrical signal to be amplified by itself. This principle is useful at all wavelengths, but it is essential for most infrared detectors. Similar procedures are sometimes possible at radio frequencies by switching a signal from an antenna on and off before it reaches the receiver.

Chopper Circuits. The simplest circuit is the one shown in Fig. 12.8. The d-c signal is passed through a resistor whose output side is shorted to ground for half of each cycle; a capacitor removes the d-c component from the result. An important characteristic of chopper circuits can be noticed here: if the d-c signal reverses its sign, the a-c signal reverses its phase. The ϕSD is then able to preserve the polarity of the original signal. This circuit leaves one contact of the chopper free; it can be used to chop another signal in a large system, or for the ϕSD.

If the source has a low impedance, it is possible to use a transformer to increase the voltage of the chopped signal, as in Fig. 12.9; the circuit is identical with that of the power chopper in Fig. 9.20. The transformer must be especially designed to work at the low frequency of the carrier, and should also be very carefully shielded. For microvolt signals, this technique allows the signal to be kept larger than the amplifier noise (Chapter 16).

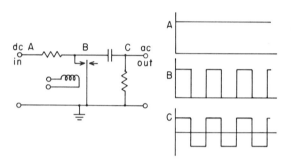

Fig. 12.8 Half-wave chopper and waveforms.

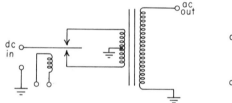
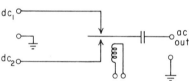

Fig. 12.9 Full-wave chopper for low-
impedance sources.

Fig. 12.10 Differential chopper
circuit.

The circuit of Fig. 12.10 produces an output proportional to the difference between two inputs; it is useful in feedback systems and elsewhere when a differential d-c amplifier is needed.

Amplifiers. The design of the a-c amplifier is straightforward, and it is merely necessary to provide the gain and power output required for the application. If the signal level is small, it is usual to restrict the bandwidth with the help of a twin-T circuit, as described in Chapter 11. However, the bandwidth should be made only narrow enough to keep the undesired "noise" voltages from overloading the system. Many ϕSD circuits require that the output be transformer coupled, and it is necessary to choose a transformer that will work properly at the carrier frequency. Although the chopper produces a square wave, only the fundamental frequency need be amplified and detected.

Phase-sensitive Detectors. The function of the ϕSD is exactly the opposite of that of the chopper: it converts the amplified alternating current back into direct current, preserving the original d-c polarity. It is supplied with a *reference voltage*, which is similar to the driving or carrier voltage of the chopper, and it has the useful property of discriminating against signals whose frequencies differ from the reference frequency. The theory of the ϕSD and a selection of practical circuits are presented in the next chapter, since they fit in with its theme of modulation. If the output is to be a stable, amplified replica of the input to the chopper, there must be a fixed phase relationship between the chopped signal and the reference voltage to the ϕSD. Usually this relationship is ensured by driving the chopper and the ϕSD from the same source; in many cases the source is the a-c power line, or in a cam-driven system the ϕSD will be a switch driven by another cam on the same shaft. In a system using a light chopper it is best to derive the reference voltage from the rotating shaft, or again to drive a switch by a cam on the shaft.

EXAMPLES

A simple chopper amplifier with a gain of about -1000 is shown in Fig. 12.11. The chopper of Fig. 12.8 and a similar ϕSD are combined, using the two contacts of a single vibrator. The amplifier can use two

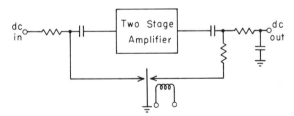

Fig. 12.11 Chopper amplifier with a gain of -1000.

sections of a twin triode; more stages can be added if higher gain is required. An R-C filter network at the output filters the ripple from the ϕSD. The amplifiers are commercially available as plug-in units.

An important application of the chopper amplifier is in *self-balancing potentiometers*, of which Fig. 12.12 shows an example. The chopper is of the type shown in Fig. 12.8, but connected to chop the difference between the input signal and the voltage from the slide-wire. If they

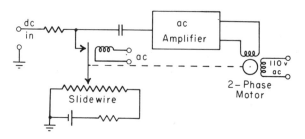

Fig. 12.12 Self-balancing potentiometer.

are not equal, the a-c voltage is amplified to a power level of several watts and applied to one winding of a two-phase induction motor. The other winding is connected to the a-c line, from which the chopper coil is also fed. The direction in which the motor rotates depends on the phase of the amplifier output; it can therefore be arranged to operate the slider, and always drive it towards balance. At balance, the chopper gives no a-c signal and the motor stops. This is, of course, a feedback or servo system, and the characteristics of the amplifier determine only the accuracy of balance. The linearity depends only on this and on the linearity of the slide-wire. Normally, the motion of the slider is reproduced by a pen which draws a line on a moving chart. Chart recorders are widely used to plot variables against time in scientific laboratories and in industry.

Differential Input Stages. We now return to the question of amplifiers without choppers, which are useful when drifts of a few millivolts are tolerable. The sources of drift in a tube amplifier have been discussed in Section 7.3, since these drifts are important in high-performance voltage regulators. Drift is chiefly a result of changes in the emission velocity of electrons, caused by changes in cathode temperature or work function. Nothing can be done about the changes in work function, but the drift from changes in cathode temperature can be made very small by regulating the heater current or by using a balanced differential amplifier to compensate for the changes. With such arrangements the drift can be of the order of 5 mv in several hours, and perhaps 25 mv in a week.

In transistor amplifiers, drift is caused by changes in temperature. These changes may be in the ambient temperature or in the equipment, and it is therefore wise to minimize the heat dissipation in the latter. It is essential to use a balanced circuit, and the usual long-tailed pair is shown in Fig. 12.13. Although this differential arrangement cancels

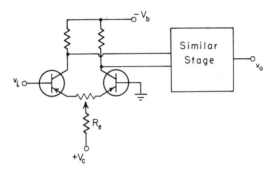

Fig. 12.13 Low-drift transistor input stage based on the long-tailed pair.

many of the drifts, it is still wise to keep them as small as possible in the first place. Analysis shows that the chief causes of drift are changes in the emitter-base voltage, and changes in the current amplification factor β. The balanced circuit must be relied upon to cancel the former, but the latter changes can be made less harmful by use of a very small emitter current and by careful choice of transistors. The cutoff current should be small; if high temperatures are expected, silicon transistors are preferable. For operation near room temperature, however, germanium units have smaller gain variation.

Fig. 12.13 shows a balance control between the emitters; this may be used to compensate for small differences between the two transistors, although they should be selected for matched characteristics at the outset. The differential output is taken to the input of a second similar stage; from there on, the amplifier may be made fully differential, or output may be taken from one collector of the second stage and the later stages made single-ended. It must be remembered that the drift cancellation of the symmetrical amplifier depends on the equality of the temperatures of the two transistors. To ensure this equality, the transistors should be clamped firmly to a massive piece of metal.

When all of these precautions are taken, the drift is of the order of $20\,\mu v$ per degree C, so that it can remain below a millivolt for a substantial range of temperature. This performance is considerably better than that of the best tube amplifiers; however, because it is difficult to obtain high input impedance with transistors, the tube version may be preferred.

12.4 SPECIAL AMPLIFIERS

Sometimes a high voltage gain is required in addition to the high current gain of an electrometer. The chopper is basically a low-impedance device and cannot be used. The solution is to use a *vibrating-reed* modulator, also called *vibrating-capacitor* modulator. In principle, this device is not unlike a chopper, but the reed does not touch any contacts; it is arranged to have a moderately large capacitance to a fixed plate, and this capacitance varies as the reed vibrates. Because the arrangement is highly susceptible to the presence of spurious potentials, the modulator must be very carefully made; normally it is gold plated and sealed in a vacuum. A suitable circuit is shown in Fig. 12.14. The capacitor is isolated from the input by a large resistor

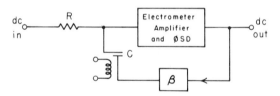

Fig. 12.14 Vibrating-reed amplifier.

R, chosen so that as the capacitor vibrates the charge on it remains essentially constant. Since the voltage on a capacitor is $V = Q/C$, the oscillating value of C produces an oscillating voltage unless Q is zero; that is, unless the average value of V is zero. The modulated voltage can be amplified and detected as usual; however, it cannot be expected to be proportional to the original d-c voltage, since the amplitude of oscillation of the reed may change. Therefore, negative feedback must always be used; this has other advantages as we have seen in Section

12.2. Since voltage gain is required, only a fraction β of the output is fed back, as Fig. 12.14 shows. When the feedback voltage is equal to the source voltage, the modulator has nothing to modulate. This principle can be incorporated directly into a self-balancing potentiometer, if desired.

PROBLEMS

Consider a modulator in which the average electrode spacing is A, and whose reed oscillates at frequency ω and amplitude B. Show that the capacitance is proportional to $1/(A + B \sin \omega t)$, but that the voltage output is sinusoidal nevertheless.

Chopper-stabilized Amplifiers. Another requirement which is not met by the chopper amplifier is that of good high-frequency response along with low drift. This performance can be attained by building an ordinary d-c amplifier, which has the required frequency response

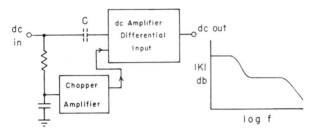

Fig. 12.15 Chopper-stabilized operational amplifier and its frequency response without feedback.

but high drift, and combining it with a chopper amplifier to reduce the drift. The simplest scheme of this kind is shown in Fig. 12.15; the unstabilized amplifier has a differential input, and the output of the chopper amplifier is connected to it. If the capacitor C is omitted, the drift of the amplifier is reduced by a factor equal to the gain of the chopper amplifier; if it is included, the only drift is that of the chopper amplifier itself. These statements are true when the gain is controlled by negative feedback; without feedback, the gain is increased, rather than the drift being reduced. The usual application of this arrangement is in the operational amplifiers of an analog computer, where the large amount of feedback required is always present. The gain without feedback has the unusual shape sketched in Fig. 12.15, but this curve is smoothed out by the feedback. The small chopper amplifier of Fig. 12.11 is suitable for this service.

Output Circuits. The load of many d-c amplifiers is a milliammeter or similar instrument with a low resistance in which the important variable is the current rather than the voltage. The most usual circuit is shown in Fig. 12.16, along with its equivalent circuit and a simplified

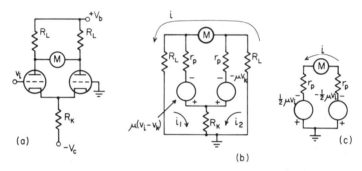

Fig. 12.16 (a) Meter output circuit. (b) Equivalent circuit. (c) Simplified equivalent circuit.

circuit which recognizes that effectively half the input is applied to each tube because of the cathode coupling. If the meter resistance is zero, it can be seen that the current is

$$i \doteq \frac{\mu v_i}{2r_p} = \frac{g_m v_i}{2}$$

This can be doubled if $(-v_i)$ is applied to the other grid, as would be done in a fully differential amplifier.

An accurate analysis can be based on the equivalent circuit of Fig. 12.16(b); the mesh equations take the following form if the cathode voltage is written $(i_1 + i_2)R_k$:

$$i_1(R_L + r_p + R_k) + i_2 R_k - iR_L = \mu(v_i - v_k) = \mu[v_i - (i_1 + i_2)R_k]$$
$$i_1 R_k + i_2(R_L + r_p + R_k) + iR_L = -\mu v_k = -\mu(i_1 + i_2)R_k$$
$$-i_1 R_L + i_2 R_L + 2iR_L \equiv 0$$

The determinant is

$$\Delta = \begin{vmatrix} R_L + r_p + (\mu + 1)R_k & (\mu + 1)R_k & -R_L \\ (\mu + 1)R_k & R_L + r_p + (\mu + 1)R_k & R_L \\ -R_L & R_L & 2R_L \end{vmatrix}$$

$$= 2r_p R_L [r_p + 2(\mu + 1)R_k + R_L]$$

The last form follows after some reduction of the determinant. The substituted determinant for the meter current is

$$\Delta_m = \mu v_i [2(\mu + 1)R_k R_L + R_L(R_L + r_p)]$$

$$= \mu R_L v_i [r_p + 2(\mu + 1)R_k + R_L]$$

Then $i = \Delta_m/\Delta = g_m v_i/2$, as before. A much more complicated result is found if the meter resistance is appreciable, but as long as it is small compared with r_p and R_L, the approximation is good.

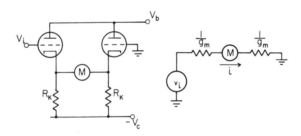

Fig. 12.17 Another meter output circuit.

An alternative arrangement is the balanced cathode follower shown in Fig. 12.17. To a good approximation, the cathode follower reproduces its input through a resistance of $1/g_m$; this leads to the equivalent circuit in Fig. 12.17. The meter current is $g_m v_i/2$, the same as for the long-tailed pair of Fig. 12.16. The cathode follower may be used if a high degree of electromagnetic damping of the meter is required, since it delivers the current from a much smaller output impedance. Usually this damping is undesirable, and the long-tailed pair is preferred.

These tube circuits are very inefficient at delivering current to low-resistance loads like a meter, and the job can be done more neatly by transistors. Fig. 12.18 shows a transistor long-tailed pair, which is closely analogous to the tube version of Fig. 12.16. Unfortunately, the analysis of this circuit is somewhat cumbersome and must be omitted. It shows that the current gain is essentially β to a low-resistance load, and the input impedance is twice the value for a single grounded-emitter stage, or approximately $2\beta r_e$. High efficiency results, since a supply of only a few volts is required, instead of the hundreds used by the tubes, to deliver a fraction of a volt to the meter.

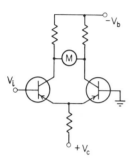

Fig. 12.18 Meter output circuit using transistors.

If one side of the load must be grounded, the complementary emitter follower shown in Fig. 9.13 is suitable. It would normally be biased for Class A or Class AB operation unless efficiency is more important than linearity. This circuit can be built with power transistors to operate the high-power galvanometers used in high-speed pen recorders.

REFERENCES

G. E. Valley and H. Wallman, eds., *Vacuum Tube Amplifiers* (New York: McGraw-Hill Book Company, Inc., 1948) contains a good chapter of tube amplifiers. The S. Schwartz handbook, *Selected Semiconductor Circuits Handbook* (New York: John Wiley & Sons, Inc., 1960) gives a selection of transistor d-c amplifiers. Many circuits and techniques are discussed in *Electronic Analog Computers* by G. M. Korn and T. A. Korn (New York: McGraw-Hill Book Company, Inc., 1956).

CHAPTER 13

Modulation

Modulation is the process of impressing one signal upon another so that they are transmitted together. We have seen one example of this in the chopper-type d-c amplifier, and a closely related process is used in radio broadcasting. In both cases a *signal* is said to be impressed upon a *carrier*. Other topics conveniently treated at the same time are *beating* or *heterodyning*, and *intermodulation* distortion in amplifiers.

13.1 AMPLITUDE MODULATION

In an amplitude-modulated wave, the signal controls the variations in amplitude of the carrier; an example is shown in Fig. 13.1, where a carrier of angular frequency p is modulated by a signal of angular frequency q. This signal can be represented by

$$v = V_c(1 + m \cos qt) \sin pt$$

The number m is known as the *modulation index* or *factor*, and is normally less than 1. (It can be much larger in systems with phase-sensitive detectors, but this case is best treated by itself.) The choice of sine and cosine functions in this expression is arbitrary and has been made for convenience in the following transformation. Writing out the bracket, we find

$$v = V_c \sin pt + m V_c \cos qt \sin pt$$
$$= V_c \sin pt + \frac{m V_c}{2} \sin (p + q)t + \frac{m V_c}{2} \sin (p - q)t \qquad (1)$$

using the identity

$$2 \sin a \cos b = \sin (a + b) + \sin (a - b)$$

The modulated wave contains three pure components: the carrier of amplitude V_c and frequency $p/2\pi$, and two *sidebands*, each having amplitude $mV_c/2$ at frequencies $q/2\pi$ higher and lower. Thus, a modulated wave occupies a frequency band with a width of $2q/2\pi$. If

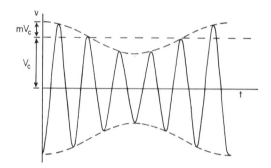

Fig. 13.1   A modulated wave with carrier amplitude
V_c and modulation index m.

the original signal is complex, as in radio broadcasting, and occupies a band extending up to a frequency f, the corresponding modulated wave requires a band with a width of $2f$. This result has already been used in the discussion of tuned amplifiers in Chapter 11.

The modulated wave produced by a chopper contains no component at the carrier frequency, and is known as a suppressed-carrier wave. This is most easily seen from the fact that the carrier is not present when there is no signal. In radio communication, both the carrier and one sideband are frequently removed in order to conserve space in the radio spectrum. The techniques for producing and detecting these waves are too specialized to be treated here.

The commonest way of producing an amplitude-modulated wave for broadcast is to vary the plate voltage of a Class C amplifier; a suitable arrangement is shown in Fig. 13.2. It was shown in Section 11.2 that the amplitude of the output wave of a Class C amplifier is nearly equal to the supply voltage; if this voltage is varied, the amplitude will therefore vary along with it. The variations are introduced by means of an audio-frequency transformer in series with the supply. Equation (1) shows that the power in the sidebands is $m^2/2$ times the power in the carrier. Thus, at full modulation, the modulating signal must supply half as much power as the d-c supply. For a powerful broadcasting station, this may be many kilowatts, and a large Class B audio amplifier must be used along with a transformer that can handle the power.

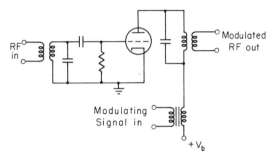

Fig. 13.2   Plate-modulated Class C amplifier.

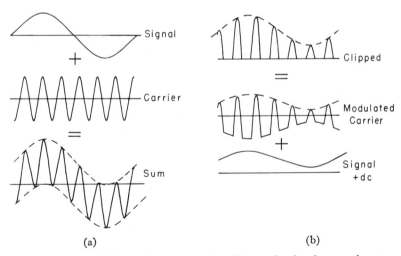

(a)   (b)

Fig. 13.3   (a) Addition of two waves in a linear circuit; the sum is not a modulated wave.   (b) Clipping of the sum generates a signal containing a modulated wave as well as other components.

Let us now consider an entirely different process. Take the signal and carrier waves and *add* them as in Fig. 13.3(a). The result is not a modulated wave, and in a linear system only the two original frequencies are present. Now let the bottom half of the compound wave be clipped off by a diode. The result is as shown in Fig. 13.3(b), which also shows that it is made up of a modulated wave combined with a reduced amplitude of signal frequency and some d-c voltage. There will also be some harmonics of the carrier frequency because of the square bottoms. The modulated wave can easily be separated from the others by filtering. This is an extreme example of modulation produced by a nonlinear element. We shall next discuss quantitatively the effect of a milder nonlinearity, which can be represented by two terms of a power series. Suppose that some device has a transfer characteristic that can be represented by

$$v_o = K(v_i + b v_i^2)$$

An example which we have already met is a single-ended triode power amplifier. Let the input be of the form represented in Fig. 13.3(a), namely

$$v_i = P \sin pt + Q \cos qt$$

For the present we shall consider that p, the carrier angular frequency, is much greater than q, but later this restriction will be dropped. Substitution gives

$$
\begin{aligned}
\frac{V_o}{K} &= P \sin pt + Q \cos qt + b(P \sin pt + Q \cos qt)^2 \\
&= P(1 + 2bQ \cos qt) \sin pt + Q \cos qt \\
&\quad + \frac{bP^2}{2}(1 - \cos 2pt) + \frac{bQ^2}{2}(1 + \cos 2qt)
\end{aligned}
$$

The terms have been arranged to show the following components:

    (1) a modulated wave with $m = 2bQ$
    (2) an angular frequency q
    (3) a d-c component equal to $b(P^2 + Q^2)/2$
    (4) second harmonics of p and q

Notice that no harmonics above the second are produced, and that the modulated wave carries an undistorted signal. In telephone service, use is made of *square-law* modulators to impose long-distance conversations on a carrier; a pair of wires can then transmit twenty or more carriers, each modulated by a conversation. A balanced circuit, closely resembling the ϕSD of Fig. 13.11, is used to cancel odd harmonics and accentuate the second harmonic; this principle is just the opposite of that behind a push-pull amplifier. Fig. 13.11 will be explained in terms of a switching mode of operation; but for very small signals, it is better regarded as a device with a square-law characteristic.

Intermodulation. So far, we have considered modulation to be a desirable effect of a purposely nonlinear circuit. However, at times it is an undesirable effect in a circuit that is supposed to be linear but contains a small nonlinearity. A common example is the audio-frequency power amplifiers used in radio, television, and phonograph systems, both low and high fidelity. In this context, the effect is usually called *intermodulation*. Again, we represent the nonlinearity by a power series terminated at the square term, but write the expansion in the following way:

$$\frac{V_o}{K} = \frac{b}{2}(P^2 + Q^2) + P(\sin pt - \frac{bP}{2}\cos 2pt) + Q(\cos qt + \frac{bQ}{2}\cos 2qt)$$

$$+ bPQ[\sin (p + q)t + \sin (p - q)t]$$

The last term has been treated as in equation (1). These terms represent

(1) a d-c component as before
(2) and (3) p and q, with second-harmonic distortion of 50 bP and 50 bQ percent
(4) intermodulation distortion, consisting of frequencies $(p + q)/2\pi$ and $(p - q)/2\pi$ with amplitude proportional to bPQ.

The ear is rather tolerant of harmonic distortion, and the audible effect is very small unless the distortion exceeds 5 percent. This statement is especially true since most natural tones already contain many harmonics. But intermodulation is a different matter; if two or more tones are present at once, the sum and difference frequencies that are created can be very objectionable, since they are usually not harmonically related to the original frequencies. A high-fidelity amplifier is expected to have a harmonic distortion of less than 1 percent at full power output, along with the accompanying low intermodulation.

Intermodulation is particularly noticeable in the reproduction of the loud and complex sounds of a choir, and in duets between two wind or stringed instruments or between these instruments and a voice. The negative feedback that is always used in a high-fidelity amplifier has the effect of straightening the transfer characteristic, so that all kinds of distortion are reduced. At the same time, it should improve the transient response so as to give good reproduction of piano tones and drumbeats, for example. This requires not only linearity, but also stability, so that the transient does not set the amplifier "ringing". Unfortunately, feedback tends to produce just this kind of instability, and it must be applied carefully.

Beats or Heterodynes. The names *beats* and *heterodynes* are given to the sum and difference frequencies in applications where they are desired. One example is the beat-frequency audio oscillator, in which the difference is much smaller than the original angular frequencies p and q. Suppose $p/2\pi$ is 200 kc and $q/2\pi$ is variable from 200 to 220 kc, a variation that is easy to achieve. The beat then covers the complete audio range, 0 to 20 kc. If the original waves are sinusoidal and the modulator or *mixer* has a square-law characteristic, the audio-frequency wave can have a distortion as small as 1 percent. Moreover, the amplitude of q is readily kept constant over its small relative frequency range, and the resulting output also has constant amplitude.

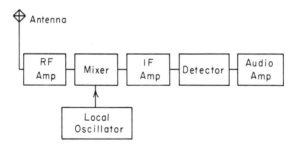

Fig. 13.4   Block diagram of a superheterodyne radio receiver.

A very common application is in the *superheterodyne* radio receiver. In this case, the beat frequency is ultrasonic. (The word *supersonic* was once used with this meaning before it was applied to aircraft and missiles.) In a broadcast radio receiver, the beat frequency is normally

456 kc; it is called the *intermediate frequency*. A block diagram of such a receiver is shown in Fig. 13.4. Suppose a station at 1000 kc is to be received. The local oscillator is tuned to 1456 kc and its output applied to the mixer at an amplitude much greater than that of the incoming signal. Under these conditions, the important beats are all between carrier and sidebands of the signal, on the one hand, and the local-oscillator voltage on the other. Therefore, a new modulated signal is generated with carrier at 456 kc, and with all sidebands intact with the same frequency differences as before. This can be amplified in the intermediate-frequency (i-f) amplifier, which can be very efficient since it is tuned to a fixed frequency. The signal is then detected and the resulting audio signal amplified to the required power level.

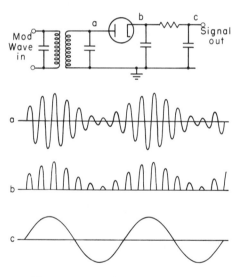

Fig. 13.5 Diode detector and wave forms illustrating its operation.

A difficulty with this type of receiver is *image* response: reception simultaneously of another signal, which would have a frequency of 1456 + 456 = 1912 kc. The radio-frequency (r-f) amplifier, which precedes the mixer in Fig. 13.4, is tuned to 1000 kc and will reject the image signal unless it is exceedingly strong. The grid circuit of the mixer is tuned as well, and in many receivers the antenna is connected directly to it, with no r-f stage at all. Receivers for higher frequencies often use a higher intermediate frequency as well, to aid in rejection of the image. For example, frequency modulation (FM) receivers, working near 100 mc, use an intermediate frequency of 10.7 mc, and frequencies of 30 and 60 mc are used for radar receivers, which operate in the thousands of megacycles.

Detection. The term *detection* is used for the process of recapturing the signal from a modulated wave; the word *demodulation* is also in use. Any nonlinear circuit will give some output at the signal frequency, but it is usual to use a diode rectifier with capacitor input, followed by an *R-C* filter, as shown in Fig. 13.5.

13.2 PHASE-SENSITIVE DETECTION

The use of phase-sensitive detectors in d-c amplifiers was introduced in the preceding chapter. We shall now consider the theory of their operation and some actual circuits. A theoretical model of a ϕSD is shown in Fig. 13.6; it is a multiplying device followed by a low-pass

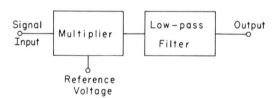

Fig. 13.6   Theoretical model of a phase-sensitive detector.

filter. The two inputs to the multiplier are the signal to be detected and the reference voltage, usually a sine wave or a square wave; we shall consider only the former. Consider an angular frequency ω_1 in the signal, and let the reference angular frequency be ω_2, with $\omega_1 \doteq \omega_2$ The output of the multiplier will be

$$2 \sin \omega_1 t \cos \omega_2 t = \sin (\omega_1 + \omega_2)t + \sin (\omega_1 - \omega_2)t$$

Here, as in equation (1) at the beginning of the chapter, the choice of sine and cosine has been made for convenience, and the factor 2 has been added for the same purpose. The low-pass filter will remove the high-frequency component of the output and leave only the difference frequency. In particular, if ω_1 and ω_2 are exactly equal, this component will be at zero frequency, or direct current. This case requires special treatment, since the phase difference between the two inputs becomes important. Thus, we have

$$2 \sin (\omega t + \phi) \cos \omega t = \sin (2\omega t + \phi) + \sin \phi$$

After filtering, the result is $\sin \phi$. When ϕ is 90 degrees, the two waves are in phase and the output is a maximum. The beat frequency when ω_1 and ω_2 are not equal can be regarded as generated by a continuous variation of the phase difference at $|\omega_1 - \omega_2|$ radians per sec.

If the signal in Fig. 13.6 contains a spectrum of frequencies near the desired frequency, this spectrum will be transformed to a similar spectrum about zero frequency. However, since negative frequencies have no physical significance, the negative half of this spectrum will be folded on top of the positive half. A signal whose frequency is exactly that of the carrier is converted to direct current, having a maximum value when the signal and reference are in phase. The ϕSD is valued because of the two following properties: (1) if the phase of the signal reverses, the sign of the output reverses, an important feature in d-c amplifiers and servo systems; (2) it is able to select a signal out of a wide spectrum of unwanted frequencies (see Chapter 16 on *noise*). Although the second property would appear to be valuable in radio receivers, it should be remembered that a reference voltage is needed, and this can be generated only with some difficulty in a receiver. However, many sensitive measuring devices use a ϕSD in a modulation-amplification-detection scheme, and its noise rejection is then essential.

The ability of a ϕSD to pick a signal out of noise is reflected in other names that are sometimes given to it: synchronous detector, coherent detector, lock-in amplifier, homodyne detector. If the filter is an *R-C* circuit with time constant τ, the effective bandwidth is $1/4\tau$ (Chapter 16). It does not depend at all on the bandwidth of the preceding a-c amplifier; however, this amplifier should have a reasonably narrow band to prevent the noise from overloading the system and driving it into nonlinear operation.

Many actual ϕSDs multiply the signal by a square wave instead of a sine wave; for example, the effect of multiplication may be achieved by switching, which is much easier than true multiplication. The output generated in the two cases is shown in Fig. 13.7; phase differences of 0 and 90 degrees are shown, and the results for 180 and 270 degrees are similar but of opposite sign. An entirely different class of ϕSD, to

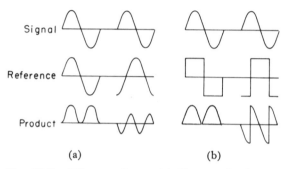

Fig. 13.7 ϕSD wave forms. (a) Sine-wave reference.
(b) Square-wave reference.

be illustrated later, operates by addition of signal and reference followed by peak detection. Detectors such as these may not completely reject harmonic frequencies if they are present in the signal; usually this property is of no consequence, since the preceding amplifier is tuned and passes only a narrow band of frequencies.

PROBLEM

Draw the waves as in Fig. 13.7 for phase differences of 180 and 270 degrees.

ϕ**SD Circuits.** Since true multiplying devices are complicated, it is usual to produce the effect of multiplication by switching, as already mentioned. An excellent circuit is shown in Fig. 13.8; it is merely the chopper circuit of Fig. 12.9 turned around. A push-pull signal is produced, usually by a transformer, and the switch alternates the two outputs at the required frequency, giving the result shown in Fig. 13.8. The filter may be a simple R-C combination or it may be more complicated; some details are given in Chapter 16.

Fig. 13.9 shows a half-wave ϕSD, equivalent to the chopper of Fig. 12.8. As the sketches show, it shifts the d-c level of the signal until the two shaded areas are equal, giving the required d-c output super-posed on a rather large ripple at the signal frequency.

ϕSD circuits that do not use mechanical choppers are popular because they are cheaper and last longer; normally, they also require

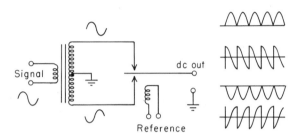

Fig.13.8 Basic transformer-coupled phase-sensitive detector or ϕSD.

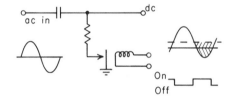

Fig. 13.9   Half wave ϕSD.

much less reference power. Since the signal level at the detector is usually large, the low d-c drift of the mechanical chopper is not an advantage. Most of these circuits use diodes connected in such a way as to act as switches. The diode equivalent of Fig. 13.8 is shown in Fig. 13.10; however, the ground point has been shifted to the chopper arm and the output is taken from the tap on the transformer. Each diamond of diodes acts as a single-pole single-throw switch, as shown in Fig. 13.10(b). Suppose that the reference voltage is driving 2 ma through the resistors; each diode then carries 1 ma if no signal current is flowing from A to B. But if 1 ma flows from A to B, two diodes carry 1.5 ma and two carry 0.5 ma; therefore A and B are effectively connected together by a switch that can carry up to 2 ma. When the reference voltage has the opposite polarity, each diode is back-biased unless the signal voltage exceeds the reference voltage; therefore, the switch is open. In the ϕSD circuit, the two switches are arranged so that each one is closed when the other is open. Clearly, four diodes can be used to make a half-wave ϕSD as in Fig. 13.9.

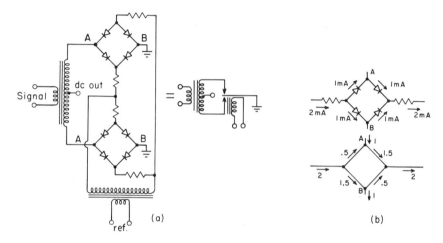

Fig. 13.10 (a) ϕSD using diode switches. (b) How the switches work.

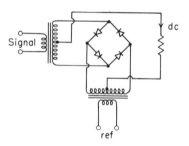

Fig. 13.11   Ring bridge ϕSD.

A remarkable circuit, which gives full-wave detection with only four diodes, is the *ring bridge* shown in Fig. 13.11. Note that the diodes in this circuit all point around the ring in the same direction, in contrast to the diamonds in Fig. 13.10, so that only one side can conduct at any one time. This circuit works particularly well with current signals and silicon diodes. Suppose that reference current is flowing to the right through the lower two diodes; the forward drop of about 0.5 volts across each one biases off the other two. Then the current from the lower half of the signal transformer is passed through the conducting diodes, much as in Fig. 13.10(b), through the reference transformer secondary, and through the load, which must approach a short circuit so that large voltages cannot be developed; otherwise, the other two diodes may conduct. On the other half cycle, the other two diodes conduct, and the load current comes from the top half of the signal transformer. If the signal source approaches a current generator, and the load approaches a short circuit, the operation is essentially ideal. If the appropriate conditions can be met, this circuit is also an excellent chopper.

An entirely different class of ϕSD is based on addition of reference and signal voltages, followed by diode detection. One of the better

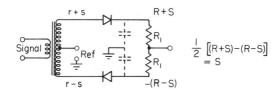

Fig. 13.12 ϕSD based on addition and subtraction
followed by detection.

circuits is shown in Fig. 13.12. The reference and signal are added in the secondary of the transformer, so that if they are in phase, the voltages $(r + s)$ and $(r - s)$ are applied to the diodes. If the capacitors are included, each diode generates a d-c voltage equal to the peak value of this, as shown. Without capacitors, a current proportional to the area of the positive (or negative) part of the sum is contributed to the output. In either case, when the two currents are combined at the output node, a phase-sensitive d-c voltage is developed; but the contributions from the reference voltage are canceled. For correct operation, the reference voltage must always be greater than the signal voltage, including all noise components.

It is possible in ϕSD circuits to use tubes and transistors that give some voltage gain at the same time. We have concentrated on the types using switches and diodes because these essentially passive devices give a completely predictable performance that is better suited for measurement applications.

13.3 FREQUENCY MODULATION

Frequency modulation (abbreviated FM) is used for high-quality broadcasting because it is much less subject to interference than AM or amplitude modulation. Amplitude-modulated waves are radiated by lightning discharges and by many types of electric machinery, and produce "static" in AM receivers. An FM signal can be distinguished readily from interference, and can be received very well under conditions that make AM reception nearly impossible. The principle is to change the frequency of the carrier from its mean value in accordance with the waveform of the signal, as shown in exaggerated form in Fig. 13.13. We shall not take the time to perform a frequency analysis of

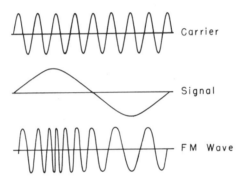

Fig. 13.13   A frequency-modulated wave.

this wave; it is found to contain a large number of closely spaced sidebands, with the strong ones nearly all in the range covered by the instantaneous frequency. This maximum deviation is normally 75 kc for FM broadcasts; most of the sidebands are therefore contained in a 150 kc band, as compared with the 10 kc allowed for AM broadcasts. This contributes to the high signal-to-noise ratio achieved by the system, but requires that the carrier frequency be high in order that the required spectrum space will be available; the FM broadcast band extends from 88 to 108 mc. These frequencies are not normally reflected by the ionosphere, so that the broadcasts do not reach past the horizon as lower-frequency ones do.

An interesting method of producing FM is to connect a *reactance tube* across the tuned circuit of an oscillator. Oscillators are introduced

in the next chapter; for the present, it is sufficient to note that r-f
oscillators contain a tuned circuit to define the frequency. An example
of a circuit producing a capacitive reactance appears in Fig. 13.14.
The components in the grid circuit are
chosen so that $\omega RC \ll 1$ at the operating
frequency, typically about 5 mc; therefore, the voltage fed back from plate to
grid is differentiated to a good approximation:

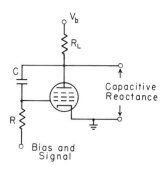

$$v_g \doteqdot RC \, \frac{dv_p}{dt}$$

For a pentode, another good approx-
imation is that $i_p \doteqdot g_m v_g$; we may therefore write

Fig. 13.14   Reactance tube.

$$i_p \doteqdot g_m RC \, \frac{dv_p}{dt}$$

which represents the current through a capacitance $g_m RC$. By shifting
the phase of the grid voltage 90 degrees, the plate voltage and current
have been made to resemble those of a capacitor. Some resistance
appears in parallel with the capacitance; this is made up of R_L and r_p
in parallel with an effective resistance caused by imperfect differentiation of the feedback voltage. These resistances will lower the Q of the
tuned circuit, but not seriously.

To vary the reactance of the tube, it is necessary to change its
transconductance over at least a small range. For some tubes the
transconductance is nearly a linear function of the grid voltage; the
6SJ7 is an example. The modulating signal is applied to R so as to
vary the bias in this linear range. By keeping the variation small,
highly linear modulation is possible. The frequency is then multiplied
by 18 in a series of stages, and the deviation is multiplied by the same
amount. As we have seen, a Class C amplifier will multiply by 2 or 3
with good efficiency, and one doubler with two triplers will give the
required factor. Other reactance-tube circuits are possible; an inductance can be produced by integration of the feedback, and R-L
integrators or differentiators can be used.

Variable-capacitance diodes, mentioned in Chapter 8, give an alternative to the reactance tube. A change in the bias of the diode alters the capacitance seen by a small variational signal. If the diode is part of a resonant circuit, the resonant frequency can therefore be controlled.

Detection of FM. An FM detector is usually called a *discriminator*; the name is also used when the circuit is intended to detect slow deviations of a frequency from a desired value. Probably the best circuit is the one

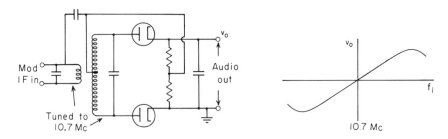

Fig. 13.15   FM discriminator and its characteristic.

shown in Fig. 13.15. It is a phase-sensitive detector, similar to the one shown in Fig. 13.12, but with both diodes facing the same way in order to preserve complete symmetry; the result is a differential output, but fortunately one side of the output can be grounded. The reference voltage is simply the primary voltage coupled through a capacitor, which is large enough to cause no phase shift. It can be shown that at resonance the secondary voltage is shifted 90 degrees with respect to the primary voltage, which is the reference; therefore, the output is zero. For other frequencies, the phase-shift differs from 90 degrees and a positive or negative output results. The relation between output voltage and frequency is linear over a considerable range if the total voltage across the secondary is twice the reference voltage, as sketched in Fig. 13.15.

A disadvantage of this detector is that it is sensitive to AM as well as FM, and therefore does not give the required immunity to interference. The usual practice is to arrange one or two i-f stages as *limiters*: they operate at a low plate voltage so that the output amplitude is constant as long as the input exceeds a certain threshold. The plate current is a square wave, but the resonant transformers restore a nearly sinusoidal voltage.

FM Tape Recording. Another important use of frequency modulation is in the tape recording of low-frequency and d-c signals. The response of a magnetic tape moving past a pickup head is proportional to frequency up to a limit reached when the wavelength on the tape becomes almost as small as the gap between the poles of the head. In audio-frequency

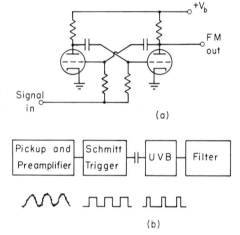

Fig. 13.16 (a) A multivibrator used as a frequency modulator for tape recording. (b) Block diagram of a detector for recovering the signal.

recording, this characteristic is compensated by the introduction of appropriate *R-C* networks, but below a few tens of cycles per second, this is not feasible, and the d-c response is zero. If it is desired to record a physical variable in the range from zero to a few hundred cycles, an FM carrier system is convenient and accurate; a carrier frequency centered at a few thousand cycles can be used with normal tape speeds. A simple and effective modulator is a multivibrator, with the signal applied to the two grid resistors, as in Fig. 13.16(a). The more positive the input, the shorter the timing waves and therefore the higher the frequency of oscillation. It is found that an input variation from 0 to +150 volts produces a nearly linear variation of frequency over a range of about 3 to 1. The square-wave output can be recorded directly. A highly linear detection scheme is shown in Fig. 13.16(b); the amplified signal is applied to a Schmitt trigger circuit, which makes a transition each time the signal crosses the axis. The resulting square wave is differentiated and the pulses are used to trigger a univibrator, which delivers a standard pulse each time. When this pulse train is averaged by a filter, a replica of the original signal results. Alternatively, the "diode pump" counting-rate meter discussed in Section 15.3 can be used.

CHAPTER 14

Oscillators

The oscillators to be considered in this chapter are used to produce wave trains at a specified frequency that is defined by a tuned circuit or a phase-shift network. Their operation is basically linear, in contrast to the relaxation oscillators discussed in Chapter 10, which operate by switching. As with tuned amplifiers, we shall discuss two groups: those with tuned circuits, usually for radio frequencies, and those using R-C networks, usually for audio frequencies. It also happens that the former normally operate in Class C and the latter in Class A.

Oscillators are based upon a positive feedback loop with a loop gain of unity or greater. If it is exactly unity, an output is generated with no input, and the amplitude is constant. The feedback circuit sees to it that this takes place at only one frequency. If the loop gain is greater, the amplitude of oscillation rises until the tube (or transistor) overloads; during the times when it is cut off or bottomed the gain is nearly zero, and the amplitude adjusts itself until the loop gain, averaged over a complete cycle, is unity.

14.1 TUNED-CIRCUIT OSCILLATORS

The majority of tuned-circuit oscillators use the tuned circuit to produce the reversal required to give positive feedback in a single stage. At the same time, the frequency of oscillation is defined at a value near the resonant frequency of the circuit. Two basic arrangements are shown in Fig. 14.1; they are known as the Hartley and

287

Colpitts circuits, but they are basically the same. In the former, the coil is tapped for the cathode connection; in the latter, it is the capacitor that is effectively tapped. It is also possible to have a circuit resembling the Hartley, but with two separate coils coupled together, instead of a single one with a tap.

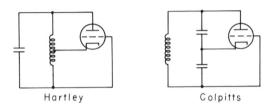

Fig. 14.1   Two basic oscillator circuits—Hartley and Colpitts.

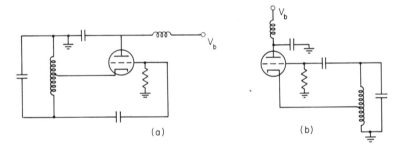

Fig. 14.2   (a) Actual circuit of a grounded-plate Hartley oscillator; (b) The same circuit as it might be drawn in practice.

To understand their operation, let us assume that the tuned circuit is already oscillating at its resonant frequency. With respect to the cathode tap, the voltages at the two ends are 180 degrees out of phase. Since one of these is applied to the grid, the resulting changes in plate voltage reinforce the original oscillation. As already described, it builds up until it is limited by overload of the circuit. Any small disturbance is sufficient to initiate this build-up; if nothing else, the voltages caused by thermal agitation of the electrons in the circuit will suffice.

The circuits used in practice may bear little resemblance to Fig. 14.1 unless they are carefully rearranged. There are several reasons for this; it is necessary to isolate plate and grid for direct current, and to provide grid-leak bias; chokes may be inserted to provide paths for direct current; and the r-f ground may be established at any of the three terminals. A grounded-plate Hartley circuit is shown in Fig. 14.2; at (a) it has been arranged to show its identity with Fig. 14.1, and at (b) it has been drawn as it might well appear in a circuit diagram. This time, the fact that the plate is connected to one end of the coil is not at all obvious. The r-f choke in the plate supply is not strictly necessary, but it serves to keep the oscillations from being transmitted to the supply line.

The tuned-plate-tuned-grid oscillator in Fig. 14.3 operates on an entirely different principle. It should first be noted that there is no magnetic coupling between the two coils; instead, the feedback is through the plate-grid stray capacitance. Since this is very small, it gives a phase shift of nearly 90 degrees. A further shift of nearly 90 degrees is provided by the tuned circuit in the plate, which is tuned to a frequency higher than the operating frequency. The remaining few degrees are contributed by the grid circuit, since the frequency of oscillation is a little lower than its resonant frequency.

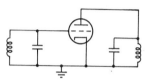

Fig. 14.3 Tuned-plate-tuned-grid oscillator.

One reason for the importance of this circuit is that it is often produced inadvertently. It will be noted that the circuit is identical with that of the Class C tuned power amplifier (Fig. 11.9); such an amplifier will almost certainly oscillate if the plate circuit is tuned to a higher frequency than the grid. This difficulty is avoided in one of two ways: use of a tetrode or pentode to reduce the grid-plate capacitance; and the process of *neutralization*, of which the simplest example is tuning the grid-plate capacitance with a coil in parallel. The important point is to eliminate or balance out the feedback voltage. Oscillator circuits may also arise in the chokes and capacitors that are included in practical oscillator circuits, resulting in *parasitic* oscillation at a low frequency. Very-high-frequency parasitic oscillations may also be produced, with the inductance provided by the leads to the tube. Once the basic causes of such behavior are understood, it is usually not difficult to find a remedy.

Frequency Stability. In most radio applications, highly stable frequencies are required. Frequency drift can be caused by two different effects: change in the resonant frequency of the tuned circuit, and oscillation at a frequency slightly different from the resonant value. The higher the Q of the circuit, the less important is the latter cause, and it can be further reduced by careful design. Tube capacitances may change because of the Miller effect, especially if the loading of the output changes. Finally, the values of the components themselves may change; for example, a coil usually has a positive temperature coefficient of inductance as the wire expands and increases the diameter. This change can be compensated for by special capacitors with a negative temperature coefficient. With a stable tuned circuit of high Q, excellent performance is possible with the *electron-coupled* design of

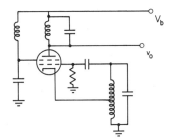

Fig. 14.4 Electron-coupled Hartley oscillator; the screen is the "plate" of the oscillator.

Fig. 14.4. Here the screen of a pentode or tetrode is used as the plate of the oscillator proper, shown in this case as in Fig. 14.2(b). The electron stream to the plate is modulated at the frequency of oscillation, and power can be taken from the plate with very little disturbance to the operation.

If the frequency is not required to be variable, very much better performance can be achieved by use of a quartz crystal as the resonant element. A crystal can be used in this way because of the *piezoelectric* (pressure-electric) effect: mechanical strain of the crystal sets up an electric field and a surface polarization, and vice versa. If a suitable slice of crystal quartz is mounted between electrodes, vibration of the crystal induces a corresponding a-c voltage on the plates, and application of an external a-c voltage causes the crystal to vibrate. Because of the near perfection of the crystal structure, this resonant system has an extremely high Q; values around 10,000 are common, and 500,000 can be reached with special precautions. The resonant frequency is temperature dependent, but slices cut from the crystal at suitable angles have a greatly reduced variation, and a thermostat may be used in critical applications. With almost no precautions, a stability of one part in 10^4 is possible, and with great care, one part in 10^8 can be reached. The short-term stability is much better even than this, and frequent comparison with an atomic oscillator permits an accuracy of one part in 10^{10}. One difficulty with such accuracy is that it is much better than the stability of the earth's rotation, and it has been necessary to use the orbital motion of the planets as the basic time standard instead.

Many of the circuits already described can be adapted to a crystal by simply replacing the tuned circuit; it can be considered as a parallel resonant circuit in such cases. It will also behave like a series circuit at a slightly higher frequency, and some circuits use it in this mode.

14.2 R-C OSCILLATORS

For the same reasons discussed in Section 11.3, resonant-circuit oscillators are not popular at audio frequencies. Moreover, it is usually desired to tune an audio oscillator over a wide range, and this is inconvenient with an *L-C* circuit, since the frequency varies only as the

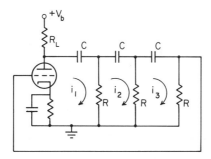

Fig. 14.5 Phase-shift R-C oscillator.

square root of *C*. Nevertheless, the first circuit to be discussed is useful for a fixed frequency or one that is to vary only a few percent at most. It is the *phase-shift* oscillator, in which a three-stage *R-C* network is used to shift the plate voltage by 180 degrees before it is applied to the grid. The phase shift varies rapidly with the frequency, and oscillation takes place at the frequency giving the correct value. A suitable tube circuit is shown in Fig. 14.5. Roughly speaking, each section of the network gives 60 degrees of the total phase shift; but this statement needs correction because the later sections load the earlier ones. At harmonic frequencies the phase shift is small, and there is large negative feedback which helps to keep the waveform pure. To analyze the circuit, we shall assume that the tube has a gain K, which must be calculated with due allowance for the loading of the network. Writing Kv_g for v_p, we shall set up the network equations and put the determinant equal to zero. This condition implies that outputs exist in the circuit without any input; in other words, it is oscillating. Using the abbreviation $X \equiv -1/\omega C$, we find for the first equation

$$(R + jX)i_1 - Ri_2 = v_p = Kv_g = KRi_3$$

It is assumed that the output resistance of the tube with R_L is negligible although the extra resistance could easily be added into the first term, The equations are

$$
\begin{aligned}
(R + jX)i_1 \quad & - Ri_2 \quad & - KRi_3 \quad & = 0 \\
- Ri_1 \quad & + (2R + jX)i_2 \quad & - Ri_3 \quad & = 0 \\
0 \quad & - Ri_2 \quad & + (2R + jX)i_3 \quad & = 0
\end{aligned}
$$

We now set the determinant Δ equal to zero:

$$
\Delta = \begin{vmatrix}
R + jX & -R & -KR \\
-R & 2R + jX & -R \\
0 & -R & 2R + jX
\end{vmatrix} = 0
$$

Note that the determinant is not symmetrical, since this is not a passive network. Expansion of the determinant gives

$$(R + jX)(3R^2 - X^2 + 4jRX) + R[-(K + 2)R^2 - jRX] = 0$$

As usual, the real and imaginary parts must be satisfied separately. The imaginary part yields

$$X(3R^2 - X^2) + 4R^2X - R^2X = 0$$

$$6R^2 = X^2 = \frac{1}{\omega^2 C^2}$$

$$\omega = \frac{1}{\sqrt{6}RC}$$

The last equation gives the angular frequency of oscillation. We now write the real part and substitute $X^2 = 6R^2$:

$$R(3R^2 - X^2) - 4RX^2 - (K + 2)R^3 = 0$$
$$3R^2 - 6R^2 - 24R^2 - (K + 2)R^2 = 0$$
$$K = -29$$

With this gain, oscillations will be just maintained. In practice, a slightly larger gain is used; the amplitude of the oscillations then grows until at the large amplitude the average gain is just -29. The waves will be slightly clipped or at least rounded, but because of the negative feedback at harmonic frequencies a remarkably good sine wave is generated all the same.

A transistor version of this oscillator is readily made; the circuit is like Fig. 14.5, except for the substitution of a grounded-emitter transistor, which again must have a gain of -29. The values of the components may be different, but the shape of the circuit is the same. A value of 10 K is appropriate for R.

Occasionally it is difficult to get a gain as large as -29, especially if appreciable power output is required. Lower gains are needed if the phase-shift network is "tapered"—that is, in each successive section, R is made larger, and C smaller, by a factor n. This tapering maintains the time constants while reducing the loading of the earlier stages by the later. For example, with $n = 2$, the gain must be -16, and with $n = 5$, -10.7 is sufficient.

PROBLEM

Carry through the analysis for this case and verify the results just given.

Wien-bridge Oscillator. The *Wien bridge* circuit is more suitable than the phase-shift type when the frequency must be adjustable. The feedback network produces zero phase shift at the operating frequency, and therefore the amplifier must have two stages if positive feedback is to be achieved. The Wien bridge, shown in Fig. 14.6(a), has occasionally been used to measure frequency in terms of resistance and capacitance, since it balances at only one frequency. The oscillator can be regarded, as in Fig. 14.6(b), as having a differential amplifier operating from the two sides of the bridge, and driving the top of the bridge from its output. However, it is more fruitful to regard the resistive negative feedback as defining a certain gain, and the positive feedback through the R-C network as producing oscillation at the frequency of zero phase shift. It is possible to use the same type of analysis

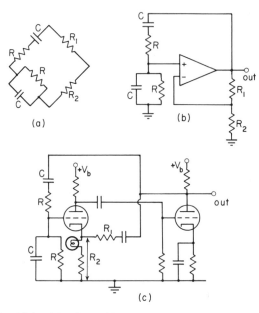

Fig. 14.6   (a) Wien bridge. (b) Wien-bridge oscillator, with differential amplifier. (c) An actual circuit, with a tungsten lamp to stabilize the amplitude.

that was applied to the phase shift oscillator, but for the sake of variety we shall use another method. This is to consider the R-C network by itself, and find the conditions for zero phase shift. The attenuation at that frequency can then be found, and the gain of the amplifier must be the reciprocal of this value. The positive feedback network is simply a voltage divider, with impedances $R + 1/j\omega C$ above, and $R/(1 + j\omega\tau)$ below, where $\tau \equiv RC$. Therefore, its attenuation is

$$\frac{R/(1 + j\omega\tau)}{R + 1/j\omega C + R/(1 + j\omega\tau)} = \frac{j\omega\tau}{(1 + j\omega\tau)^2 + j\omega\tau}$$

$$= \frac{j\omega\tau}{1 - \omega^2\tau^2 + j3\omega\tau}$$

The specified phase shift of zero occurs when this expression is real; and since the numerator is pure imaginary, so must be the denominator. This will be so if its real part is zero, or

$$\omega\tau = 1$$

This relation gives the frequency of oscillation. When it is satisfied, the attenuation is 1/3; therefore, the amplifier must have a gain of 3. The negative feedback network must have the same attenuation if the loop gain is large; this will be true if $R_1 = 2R_2$. If R_1 and R_2 are fixed, the oscillations will almost certainly either die away or grow until the amplifier clips. However, it is possible to make one of them a thermally sensitive resistor whose value is altered as it is heated by the a-c power dissipated in it. With suitable adjustment, the amplitude of oscillation can be kept constant in this way over a very wide range of frequency, line voltage, and tube characteristics. In Fig. 14.6(c), a simple version using tubes is shown; R_2 consists partly of a small tungsten lamp (3 watts, 110 volts), which has a positive temperature coefficient. This technique fails below about 20 cps, since the lamp resistance begins to follow the power fluctuations in the individual cycles. A *thermistor*, having a negative temperature coefficient, can be used for R_1. This device is especially valuable in transistor oscillators, which often do not develop enough voltage to heat the available lamps appreciably. Otherwise, a transistor version may look very similar to Fig. 14.6(c), with a two-stage grounded-emitter amplifier. For some purposes it may be desirable to refine this, for example by using an emitter follower at the input to reduce the loading of the feedback network. For low frequencies it may also be worthwhile to use direct coupling in the amplifier, so as to avoid phase shifts in the coupling capacitors.

Phase Shifters. It is often required to adjust the phase of a wave to a required value, particularly in circuits with phase-sensitive detectors. It is possible to use simple R-C networks as *phase shifters*, as in Fig. 14.7(a), but they have the disadvantage that the amplitude changes along with the phase. A much better arrangement is shown in Fig. 14.7(b), in which the network is fed a push-pull voltage from a tapped transformer or a split-load phase splitter. Relative to the bottom point at $-v$, the output is

$$v_o - (-v) = 2v\frac{j\omega\tau}{1 + j\omega\tau}$$

With respect to ground, the output is

$$v_0 = v\left(\frac{2j\omega\tau}{1 + j\omega\tau} - 1\right) = -v\frac{1 - j\omega\tau}{1 + j\omega\tau}$$

The magnitudes of numerator and denominator are always the same; therefore, the magnitude of v_0 is constant; but the phase varies by

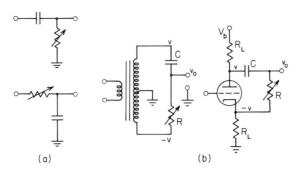

Fig. 14.7 Phase shifters. At (a) are very simple types that vary the amplitude along with the phase. The type shown at (b) gives a constant amplitude; the push-pull signal required can be produced by a tapped transformer or a split-load phase inverter.

180 degrees as τ (or R) changes from zero to infinity. It must be remembered that the phase shift depends on frequency; there is no simple solution to the problem of producing a phase shift independent of frequency.

REFERENCES

Radio-frequency techniques are thoroughly covered in a practical manner in *The Radio Amateur's Handbook* (West Hartford, Conn.: American Radio Relay League, 39th ed., 1962).

CHAPTER 15

Computation, Wave Shaping, and Gating

15.1 ANALOG COMPUTERS

An analog computer is a device that represents the terms of an equation by physical variables, and solves the equation by measurement of their variations. A familiar example is the slide rule, which represents the logarithms of numbers by distances, and performs multiplication and division by adding and subtracting these distances. We are concerned with electronic analog computers in which the variables are voltages. We shall see that the operations of addition, subtraction, multiplication by a constant, integration, and differentiation can be carried out with ease and accuracy. Multiplication and division of two variables is much more difficult, but some ways of performing these operations will be considered.

Operational Amplifiers. The ease and accuracy of the linear operations just mentioned depends on the use of negative feedback in an operational amplifier. This is a d-c amplifier with a high negative gain ($-10,000$ or more); the high-frequency gain characteristic is shaped to give stability under all conditions of feedback. For additional versatility and reduction of drift, a differential input is often provided. For all the applications we shall consider, such an input would be grounded or connected to a zero adjustment. Even lower drift, which is sometimes required, can be obtained by chopper stabilization, as

297

discussed in Section 12.4. A large variety of operational amplifiers is available commercially to be plugged or soldered into circuits as required; they may use either tubes or transistors and may or may not include chopper stabilization.

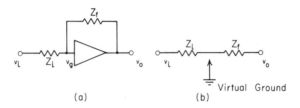

(a)   (b)

Fig. 15.1   (a) General circuit of an operational amplifier. (b) Use of the "virtual ground" concept to understand its behavior.

The basic circuit used with operational amplifiers is shown in Fig. 15.1(a). It was shown in Section 6.5 that because of the large loop gain, the gain is closely given by

$$\frac{v_o}{v_i} = -\frac{Z_f}{Z_i}$$

The operation can be visualized in terms of a "seesaw" as in Fig. 15.1(b); the high gain means that the grid voltage v_g must always be very small so that the output voltage will be within the normal range. The amplifier input is therefore a *virtual ground*, maintained by suitable variation of the output without any flow of current directly to ground.

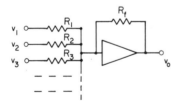

Fig. 15.2   Adding circuit.

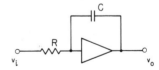

Fig. 15.3   Integrator.

If both Zs are resistances the device is an amplifier, or (if $R_i = R_f$) an inverter with a gain of -1; the gain in the more general case is $-R_f/R_i$. Because of the virtual ground, the input impedance is R_i, and this must be taken into account if the source resistance is appreciable. If several input resistors are used, the amplifier becomes an adder, as in Fig. 15.2. Since the sum of the currents flowing in must equal the current flowing out through R_f, we have

$$\frac{v_1}{R_1} + \frac{v_2}{R_2} + \cdots = -\frac{v_o}{R_f}$$

$$v_o = -R_f\left(\frac{v_1}{R_1} + \frac{v_2}{R_2} + \cdots\right)$$

The usual case has all the input resistors equal; the output is then the sum of all the inputs, multiplied by a negative constant.

For integration, Z_f is a capacitor, as shown in Fig. 15.3. Again making use of the virtual ground concept, we find

$$i_R = v_i/R, \qquad i_C = -C\dot{v}_o$$

where the dot represents differentiation. If these are set equal, the result is

$$C\dot{v}_o = -v_i/R \qquad v_o = -\frac{1}{RC}\int v_i\,dt + \text{constant}$$

The constant of integration is the original voltage on the capacitor at time zero. Initial conditions can be applied by connecting a floating voltage source across the capacitor, and quickly removing it when computation is to start.

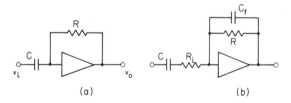

(a)   (b)

Fig. 15.4   (a) Ideal differentiator. (b) Practical arrangement with high-frequency cutoff.

For differentiation, the resistor and capacitor are reversed, as in Fig. 15.4(a). By exchanging v_i and v_o in the expression for the integrator, we see that

$$v = RC\dot{v}_i$$

However, perfect differentiation of a function is a mathematical ideal, which can never be applied to a physical variable. This is easily seen on the steady-state frequency-response picture, since a gain proportional to frequency without any limit is implied. In practice, if one is differentiating a curve, he always smooths it first to remove the small-scale irregularities. This idea can be applied to the operational differentiator as shown in Fig. 15.4(b); a small resistor is placed in series with C, and a small capacitor in parallel with R. For very short times, or high frequencies, the circuit acts as an integrator; but for slower changes, or low frequencies, it is still a differentiator. The frequency response rises with frequency to a certain point, but then turns over and falls in inverse proportion. Because of this difficulty, differentiators are avoided wherever possible in the solving of equations by analog computers; as we shall see, it is normally possible to set up a differential equation with integrators only. However, it is sometimes desired to differentiate data as they are produced by a measuring instrument, and then the remarks just made are relevant.

Many other more complicated responses are possible by the use of suitable input and feedback networks. A large number are listed, for example, in *Electronic Analog Computers* by Korn and Korn, referred to at the end of this chapter.

As an example of analog computation, we shall now consider the solution of the familiar second-order linear differential equation, which represents damped harmonic motion, oscillations of a tuned circuit, and other physical systems. Undamped and damped oscillations, critical damping and overdamping, can all be demonstrated, with any desired initial conditions. It is even possible to get negative damping, with growing amplitude of oscillation. The equation can be written

$$\ddot{y} + 2b\dot{y} + \omega^2 y = 0$$

Then for small damping the angular frequency is ω, and critical damping occurs when $b = \omega$. The terms are generated by integrating $\ddot{y}$ in order to avoid the use of differentiators; thus, if both integrators have the same value of $RC \equiv \tau$, one integration produces $-\dot{y}/\tau$, and the second y/τ^2. If the first of these is inverted and then added to the second, with appropriate weighting factors, the result is $-2b\dot{y} - \omega^2 y$, which should be equal to $\ddot{y}$; it is, therefore, fed back to be integrated in the first place.

The corresponding circuit is shown in Fig. 15.5; as already noted, initial conditions are applied as voltages across the two capacitors, and rapidly switched out when computation is to start. Either y or its derivatives can be observed as desired at different points in the circuit. If the response to a forcing function is required, as in plotting frequency response, it can be applied at A.

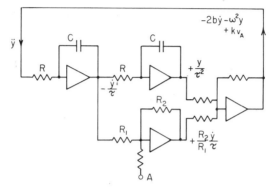

Fig. 15.5   Analog computer set up to simulate damped harmonic motion.

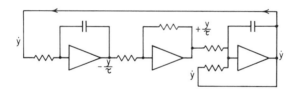

Fig. 15.6 Simplified circuit for damped harmonic motion.

An ingenious simplification of the circuit is shown in Fig. 15.6; it is based on the use of a summing integrator and solves the equation in the form

$$\dot{y} = -\int (2b\dot{y} + \omega^2 y)\, dt$$

The only disadvantage is that $\ddot{y}$ cannot be observed, since it does not exist anywhere in the circuit.

Naturally, an analog computer would not normally be used to solve an equation as simple and well-known as this one, but its very familiarity makes it a good example to study. Commercial analog computers may contain tens or dozens of operational amplifiers, along with function multipliers and function generators, and are used to study systems of equations that cannot be solved at all or whose solutions are too complicated for numerical study in a short time.

PROBLEM

Derive the frequency response of the practical differentiator in Fig. 15.4(b).

Multiplication and Division. There is no completely satisfactory solution to the requirement of multiplying or dividing two variables, especially when contrasted with the simple elegance of the operational amplifier. However, it is easy to convert a multiplier into a divider, or vice versa, as Fig. 15.7 shows. A differential operational amplifier is

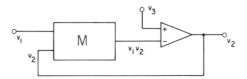

Fig. 15.7 Conversion of a multiplier into a divider with the help of an operational amplifier.

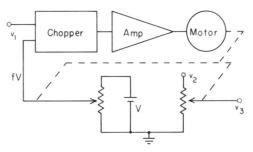

Fig. 15.8 Servo-multiplier in which a motor drives a pair of potentiometers.

required; because of its high gain it must keep its two imputs essentially equal by producing the appropriate v_2 at its output. Since $v_1 v_2 = v_3$, the output v_2 is equal to v_3/v_1 as required. In any divider, the user must ensure that the denominator is not allowed to become too small.

The best multiplier uses a servo-driven potentiometer as shown in Fig. 15.8. Basically, this device is exactly the same as the self-balancing potentiometer shown in Fig. 12.12, in which the potentiometer balances against one input v_1. But coupled to the slide-wire is a second identical slide-wire, to which is applied the second input v_2. The fraction of v_2 appearing on its slider is therefore proportional to v_1 as well as v_2, and is the required product. Algebraically, this is shown as follows: if the fraction tapped by the two slide-wires is f, then because of the servo $v_1 = fV$ and also $v_3 = fv_2$. Dividing these expressions gives

$$\frac{v_3}{v_1} = \frac{v_2}{V} \quad \text{or} \quad v_3 = \frac{v_1 v_2}{V}$$

It might be thought that division could be performed by applying a variable voltage instead of the constant V; however, it turns out that this arrangement leads to serious difficulties in keeping the servo stable, since its loop gain effectively depends on f. High-performance servos are needed to make the speed of response as high as possible, and this additional trouble cannot be tolerated. Even the best servo cannot follow changes in v_1 at more than a few cycles per second, and the speed of computation must be adjusted accordingly. This low speed, along with high cost, are the disadvantages of the servomultiplier. For some purposes the slow speed can be tolerated if only one variable changes rapidly, since the only limitation on the speed of v_2 is due to stray reactances, and these are never appreciable at computing frequencies. It must also be remembered that the output resistance is large and variable, since the output is often required to drive an operational amplifier with its low input resistance. A clever way of allowing for this loading is to load the feedback slide-wire with an equal resistance, so that the error is the same in both and cancels out.

For speeds too high to be handled by a servo, fully electronic multipliers must be used. It is usually not difficult to design these multipliers for fast operation, but they are seldom highly accurate, with errors of one to a few percent of full scale being typical. The variety of available systems in itself shows that none is fully satisfactory. We shall not consider the details of any of these devices, but shall point out that many of them are based on the *quarter-square* principle. This uses the identity

$$(x + y)^2 - (x - y)^2 = 4xy$$

Thus, the product xy can be obtained by use of the operations of addition, subtraction, division by a constant, and squaring. All of these but the last can be done by operational amplifiers, and squaring with moderate accuracy is not difficult. It uses nonlinear elements, frequently in balanced circuits to cancel the odd terms from the power series representing the transfer characteristic.

15.2 WAVE SHAPING

In this section we shall be chiefly concerned with methods for the accurate generation of linear sawtooth waves, which are useful for oscilloscope sweeps and generating time delays. In Chapter 10 we saw that an approximately linear rise can be generated by using the initial part of an R-C charging wave. The departure from linearity can be considered as due to the buildup of voltage on the capacitor, which diminishes the voltage across the resistor and therefore the charging current. The methods to be discussed act to keep the current constant, and therefore to keep the rate of change of voltage constant.

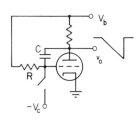

Fig. 15.9 Miller integrator for generating a linear sawtooth.

One method is to use a feedback integrator, as discussed in the preceding section. The feedback maintains the voltage at the amplifier input constant to give the required effect. For most purposes it is not necessary to have an operational amplifier; a single stage gives enough gain to produce a highly linear rise. Fig. 15.9 shows a circuit of this type, usually called a *Miller integrator*, since its action is closely related to the Miller effect. The switch represents a thyratron or a vacuum tube controlled by a square gate. When it is open, current flows down from V_b and into the capacitor, but nearly all of the resulting potential appears at the plate side of the latter. The result is a close approximation to a linear fall of plate voltage, since the voltage across the resistor R hardly changes. The circuit can be regarded as integrating the square pulse into a triangle.

In terms of the Miller effect, the tube can be considered as developing an apparent input capacitance $C(1 - K)$, where K is its gain. This technique is occasionally useful when a very large effective capacitance is needed.

Another circuit for producing a linear sweep is the *bootstrap integrator*, shown in Fig. 15.10. The prototype version at (a) uses a floating battery to produce the charging current; the capacitor voltage is reproduced by a cathode follower, so that the negative end of the

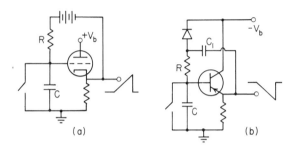

Fig. 15.10   Bootstrap integrators.   The tube version at (a) demonstrates the principle; the transistor circuit shows how the battery may be replaced by a capacitor and diode.

battery rises almost as fast as the positive end of the capacitor. Therefore, a nearly constant voltage is maintained across R, and the result is a nearly linear rise. The name of the circuit arises because the battery "lifts itself by its own bootstraps." Curiously enough, this circuit is, in principle, identical with the Miller integrator, differing only in the position of the ground and the arrangement of the supply voltage. The same tube with the same supply voltage and load will give the same approach to linearity. In the Miller integrator, the lack of perfection comes from finite gain, with the result that the grid voltage does rise slightly; in the bootstrap circuit, the same result appears because the gain of the cathode follower is less than unity.

To avoid the floating battery, it is usual to use a capacitor and a diode, which allows the top of R to rise above the supply potential. This is shown in Fig. 15.10(b) in a transistor version. The feedback capacitor C_1 must be much larger than C so that it can supply the required charge without much drop in potential. When the output returns to zero, the lost charge is restored in a burst through the diode.

Clipping and Differentiating. The processes of *clipping* and *differentiating* find their main application in timing devices. Suppose, for example, that a train of short pulses spaced by 100 μsec is required for calibrating an oscilloscope sweep. We start with a stable 10 kc sine-wave oscillator, as illustrated in Fig. 15.11. The output is amplified and clipped to produce a square wave; if it is not square enough, the process may be repeated. An *R-C* differentiating network converts the

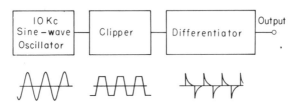

Fig. 15.11   Generation of a series of timing pulses by clipping and differentiation.

square wave to the desired train of short pulses; in many applications the negative pulses can be left in, but they can be removed by a diode if necessary. A similar process can be used to produce pulses for very accurate and stable synchronization of a sweep circuit to an incoming wave, a common practice in high-quality oscilloscopes.

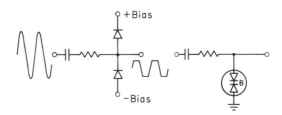

Fig. 15.12   Clipping of a large input wave by biased diodes or by a symmetrical breakdown diode.

The most straightforward way to clip a wave is to use biased diodes, as in Fig. 15.12. The bias sources must have a low impedance, because they must absorb the current through the resistance when the diodes are conducting. In a symmetrical circuit such as this, capacitor coupling is possible; but if only one diode is used, the capacitor will develop a voltage nearly equal to the peak value of the wave, and the clipper will no longer clip. This is the same process that produces grid-leak bias in Class C amplifiers, and that is used in clamping, to be discussed in the next section. Fig. 15.12 also shows a very simple and effective clipper using a breakdown (or Zener) diode. These diodes are commercially available in "double-anode" form, amounting effectively to a pair of equal diodes back-to-back; when either one breaks down, the other is in forward conduction. Otherwise, a pair of separate diodes can be used.

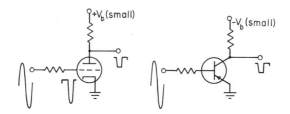

Fig. 15.13   Clipping by an overloaded tube or transistor
with a small supply voltage.

Clipping and amplification can be combined as in Fig. 15.13; the grid is used as a diode plate to clip the top of the wave, and cutoff of the tube cuts off the other side, which after amplification is also the top. This works especially well if the supply voltage is low. Since the grid draws current, care must be taken to avoid the building up of grid-leak bias. A transistor amplifier with a large input and a small plate voltage works just as well, the collector alternately bottoming and cutting off.

Finally, a regenerative clipper can be used. This is a Schmitt trigger circuit with a small hysteresis, biased to trigger one way for positive input and the other way for negative. This circuit was shown in the FM tape detector at the end of Chapter 13. It gives a large output for a small input, but is less reliable than the simple clippers, since the adjustment is fairly critical.

15.3 CLAMPING AND PULSE STRETCHING

Clamping is the process of automatically adjusting a certain part of a wave to a specified potential. Most often this potential is at ground, and the part clamped is the most positive or most negative peak, but neither of these restrictions is necessary. As a simple example, consider Fig. 15.14, in which a rectangular wave has been fed through a capacitor, so that the areas above and below ground potential must be equal.

The clamping is provided by a shunt diode to ground; if the wave goes negative, the diode conducts and charges the capacitor with the polarity shown. As long as the time constant RC is much greater than the period between pulses, the potential on the capacitor will be nearly constant at the value required to clamp the bottom of the wave

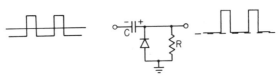

Fig. 15.14   The diode clamp places the most negative
part of the wave at ground potential.

to ground. The longer this time constant, the more accurate will be the clamping, but if the amplitude of the signal changes, the clamp will be sluggish in responding.

If the diode is reversed, the top of the wave will be clamped instead of the bottom. This is what happens in the special case called grid-leak bias. If the diode is returned to a low-impedance bias source, the appropriate part of the wave is clamped to the bias potential.

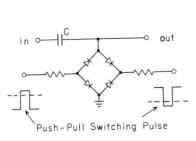

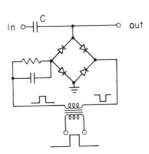

Fig. 15.15 Switched clamp turned on by push-pull switching pulses.

Fig. 15.16   Switched clamp with a transformer-coupled gate.

If the part of the wave to be clamped is not the top or bottom, a switched clamp must be used. To operate the switch, a control pulse or gate is necessary; this pulse will ordinarily be generated by a suitable combination of trigger circuits. A suitable switch is shown in Fig. 15.15; its action is explained in Chapter 13 and illustrated in Fig. 13.10(b). It is normally held open by the positive and negative biases applied to the switching terminals; but a push-pull gate causes the diodes to conduct, and clamps the signal to ground. If the gates recur regularly, the two bias potentials will be generated automatically by the grid-leak process. If the gate must be very short, it can be applied directly to the diode bridge through capacitors, thus avoiding the time constant introduced by the presence of the resistors. As with all diode switches, the bias must be larger than the maximum of the signal voltage. There is no need for the resistor R which appeared in Fig. 15.14, since this switch can conduct in either direction when the voltage on C is required to change.

Another form of this switch is shown in Fig. 15.16; here the gate is coupled through a transformer, and the bias that holds the switch opened is again generated by the grid-leak process. Various switches using only two diodes are also possible, particularly if only unidirectional conduction is required. For very slow signals, it should not be forgotten that mechanical contacts make excellent switches.

Pulse Stretcher. The univibrator and other trigger circuits can deliver a pulse of any desired length when they are actuated by a suitable input pulse. However, the output always has an amplitude that is independent of the input amplitude. Sometimes it is desired to lengthen a pulse while preserving the amplitude; most often this is done so that the amplitude can be measured accurately at relative

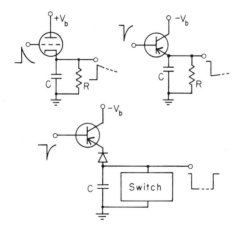

Fig. 15.17   Three versions of the pulse stretcher.

leisure. This requirement is met by the circuit shown in several variations in Fig. 15.17. It is a cathode follower or emitter follower with a
capacitor for a load; either a resistor R or a switch discharges the
capacitor. In the tube version, a positive input pulse causes the tube
to conduct very heavily, charging the capacitor to the peak voltage of
the input. After the input disappears, the tube cuts off and the voltage
remains on the capacitor, leaking off slowly through R and the tube.
The capacitor must be chosen small enough so that the available current is able to charge it to the required voltage in the short time the
input is present. As a result, the capacitor must often be so small that
its charge leaks away rapidly. In some cases, two or even three successive stages of stretching are needed. The transistor version shown uses
a p–n–p transistor, and therefore works on negative pulses. The performance of either kind can be improved by use of a diode to ensure
that the capacitor is not discharged through the cathode or emitter.
Also, in some cases R is replaced by a switch so that the stretched pulse
can be terminated quickly.

Counting-rate Meter. The circuit of Fig. 15.18, often called a
diode pump, produces an output voltage v_o that is proportional to the
pulse-recurrence frequency at the input, under certain conditions. It

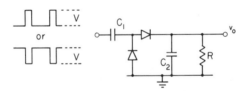

Fig. 15.18   "Diode pump" counting-rate meter.

can thus be used as a frequency meter or to give an indication of
counting rate in experiments in nuclear physics. Suppose the pulses
are positive and of amplitude V, and that the output v_o is much less
than V. Each time a pulse occurs, C_1 is connected in parallel with C_2
by the second diode, and transfers a charge $C_1 V$ if C_2 is large enough.
When the pulse ends, the output side of C_1 goes negative for an instant
and recharges through the first diode. Thus, C_1 can be thought of as a
"bucket," which transfers charge to the "tank" C_2. If the pulses are
negative, C_1 is filled at the leading edge and emptied at the trailing

edge, but the same charge is transferred at each pulse. If the pulses recur at an average frequency f, and each transfers charge $C_1 V$, the average current through R is $C_1 V f$, and the voltage developed is

$$v_o = R C_1 f V$$

This voltage must be much less than V if the full charge is to be transferred by each pulse. If the counting rate changes, the new reading is approached with a time constant $R C_2$.

Several useful variations of this circuit are possible. C_2 may be replaced by the feedback capacitor of an operational integrator or Miller integrator, thus maintaining the virtual ground so that the charge transferred is independent of the output, but allowing a large voltage to build up. R should be kept in parallel with C_2. However, with short pulses it is useful to leave part of C_2 connected to ground to hold the charge while the amplifier reacts and develops the feedback voltage. If R is left out, the circuit counts the number of pulses fed to it and becomes an integrator. A switch must be provided to discharge C_2 either upon command or upon the accumulation of a certain number of pulses.

15.4 GATE AND LOGIC CIRCUITS

A *gate circuit* is one that allows a small length of a signal to be selected and passed while blocking the rest. For example, it may be desired to pass one out of every ten of a string of timing pulses, as shown

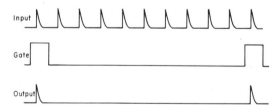

Fig. 15.19   Selection of part of an input wave by a gate circuit.

in Fig. 15.19. We shall use the word "gate" for the controlling pulse and "gate circuit" for the circuit; but the latter is also called "gate" by some writers. Gating is one of the fundamental logical operations, often called *coincidence* or AND; the name used depends more on the application than on the circuit. Other logical operations will be considered later, along with some circuits that respond only to coincident inputs, but do not preserve signal shape.

Among the simplest and most effective gate circuits is the diode type shown in Fig. 15.20. It will work only for positive signals, and uses a

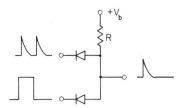

Fig. 15.20   Diode gate circuit for positive signals.

positive gate as well; both must come from low-impedance sources. If either input rises from ground by itself, its diode simply cuts off, and all of the current from R flows through the other. But if a gate is present, cutting off the lower diode, a pulse at the other terminal is transmitted as long as it is not larger than the gate. Any negative signal on either input is transmitted.

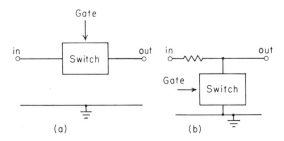

Fig. 15.21   Series and shunt switches.

If bidirectional signals must be handled, it is possible to use one of the diode switches discussed in the preceding section. As Fig. 15.21 shows, a switch can be either in series or in parallel. The series connection is the normal one for mechanical switches, but with electronic switches the choice is not as clear-cut. In particular, the series switch, shown in Fig. 15.21(a), is much more susceptible to interference by coupling of the gate into the signal line, and usually requires a transformer-coupled gate as in Fig. 15.16. The parallel switch has one terminal grounded and suffers much less from pickup; therefore, it is used more often. Other kinds of switch exist, but the ones in Figs. 15.15 and 15.16 will satisfy most requirements.

Gating is also possible in amplifying devices; in particular, a pentode may be used by applying the gate to the suppressor grid to overcome a cutoff bias. The most serious defect of such gate circuits is the production of a "pedestal"; that is, the gate pulse appears in the output with the signal on top of it. Although this can be clipped off by a diode, it is much better to have no pedestal in the first place.

Logic Circuits. The main distinction between gate circuits and the corresponding logic circuits is that the latter are concerned only with the presence or absence of signals, and not with their shapes. Every gate circuit is a logic circuit, but the converse is not true. Logic circuits are used principally in electronic digital computers, but they find many uses in special-purpose computers and in nuclear physics as well. We shall first define some of the basic logical operations.

The AND operation (coincidence) produces an output only if all inputs are present at once. Gating is a special case of this condition for two inputs. Logical variables are usually binary, as in the scale-of-2^n discussed in Chapter 10; that is, they can have only two values, 0 and 1, or off and on, or true and false. Thus, if an AND circuit has three inputs, A, B, and C, its output will be 1 only if A, B, and C are all 1; if any of them is 0, the output will be 0. If the output is called D, this relation may be written

$$D = A \text{ AND } B \text{ AND } C \quad \text{or} \quad D = ABC$$

The OR operation, also called *mixing*, produces an output if any input is present. In the example just given, the output is 1 if any one of A, B, and C is 1, and the relation is written

$$D = A \text{ OR } B \text{ OR } C \quad \text{or} \quad D = A + B + C$$

The NOT or *negate* operation turns 1 into 0 and 0 into 1; it is usually carried out by an amplifier, nowadays nearly always a transistor; however, a transformer can also be used for pulsed signals. NOT A is often written $\bar{A}$, and it is common to see NAND for AND followed by negation, and NOR for OR followed by negation. Note that the term NOR is not really derived from the corresponding English word, although the meaning can be stretched to explain it as if it were.

All other logical operations can be carried out by combinations of these three, but sometimes it is convenient to give certain ones names of their own. Perhaps the most important is the *inhibit*, abbreviated INH and sometimes called *anticoincidence*. An inhibit circuit passes one pulse (or a logical combination of them) only if an inhibiting pulse is not present. A inhibited by B is the same as a coincidence between A and $\bar{B}$; inhibition is thus a combination of NOT and AND.

A diode AND circuit is shown in Fig. 15.22; it is the same as the one in Fig. 15.20 except for the addition of several extra inputs. If all inputs are 0 (ground potential), the current through R divides equally among

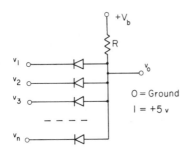

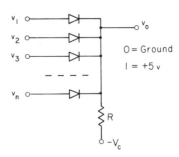

Fig. 15.22   Diode AND   circuit
for positive signals.

Fig. 15.23   Diode OR   circuit
for positive signals.

them all. If one or more rise to 1 (defined here as $+5$ volts), their diodes cut off and the current is accepted by the remaining inputs. Only if they all rise at once does the output rise along with them.

Reversal of the diodes and the supply potential gives an OR circuit (Fig. 15.23). This time, any input that rises carries the output along with it, and all the other diodes cut off. Besides its uses in computing, this circuit is useful for coupling a large number of particle counters so that a pulse from any one can be recorded; the OR circuit couples their outputs together but isolates their stray capacitances.

These two circuits illustrate a common property of most logic circuits: the same one may be regarded as either an AND or an OR, depending on which input level is defined as 0 and which as 1. If 0 is +5 volts and 1 is ground, then Fig. 15.22 is an OR and Fig. 15.23 is an AND.

A complete logical system requires amplifiers or *buffers* as well as the diode logic circuits just described, since there is some attenuation in passing through them, and since they require a fairly low source impedance to work properly. The amplifiers can also provide the inversions required for the NOT operation. Frequently the amplifier is a regenerative or trigger circuit, such as a blocking oscillator or a flip-flop. However, the small size, low power consumption, and reliability of transistors encourages their use, and by abandoning regeneration they can be incorporated right into the logic networks. The result is a class of logic circuits that can be used by themselves to produce complete logical systems, since they have power amplification and inversion built into them.

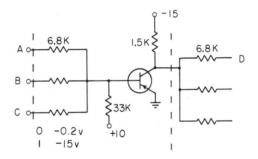

Fig. 15.24   Transistor-resistor (TRL) NOR circuit.

A remarkably simple example of this class of circuit is the NOR circuit shown in Fig. 15.24; it uses only resistors and a transistor, and is therefore often called a transistor-resistor logic (TRL) circuit. This example will accept three inputs from similar stages, and can drive up to three more. If all three inputs are near ground, the current through the $33K$ bias resistor holds the base at about $+2$ volts, the transistor is cut off, and its collector is at -15 volts, or slightly less if all the outputs are loaded. If one or more inputs are at -15 volts, the base will go negative and will be provided with a bias current of at least 1.5 ma; it therefore conducts heavily, and the collector bottoms at about -0.2 volt. If

-15 volts is defined as the binary 1, as is customary with *p–n–p* transistors, the circuit carries out an OR operation on the inputs, and inverts the output; this is the reason for the name NOR. If -0.2 volt is regarded as the 1, the operation is NOT AND, or NAND. The design shown is conservative, and can accept more inputs and drive more outputs if the conditions are not so stringent. However, the numbers are still rather small, and for the very fastest computers the circuit is a trifle slow, in comparison with TDL circuits. The TRL type is still useful for many applications.

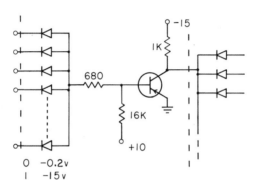

Fig. 15.25   Transistor-diode (TDL) NOR circuit.

Transistor-diode logic (TDL) circuits use the diode AND and OR circuits of Figs. 15.22 and 15.23 in combination with a transistor to give NAND and NOR combinations. For simplicity we shall discuss only the latter, shown in Fig. 15.25. Because we are using -15 volts as the binary 1, the AND circuit of Fig. 15.22 is now an OR. A small resistor is placed in series with the base to avoid drawing too much current from it. The action is much the same as for the TRL circuit, but the isolation provided by the diodes gives somewhat higher switching speeds and greater input and output capacity. Even in very conservative designs, ten inputs and six outputs are possible.

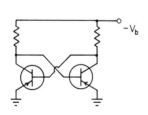

Fig. 15.26   Direct-coupled (DCTL) flip-flop.

It is also possible to couple the collector of a transistor directly to the base of another, giving a type of logic circuit called DCTL. This coupling is possible because the collector of a saturated transistor can be closer to ground than the base, enough so to cut it off. Instead of showing any logic circuits, we give a direct-coupled flip-flop in Fig. 15.26. DCTL requires special transistors, which have not been readily available in the past; as they become more common, this type of circuit may become very important, since it can be extremely simple.

EXAMPLES

First, we shall discuss two arrangements of the NOR circuit of Fig. 15.24 to show how logical systems can be built up. Fig. 15.27 shows that two TRL blocks can be coupled to each other, forming nothing less than the familiar flip-flop. In this case it can be turned "on" and "off" by −15-volt signals on the appropriate leads as shown in the figure.

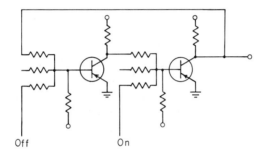

Fig. 15.27 Two TRL units combined into a flip-flop.

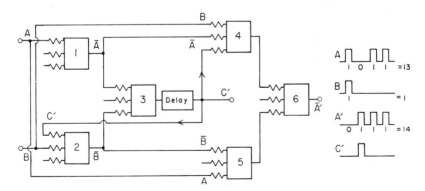

Fig. 15.28 Half adder for binary numbers built from TRL units.

Fig. 15.28 shows a device known as a *half adder*, which can take a serial binary number and add 1 to it, taking account of any carry digits that may be generated. Two half adders can be combined to make a full adder, capable of adding two serial binary numbers of any size, but the half adder is also useful in its own right. A serial number is one in which the digits follow one another in time, and for the present purpose the least significant digit must come first, just opposite to the conventional way of writing numbers. Thus, the number 13, whose binary form is 1101, would appear as a pulse, a space, and two pulses, and the 1 to be added to it would be a single pulse coincident with the first. Since $1 + 1 = 10$ in binary arithmetic, the addition of the two 1's in the first position must generate a zero and a carry pulse, which is then added to the second digit. This becomes 1 with no further carry and the new number is a space followed by three pulses, or 1110, the binary form of 14.

The rule of addition may be summarized as follows: no input, no output; one pulse in, one out; two in, none out and one to carry. The circuit of Fig. 15.28 works according to these rules; the large number is applied to A and the single digit to B. Each of these is inverted to produce $\bar{A}$ and $\bar{B}$. To generate the carry output, $\bar{A}$ and $\bar{B}$ are fed to a third TRL unit, which produces output only if they are both absent, or in other words only if A and B are both present. The carry output is delayed one digit period by a delay line for further use. The signals $\bar{A}$ and B are presented to unit 4 which generates output if they are both absent, or in other words only if A is present in the absence of B. Similarly, unit 5 receives A and $\bar{B}$ and produces a pulse if only B is present. These two outputs are combined in unit 6, which gives no pulse (NOT A') when only one of A and B is present. This is the negation of the sum digit A', and would usually have to be inverted back again for further use.

If a carry pulse is generated, it must be brought back to input B in coincidence with the second digit; by hypothesis, there is no other pulse coming to B at this time. The delayed carry pulse C' is therefore taken to unit 2 for inversion, and to unit 4 where it replaces the B input. It is this fact that the carry replaces the B input after the first digit that makes the half adder unable to add two complete binary numbers. Full adders can be made from two half adders or by an independent logical design. Simpler designs are possible by using both

AND and OR units (or NAND and NOR), but this example shows that NOR units are enough by themselves.

We now turn our attention to a different device, the diode *switching matrix*. Suppose that a binary number is stored in a series of flip-flops, which may be connected as a counter or may have received the number in some other manner. It is frequently required to convert this information into voltages on a set of wires, such that only one wire receives a signal at a time. For example, a four-stage counter can control sixteen wires, one for each of the 2^4 numbers it can hold. Part of the matrix for a three-stage system is shown in Fig. 15.29; if the least significant digit is

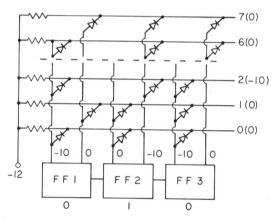

Fig. 15.29 Diode switching matrix which turns the output of three flip-flops into signals on separate wires.

at the left, the binary number in storage is 010, or 2. Each of the horizontal output wires has three diodes connected as an AND circuit to three of the six wires from the flip-flops. Only the one for which all three wires are at -10 volts will be itself at -10 volts; the other seven will all be at about ground. It is seen that wire number 2 is the one with output, as required, and that as the count advances in the flip-flops, the wires are gated in the proper succession. This kind of matrix is used in the control circuits of computers, where a binary number must be decoded so as to cause the correct operation to be performed. It is also used in changing from one binary code to another, or from binary to decimal.

References

Analog computers are thoroughly treated, from the standpoints of instrumentation and computing techniques, in *Electronic Analog Computers* by G. A. and T. M. Korn (New York: McGraw-Hill Book Company, Inc., 1956). Two standard references on gating and logic circuits are *Waveforms* by B. Chance, V. Hughes, E. F. MacNichol, D. Sayre, and F. C. Williams (New York: McGraw-Hill Book Company, Inc., 1949), and *Pulse and Digital Circuits* by J. Millman and H. Taub (New York: McGraw-Hill Book Company, Inc., 1956).

CHAPTER 16

Noise

In principle, there is no difficulty in increasing the gain of an amplifier or the sensitivity of a measuring device without limit. When this is attempted, it is always found that at some point the amplified signal is lost in some kind of *noise* which arises in the measuring device or the amplifier. In this context, noise may include unwanted signals, such as are found in radio reception; ripple and other effects caused by imperfect amplifiers; or fundamental noise generated by the currents and charges in the circuit. In a narrower sense, the term may be restricted to the last kind, and we shall devote most of our time to it. The name comes originally from the rushing or hissing sound heard in a loudspeaker when random noise is applied to it.

The most important types of fundamental noise are thermal and shot. Thermal-agitation, or Johnson, noise is produced by the random motion of the electrons in resistors, as they occasionally happen to move preferentially in one direction or the other. Shot noise is due to the fact that electric current is not continuous, but is made up of discrete charges in motion; it is most important with very small currents, but can be appreciable even with large ones. The acoustic noise produced by raindrops on a roof is a kind of shot noise. We shall also consider current and flicker noise, which are produced by slightly less microscopic fluctuations and are often met in amplifiers.

16.1 THERMAL NOISE

The type of noise resulting from thermal agitation was studied experimentally by J. B. Johnson and is sometimes given his name. At

about the same time, Nyquist gave a simple derivation of an expression
for its amplitude and frequency spectrum, and Johnson found it to
agree closely with experiment. We shall
follow Nyquist's method closely.

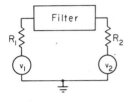

First, let us use the second law of thermo-
dynamics to establish some basic facts about
the noise spectrum. Fig. 16.1 shows two resistors R_1 and R_2, with their noise voltages
represented separately by generators in series.

Fig. 16.1 Two resistors
with their thermal noise
generators, joined by a
filter.

They are joined by a filter, which allows us to
consider different frequency bands separately
if we wish. If the two resistors are at the same
temperature, no net power can flow from one
to the other, and therefore the powers dissipated by each generator
in the other resistor must be equal. Then

$$\left(\frac{v_1}{R_1 + R_2}\right)^2 R_2 = \left(\frac{v_2}{R_1 + R_2}\right)^2 R_1$$

$$\frac{v_1^2}{v_2^2} = \frac{R_1}{R_2}$$

Thus, for any resistance, the square of the noise voltage is proportional
to R; moreover, since the foregoing result must be true regardless of
the band of frequencies that is passed through the filter, the spectrum
of the noise is the same for all resistors. We may therefore use any convenient model to find the spectrum, and we are assured that it will hold

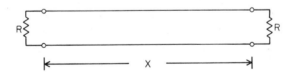

Fig. 16.2   Ideal transmission line for derivation of the
thermal noise spectrum.

universally. Since the noise voltage is a fluctuating quantity by its very
nature, it is really the *mean* square voltage we have been talking about.

Nyquist's model, used to find the noise spectrum, is an ideal two-
wire transmission line, as sketched in Fig. 16.2. We show in the next

chapter that such a line has a *characteristic impedance*, which is in this case a pure resistance R. Electromagnetic energy travels along it at the speed of light, and some is reflected when it reaches the ends, unless the ends are *terminated* by resistances R equal to the characteristic resistance. On the other hand, with a short-circuit or open-circuit termination, all the energy is reflected. We start with the Rs connected to the ends, and if the whole system is in thermal equilibrium, each one transmits a certain noise power into the line, and receives the same amount from the other one through the line. Next, we rapidly replace the Rs by short circuits, trapping in the line all the noise energy that was on it at that instant. However, a short-circuited line can support only certain modes, represented by standing waves that fit into the line exactly. It is a simple matter to count these modes and to assign to each one an energy kT, where k is Boltzmann's constant, thus giving the noise spectrum.

Let us consider the noise in a certain bandwidth B. When the short circuits were applied, the amount of energy in B caught in transit on the line was

$$dW = \frac{2x}{c}\, dP$$

where x is the length of the line, c is the speed of light, and dP is the power delivered by R in the band B. The factor 2 arises because there are two resistors, each transmitting noise power in one direction. Now we count the number of standing-wave modes in B. These are all harmonics of the lowest frequency f_1, corresponding to a wave with only two nodes, one at each end; therefore, $f_1 = c/2x$, and the harmonics have frequencies nf_1, with n being any integer. (Because we are looking for an approximation to a continuous spectrum, we must use a very long line, and n may be a very large number.) No matter how large the value of n, the spacing between adjacent modes is always f_1, and the number contained in B is B/f_1, wherever B is located in the frequency spectrum. We assign each harmonic an energy kT, since an oscillatory degree of freedom gets twice the amount $(kT/2)$ allowed for a translational degree of freedom. Therefore, another expression for the energy in B is

$$dW = kTB/f_1 = kTB \cdot 2x/c$$

Comparing the two expressions for dW, we see that

$$dP = kTB$$

This is the required result. Since the result is independent of the length of the line, we may make the line as long as we please, until the spectrum of harmonics merges into a continuum.

This expression gives the mean noise power that any resistor can deliver to a matched load. For most purposes it is more convenient to use the open-circuit mean-square noise voltage represented by v_1 in Fig. 16.1. The power delivered to an equal resistor by a voltage v is

$$\left(\frac{v}{2R}\right)^2 R = v^2/4R$$

and thus the mean-square noise voltage is given by

$$\bar{v}^2 = 4RkTB$$

Similarly, if the noise source is represented by a current generator in parallel with a conductance G, its mean-square value is

$$\bar{i}^2 = 4GkTB$$

In the calculation of actual noise voltages, it is convenient to use the value of k as 1.38×10^{-23} joule per degree Kelvin, and to note that if T is 290°K or 17°C, $kT = 4.00 \times 10^{-21}$ joule. Thus, for a 1-mc band and a resistance of 1 megohm, the mean-square noise voltage is 16×10^{-9} volt², and the corresponding root-mean-square value is 1.3×10^{-4} volt, or 0.13 mv. A very modest amplifier is enough to raise this input to a level of many volts.

PROBLEM

Verify all the results given in the last paragraph.

16.2 SHOT EFFECT

The shot effect is an important source of noise in vacuum tubes, where the fluctuations of interest are in fairly large currents. It is equally important in the detection of very small signals, such as photoelectric currents, ion currents, and counts of radioactive particles. The basic idea is very simple. Suppose that a certain number of events

N occurs on the average in a counting time T. If the events are independent, the number counted will fluctuate with a standard deviation of $\sqrt{N}$. If the events are the transit of individual charges in a current, these variations will appear as noise. Writing the rms noise current as i_n, we therefore have

$$\frac{i_n}{I} = \frac{\sqrt{N}}{N} = \frac{1}{\sqrt{N}}$$

If the current I is carried by particles of charge e, then $I = Ne/T$ and

$$i_n^2 = eI/T$$

This is the basic equation of the shot effect. However, for most purposes it is convenient to use a bandwidth B instead of a time per observation T. The transformation is best made by Fourier inversion, and the result is $B = 1/2T$; we shall give a simple justification of this in a moment. We therefore have

$$i_n^2 = 2eIB$$

The spectrum is exactly like that of thermal noise, having a constant power per unit bandwidth no matter what the location of the band in the frequency spectrum.

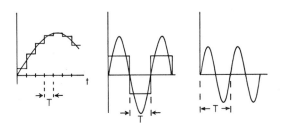

Fig. 16.3   Effect of averaging for successive times T
on sine waves of different frequencies.

Now let us see that the relation $B = 1/2T$ is a reasonable one. Fig. 16.3 shows a series of sine waves of higher and higher frequency. When the averaging time T is short compared with the period, the sequence of averages is a good representation of the original wave. When the frequency is high enough so that T is half the period, a square wave results from the averaging process, and when the period is equal to T, the wave does not show at all in the averages. When the effective width of the frequency-response function is found, it is reasonable that it should be equal to $1/2T$.

As an example of the application of the shot-noise relation, consider a photomultiplier detecting a very weak light beam which gives a photo-current of 10,000 electrons per second. The secondary-emission structure amplifies this tiny current until it can easily be measured, but adds only a small amount of noise, which we shall neglect. Suppose the amplifier has a bandwidth of 100 cps; the effective time per observation is therefore 5 milliseconds, during which an average of 50 electrons arrive. The actual value will fluctuate from this by 7 electrons on the average, and a noise equal to $\frac{1}{7}$ of the signal would be expected. Calculation of i_n in terms of the current I gives the same result: $i_n/I \doteq \frac{1}{7}$.

In vacuum tubes the currents are much larger, and the relative fluctuations are very small. However, if the tube is used to amplify a small signal, the noise from its plate current may swamp the signal if extreme care is not taken. On the other hand, the effect is also put to use in constructing noise sources for tests and calibrations. A saturated diode gives a noise signal whose magnitude can be calculated at once if the plate current and bandwidth are known. In many applications, the bandwidth also enters into the unknown and cancels out of the calculation.

PROBLEM

Calculate the mean-square noise current from a saturated diode with a plate current of 1.0 ma, and the noise voltage developed across a 50-ohm resistance.

16.3 EXCESS NOISE

Many resistors, especially the common carbon-composition type, exhibit noise in excess of thermal noise when they are carrying a current; the same is true of photoconductive cells. For this reason the phenomenon is called *current noise*; it is easily explained as being caused by fluctuations in resistance, so that the noise voltage generated is the product of the current and the resistance fluctuation. In composition resistors, the cause seems to be changes in contact resistance between individual carbon grains. Carbon-film resistors show a much smaller effect, and metal-film and wire-wound types usually show none at all; if they do, it can probably be attributed to granular structure in the very thin film or wire. The effect can be reduced by using physically large resistors or combining several in series or parallel.

The spectrum of current noise is usually such that v_n^2 is proportional to B/f, so that it is concentrated at low frequencies. (It is probable that this form changes at the very lowest frequencies, but very little is known about this because it is almost impossible to measure the noise accurately in, say, a 1-cycle band at 2 cps.) Therefore, if the frequency is high enough, usually above only a few thousand cps, the current noise is less than the thermal and can be ignored. However, high-gain audio amplifiers must be designed with current noise in mind, and plate-load resistors in the first stages should be of the wire-wound or film type.

Semiconductors also exhibit excess noise at the lower frequencies. In many cases a shot-noise component can also be identified, because the number of carriers in motion is much smaller than in conductors. Moreover, each individual carrier may last only a short time before it recombines and is replaced by a new one.

In vacuum tubes there is an excess noise with a $1/f$ spectrum arising from fluctuations in cathode emission. This is called the *flicker effect* and is especially pronounced with oxide cathodes. It is assumed to be due to the formation and disappearance of small patches of enhanced emission, probably allowed by a reduced work function. The range of lifetimes is such as to account for the observed frequency spectrum. As with current noise, flicker noise is usually negligible above a few hundred or a thousand cps. Transistors operated at low currents can give quieter amplification than tubes at low audio frequencies. This advantage is accompanied by another: a much smaller susceptibility to *microphonic* noise, which is generated in tubes by mechanical vibration of the electrodes.

Noise Figure and Noise Temperature. It is often convenient to have a number that specifies how closely an amplifier or receiver approaches ideal performance. A widely used parameter of this kind is the *noise figure* or noise *factor*, which is simply defined as

$$F \equiv \frac{\text{actual noise power}}{\text{fundamental noise power}}$$

In most applications F is expressed in decibels, but sometimes the actual ratio is more convenient. The fundamental noise is usually thermal, but in a photomultiplier, for example, it is shot noise, and the noise figure is about 1.15 because of additional fluctuations introduced by the multiplier structure. In radio receivers, the fundamental noise is the thermal noise in the antenna resistance, and noise figures of a few decibels can be achieved with tube amplifiers. However, there are two other classes of amplifier that we have not been able to discuss; these are *masers* and *parametric amplifiers*, and they can have noise figures so close to 1, or 0 db, that F is no longer convenient.

Instead, with these devices it is customary to use the *noise temperature*. This is the temperature at which thermal noise would have the magnitude of the actual noise. Although amplifiers may have noise temperatures of only a few tens of degrees Kelvin, the total noise temperature is usually greater because of cosmic noise from stars and nebulae, and because of thermal noise from the earth's surface and lower atmosphere.

Let us pause for a moment to consider this question of thermal radiation in more detail. Thermal noise in resistors, which we have been discussing, is closely related to black-body radiation. Most discussions of this radiation refer to the visible and infrared regions of wavelength, but the tail of the spectrum extends into the radio region with detectable intensity. If an ideal antenna is exposed to a field of such radiation, the voltage at its terminals is identical to the thermal noise that would be generated in an equivalent resistor, equal to the *radiation resistance* of the antenna. This is the effective resistance produced at the terminals, when the antenna is used for transmitting, by the energy lost into radiation. If a directional antenna is pointed at a source whose temperature is very low, the noise voltage observed from it is also very low, corresponding to the black-body radiation at that temperature. However, additional amounts of noise may be introduced from various sources. We have already considered the amplifier or receiver; other important sources are "losses" or resistance in the lines from the antenna, and reception of high-temperature radiation from the earth's surface by unwanted defects in the directional pattern of the antenna.

PROBLEM

Show that the noise temperature is $T_n = T_r(F - 1)$ if T_r is room temperature.

16.4 FILTERS FOR NOISE REDUCTION

As we have seen, all types of noise have a spectrum such that the rms noise amplitude is proportional to the square root of the bandwidth B. Once everything has been done to reduce the noise as closely as possible to the fundamental limits, the usual further recourse is to reduce the bandwidth, if the signal-to-noise ratio is still not high enough. In many measuring applications, the signal is slowly varying (in some sense) and the noise is filtered by R-C circuits, which determine the bandwidth. However, this filtering carries with it the penalty of a sluggish response to changes in the signal. We shall now investigate the relations between response time and bandwidth for these circuits.

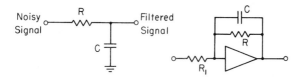

Fig. 16.4 Circuits giving a single time-constant. The simple one must be followed by a buffer amplifier; the one using an operational amplifier has a very low output impedance.

First we consider the commonest case, that of a single time constant $RC = \tau$ as shown in Fig. 16.4. It is assumed that the circuit is not loaded; for example, it may drive a cathode follower. It is also possible to incorporate the time constant into an operational amplifier as shown; the gain will be $-R/R_1$ and the time constant RC. The voltage response of the filter is $1/(1 + j\omega\tau)$ and the power response is the squared magnitude of this, $1/(1 + \omega^2\tau^2)$. The noise bandwidth is found by integrating this expression with respect to frequency:

$$B = \int_0^\infty \frac{1}{1 + \omega^2\tau^2}\,df = \frac{1}{2\pi\tau}\left[\tan^{-1}\omega\tau\right]_0^\infty = \frac{1}{2\pi\tau}\frac{\pi}{2} = \frac{1}{4\tau}$$

This is just a little more than the corner frequency of the network f_0; it is seen that $B = \pi f_0/2$. There is no single definition possible of the response time to a change in signal, since the criterion must depend on the accuracy with which the deflection approaches the asymptotic value; after a time 3τ, the error is still 5 percent, and after 5τ it is less than 1 percent.

A better combination of bandwidth and response speed is possible, as in video amplifiers, by adopting a filter that cuts off a little more rapidly. In principle this improvement could be made by adding inductance to the filter, but the size of the required inductance usually makes this method unattractive. Excellent results can be obtained with two RC time constants in cascade, but certain principles must be observed, as we shall now discuss. We shall phrase the discussion in terms of a system obeying the equation of damped harmonic motion, such as a galvanometer or an R-L-C circuit. This equation is

$$\ddot{v} + 2b\dot{v} + \omega_0^2 v = v_i$$

where v_i is proportional to the driving voltage. As would be expected, the best combination of noise bandwidth and response time occurs when the system is critically damped, that is, when $b = \omega_0$. To see how a critically damped system can be simulated by R-C circuits, it is convenient to derive the steady-state frequency response. Setting $b = \omega_0$ and replacing time differentiation by $j\omega$, we find

$$-\omega^2 v + 2\omega_0 j\omega v + \omega_0^2 v = v_i$$

$$(\omega_0 + j\omega)^2 v = v_i$$

The response of two equal R-C circuits in cascade takes the following form if the second does not load the first:

$$\frac{v_0}{v_i} = \frac{1}{(1 + j\omega\tau)^2}$$

Comparison of these two shows that they have the same form, except for a constant factor, if

$$\tau = 1/\omega_0$$

Any circuit having this frequency response will behave like a critically damped system. The bandwidth is found as before by integration of the power response:

$$B = \int_0^\infty \frac{1}{(1 + \omega^2\tau^2)^2} \, df = \left[\frac{1}{4\pi\tau} \tan^{-1} \omega\tau + \frac{f}{2(1 + \omega^2\tau^2)}\right]_0^\infty = \frac{1}{8\tau}$$

This is just half the bandwidth of the single R-C section with the same time constant.

Let us now compare the step responses of two filters having the same bandwidth: a critically damped filter with two equal time constants τ, and a single R-C section with time constant 2τ. The results are shown in Fig. 16.5, where it is seen that the output of the simple filter starts off faster, but is soon overtaken, and shortly afterwards the critically damped filter has less than half the error.

Unfortunately, a perfect critically damped response cannot be obtained by connecting the output of an R-C filter to the input of a second, since they are no longer independent. We have already encountered this effect in our study of the phase-shift oscillator in Chapter 14. A fair approximation is possible if the second section has at least ten times the impedance of the first. Alternatively,

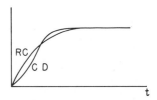

Fig. 16.5 Step response of two filters having the same bandwidth: the R-C time constant and the critically damped.

they can be isolated by a cathode follower, or an emitter follower if its input impedance is high enough. Better results are possible in a feedback system, two examples of which are shown in Fig. 16.6. In Fig. 16.6(a)

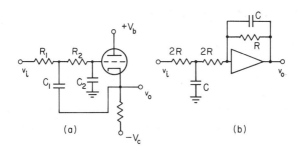

Fig. 16.6 Two methods of realizing a critically damped characteristic.

the output of a cathode follower is fed back to the lower end of C_1; perfect critical damping is achieved if the gain of the cathode follower is unity, and the performance is satisfactory with the slightly lower gain that is possible in practice. Again, an emitter follower is usable only if its input current can be tolerated. The two resistors and the two capacitors should be equal. Fig. 16.6(b) shows a circuit that can be used with an operational amplifier. With the constants shown the gain is $-\frac{1}{4}$, but it can be raised if necessary by increasing the feedback resistor while decreasing the capacitor in the same ratio.

In some applications a rather different method of filtering is used—that is, averaging or integrating the signal over definite time intervals equal to T. Perhaps the commonest example is the counting of particles in nuclear physics, where the shot noise shows up as statistical fluctuations in a series of counts that should all be equal. However, it is not difficult to apply the equivalent method to a continuous signal by using an operational amplifier as an integrator. A switch in parallel with the capacitor is used to set the integrator to zero at the beginning of each interval, and the integrated voltage is rapidly recorded at the end. (The switch should be protected by a small series resistor.) In our discussion of shot noise, we saw that the equivalent bandwidth for this method is $B = 1/2T$, to be compared with $1/4\tau$ for the R-C filter and $1/8\tau$ for the critically damped filter. The response time of the filters depends on the required accuracy, but is about 4τ and 8τ respectively, or of the order of $1/B$. With averaging, there is full response to a sudden change in a time between 0 and T, depending on when the change occurs during the interval; the average is $1/2T$ or $1/4B$. This method is therefore clearly superior; whether it is used in practice depends upon whether the extra complication is considered worthwhile.

PROBLEMS
1) Show that the operational amplifier in Fig. 16.4 has the same frequency response as the R-C circuit.
2) Derive the frequency responses of the circuits in Fig. 16.6, assuming unity gain for the cathode follower, and show that they have the critically damped form.

Noise in Modulated Systems. Many measuring systems contain a band-pass amplifier, followed by a detector and then another amplifier which also limits the bandwidth in the manner we have just been discussing. The commonest example is a radio receiver, and another is the chopper-type d-c amplifier. We must therefore now examine the effect of the detector upon the noise from the band-pass amplifier.

The full treatment is far too complicated to be included here; we shall simply give some rough arguments in justification of the results.

First we consider the linear diode detector commonly used in radio receivers (Fig. 13.5). Suppose that B_1 is the bandwidth of the band-pass amplifier before the detector; the resulting noise spectrum is sketched in Fig. 16.7(a). The detector develops a d-c voltage by

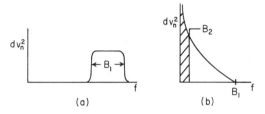

Fig. 16.7   (a) Noise spectrum incident on the detector in a modulated system such as a radio receiver. (b) Resulting spectrum after detection.

rectifying this noise, of a value proportional to its amplitude, or to $\sqrt{B_1}$. This in turn has its fluctuations which should be proportional to $B_1^{1/4}$. The power spectrum of the noise after detection has the form sketched in Fig. 16.7(b), produced by beats between the individual noise components of Fig. 16.7(a). Since the number of pairs of frequencies that can beat together is greater for smaller frequency differences, the spectrum of the detected noise is peaked at the lowest frequency. If a filter after the detector has bandwidth B_2, the noise power passed by it will be approximately proportional to $\sqrt{B_2}$ as well, and altogether will be proportional to $\sqrt{B_1 B_2}$. The noise bandwidth of the complete system is therefore $B = \sqrt{B_1 B_2}$. For low noise, the bandwidths before and after the detector must *both* be small. This is the normal case in a radio receiver, in which B_1 and B_2 are approximately equal and have the smallest value that is adequate to pass the sidebands of the signal, and the signal itself, respectively.

Next we consider a similar system, but with a phase-sensitive detector, in which each frequency component of the input beats with the reference voltage, and the output is at the difference frequency. The carrier, if it is not suppressed, gives a d-c output, and the sidebands are transformed to very low frequencies. The same is true of the noise components of the input, and only those frequencies close above and below the reference frequency are transformed to a low enough final frequency to be passed by the filter. Therefore, the noise bandwidth does not depend on B_1 at all, and has the value $2B_2$. However, if the noise level is high, it is often useful to restrict B_1 somewhat; otherwise, the amplifier or the ϕSD may be overloaded by the peaks of the noise. If this happens, the sensitivity of the system to a signal buried in the noise may be decreased, even though the signal itself is far too small to overload the system. In the extreme case in which the noise is heavily clipped, the signal may disappear altogether from the output.

It can be seen that for very narrow bandwidths the ϕSD is far superior in its noise performance to a linear detector, where it can be applied. The difficulty in most systems is to derive a reference voltage of the right frequency and phase; this is particularly true in radio systems. In some cases it is in fact possible to derive a reference voltage from the received signal, but a receiver of this kind is more complicated than an ordinary one, and is very seldom used.

Measurement of Noise. So far, we have been concerned with the measurement of a small signal in the presence of noise, so that the noise had to be rejected as much as possible. However, the problem of measuring the noise itself is also an important one—for example, in fundamental studies of the noise phenomenon and of excess noise in various devices. Another example is in studies of the natural radio emission of cosmic sources such as the sun, the planets, certain nebulae, and other galaxies. Although the spectra of such sources are seldom thermal in nature, they are sufficiently independent of frequency over short ranges that no serious error is committed in using the thermal noise spectrum in this discussion.

For the linear detector, only a slight extension of the previous discussion is necessary. The rectified noise has a d-c component whose mean-square value is proportional to B_1; its fluctuations at the output depend on $\sqrt{B_1 B_2}$. The signal-to-noise ratio at the output is just the ratio of these two figures: $\sqrt{B_1/B_2}$ for power, or $(B_1/B_2)^{1/4}$ for voltage. It is thus necessary to use a *wide* passband before the detector, in order to have as much noise as possible to rectify, and a very narrow passband, or a filter with a long time constant, after the detector. This is one reason that relatively little is known about excess noise at very low frequencies; if the passband is located at 1 cps, its width must be even less, and an extremely long time of observation is necessary for accurate measurement, or even any at all. In radio astronomy, input bandwidths of several megacycles and observing times of several minutes per point are common.

Phase-sensitive detectors are not directly applicable to noise measurement, since their characteristic narrow bandwidth is not wanted. However, many radio astronomy receivers use a modulation-detection scheme to distinguish the received noise from noise generated in the receiver, and here the ϕSD does find application. The basic idea is identical with that of the light-chopping scheme shown in Fig. 12.7 and briefly discussed in Section 12.3. The ϕSD recognizes that part of the noise that was modulated at the input, and the bandwidth B_1 is still that of the receiver.

REFERENCES

A comprehensive study of noise in theory and practice is given in *Noise* by A. van der Ziel (Englewood Cliffs, N.J.: Prentice–Hall, Inc., 1954).

CHAPTER 17

Transmission Lines

The circuit theory that we have studied up to now has implicitly assumed that changes in voltage and current are propagated instantly to all parts of the circuit, except for the effects due to the presence of energy storage in capacitors and chokes. This approximation is excellent for circuits of normal size up to frequencies of around 100 mc, or to corresponding times down to 0.1 μsec. However, it rapidly breaks down for larger circuits or faster variations. The effects of time delays were first encountered in transmission of long-distance telegraph and telephone communications, and of radio-frequency power to and from antennas. The name "transmission lines" is therefore commonly applied to studies of this kind. Moreover, the particularly simple configurations of conductors found in long lines lend themselves readily to quantitative treatment. Basically, the effects arise because electromagnetic disturbances propagate at the speed of light, or sometimes more slowly; but for analysis it is easier to use the concepts of inductance and capacitance, which are present even in simple conductors by virtue of the magnetic and electric fields that are set up around them.

17.1 LOSS-FREE LINES

In a real line, besides the inherent inductance and capacitance, there are energy losses due to the resistance of the wire and to leakage between the conductors; we shall neglect these to simplify the analysis, and therefore our results will apply best to short lengths of line. The main effect of these losses is to attenuate the signal slowly as it passes along the line. Typical lines to which our analysis applies are shown in Fig. 17.1. Fig. 17.1(a) shows a parallel-wire line consisting of two equal wires held apart by insulators at intervals, or by a ribbon of insulation; the latter form is familiar in the lead-ins from television antennas. Fig. 17.1(b) shows a coaxial line, most often made in

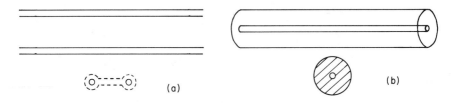

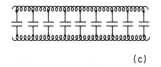

(c)

Fig. 17.1   (a) Two-wire transmission line, top view and cross section. (b) Coaxial line. (c) Equivalent circuit.

flexible form with continuous plastic insulation; it has the advantage that the electric and magnetic fields are confined to the interior, so that signals are neither radiated nor picked up. In either case we can speak of an inductance per unit length L_1, which must include both conductors, and a capacitance per unit length C_1. The equivalent circuit is shown in Fig. 17.1(c), which is more appropriate to the two-wire line; for the coaxial line, it is more natural to have all the inductance on one side, but the equations turn out the same as long as the proper value is used for L_1.

Since the line is a uniform continuous medium, the appropriate form of the circuit equations is that of differential equations, and since both distance and time are independent variables, partial derivatives must be used. Let distance along the line be measured by x, and let the voltage and current at x be V and I; then at $(x + dx)$ they are

$$\left(V + \frac{\partial V}{\partial x}\, dx\right) \quad \text{and} \quad \left(I + \frac{\partial I}{\partial x}\, dx\right)$$

by Taylor's theorem. The voltage drop across dx is due to the inductance $L_1 dx$, and is

$$V - \left(V + \frac{\partial V}{\partial x}\, dx\right) = \left(L_1\, dx\right)\frac{\partial I}{\partial t}$$

The change of current in dx is attributable to the shunt current flowing in the capacitance $C_1 dx$, and is

$$I - \left(I + \frac{\partial I}{\partial x} dx\right) = \left(C_1 \, dx\right) \frac{\partial V}{\partial t}$$

Therefore, the circuit equations are

$$\frac{\partial V}{\partial x} = -L_1 \frac{\partial I}{\partial t} \quad \text{and} \quad \frac{\partial I}{\partial x} = -C_1 \frac{\partial V}{\partial t} \tag{1}$$

To produce individual equations for V and I, we must combine these two. For example, to eliminate I, we differentiate the first with respect to x and the second with respect to t; this gives

$$\frac{\partial^2 V}{\partial x^2} = -L_1 \frac{\partial^2 I}{\partial t \, \partial x} \quad \text{and} \quad \frac{\partial^2 I}{\partial x \, \partial t} = -C_1 \frac{\partial^2 V}{\partial t^2}$$

and thus

$$\frac{\partial^2 V}{\partial x^2} = L_1 C_1 \frac{\partial^2 V}{\partial t^2} \quad \text{and} \quad \frac{\partial^2 I}{\partial x^2} = L_1 C_1 \frac{\partial^2 I}{\partial t^2} \tag{2}$$

These are standard wave equations in one dimension, and the solution of the first is

$$V = f(x \pm vt)$$

where f is any function whatever; it represents the shape of the wave at any instant. Consider the function $f(x - vt)$; at $t = 0$, $f(x)$ has some particular shape, say a short pulse at the origin. At a later time t_1, $f(x - vt_1)$ has exactly the same shape, but its new origin is at $(+vt_1)$; therefore, the whole function f has moved towards positive x by this distance. Therefore, the solution represents a disturbance traveling with speed v. If the positive sign is used instead, the disturbance travels towards negative x.

The solution is readily verified by substitution in (2). Let the symbol $\dot{f}$ represent

$$\frac{\partial f}{\partial (x \pm vt)}$$

Then

$$\frac{\partial^2 V}{\partial x^2} = \ddot{f}\left(\frac{dx}{dx}\right)^2 = \ddot{f}$$

and

$$\frac{\partial^2 V}{\partial t^2} = \ddot{f}\left(\frac{d(\pm vt)}{dt}\right)^2 = v^2\ddot{f}$$

It is seen that the wave equations (2) are satisfied if $v^2 L_1 C_1 = 1$ so that the speed of propagation is given by

$$v = \frac{1}{\sqrt{L_1 C_1}}$$

The values of L_1 and C_1 can be deduced by electromagnetic theory, or in other words, by considering the magnetic and electric fields set up around the conductors. This is easy for the simple configurations shown in Fig. 17.1, and the result is given in most texts on electromagnetism. For parallel wires, the value of L_1 increases if the wires are placed farther apart or made smaller, because there is more scope to set up a magnetic field without interference from the opposing current in the other wire. At the same time, C_1 becomes smaller, and the product $L_1 C_1$ remains exactly constant. If the wires are separated by vacuum, the velocity v is just the speed of light, normally represented by c. If the space occupied by electric fields is filled with dielectric whose relative permittivity is k, C_1 is increased proportionally to k, and the speed is therefore $c/\sqrt{k}$. The permittivity of air is so close to that of vacuum that the difference can usually be neglected. Study of the coaxial line reveals similar results; L_1 and C_1 depend on the ratio of the diameters of the outer and inner conductors, but their product is constant and the speed of propagation is the same. In this case it is much easier to be sure that a dielectric occupies the whole space in which electric fields are present, namely the inside of the line. The insulators used in most flexible coaxial cables have such a permittivity that the speed is about two thirds of the vacuum speed.

17.2 STEADY-STATE SOLUTIONS

To simplify the further analysis, we shall assume that the line carries steady-state sinusoidal voltages and currents. Thus, we take the following expressions for the time variation of V and I at a single point:

$$V = V'e^{j\omega t} \quad \text{and} \quad I = I'e^{j\omega t}$$

V' and I' are functions of x alone; they will be complex in general and may have different phases. When these forms are substituted in (2), the exponential parts cancel out (L_1C_1 is replaced by $1/v^2$):

$$\frac{d^2 V'}{dx^2} = -\frac{\omega^2}{v^2}V' \quad \text{and} \quad \frac{d^2 I'}{dx^2} = -\frac{\omega^2}{v^2}I'$$

so that now we have equations for the spatial dependence of V and I, separated from their time dependence. They are the familiar equations of simple harmonic motion, and the general solutions may be written down immediately. However, this gives four constants of integration, of which only two are independent; we therefore write the solution for I' and derive the one for V' from it:

$$I' = I_+e^{j\omega x/v} + I_-e^{-j\omega x/v}$$

The two terms represent waves propagating in the two directions. Note that the quantities $\omega x/v$ can also be written $2\pi x/\lambda$ by virtue of the relation $v = f\lambda$, with λ representing the wavelength.

To find the expression for V', we use the first of equations (1), which is

$$\frac{\partial V}{\partial x} = -L_1\frac{\partial I}{\partial t} \quad \text{or} \quad \frac{dV'}{dx} = -j\omega L_1 I'$$

$$\frac{dV'}{dx} = -j\omega L_1(I_+e^{j\omega x/v} + I_-e^{-j\omega x/v})$$

This is readily integrated, with the result

$$V' = -vL_1(I_+e^{j\omega x/v} - I_-e^{-j\omega x/v})$$
$$= -Z_0(I_+e^{j\omega x/v} - I_-e^{-j\omega x/v})$$

where Z_0 is the *characteristic impedance* of the line, equal to vL_1, or, by the expression for v,

$$Z_0 = \sqrt{L_1/C_1}$$

For the loss-free lines we are discussing, Z_0 is a pure resistance, and its value is typically 300 ohms for parallel-wire lines, and 50 to 100 ohms for coaxial cables.

Reflection Coefficients. Let us now consider a section of line with length s, driven by a voltage V_i at one end and terminated at the other by a resistance equal to Z_o. The constants in the expressions for V' and I' can be evaluated from the boundary conditions

$$V' = V_i \quad \text{at} \quad x = 0$$
$$V'/I' = Z_o \quad \text{at} \quad x = d$$

Thus, we have

$$V_i = -Z_o(I_+ - I_-)$$

and

$$-\frac{Z_o(I_+ e^{j\omega s/v} - I_- e^{-j\omega s/v})}{I_+ e^{j\omega s/v} + I_- e^{-j\omega s/v}} = Z_o \tag{3}$$

The second equation (3) gives $I_+ = 0$, and the first therefore shows that $I_- = V_i/Z_o$. Therefore the solution is

$$V' = V_i e^{-j\omega x/v} \quad \text{and} \quad V = V_i e^{j\omega(t-x/v)}$$

This represents a transmitted wave moving away from the source and completely absorbed in the terminating resistor, since there is no reflected wave. Such a result is reasonable, since the terminating resistance equal to Z_o cannot be distinguished from a further length of line, which would simply continue to transmit the wave. The termination is said to be *matched* to the line.

Now let us examine the behavior of terminations with impedance Z_L different from Z_o. Since there will now be a reflected wave, we suppress any further reflections at the generator end (which would complicate matters) by arranging a resistance Z_o in series with the generator. The boundary condition at this end is now

$$V' = V_i - Z_o I' \quad \text{(at } x = 0)$$
$$-Z_o(I_+ - I_-) = V_i - Z_o(I_+ + I_-)$$
$$I_- = V_i/2Z_o$$

This is the expected result, since the voltage V_i is applied across the resistor Z_o and the line impedance Z_o in series. At the far end of the line, the boundary condition is exactly like (3) except that the right-hand side is the load impedance Z_L. This can be written

$$-Z_0(I_+e^{j\omega s/v} - I_-e^{-j\omega s/v}) = Z_L(I_+e^{j\omega s/v} + I_-e^{-j\omega s/v})$$

$$I_+(Z_L + Z_0)e^{j\omega s/v} = I_-(Z_0 - Z_L)e^{-j\omega s/v}$$

$$\frac{I_+}{I_-} = \frac{Z_0 - Z_L}{Z_0 + Z_L}e^{-2j\omega s/v}$$

The first part of this is the amplitude reflection coefficient, since it gives the ratio of the amplitudes of the reflected and incident waves; it is real if Z_L is resistive. The second part is a phase factor depending on the number of wavelengths in the length of the line. We have already noted that $\omega s/v$ is equal to $2\pi s/\lambda$; twice this value appears in the exponent because the wave travels a distance $2s$ before returning to the origin. Thus, the reflection coefficient is

$$\frac{Z_0 - Z_L}{Z_0 + Z_L}$$

For a short-circuit termination, it has the value $+1$, and for an open-circuit termination, -1. Similar results are familiar in the reflection of a sound wave at the closed and open end of a tube. When $Z_L = Z_0$, no energy is reflected, as we have already seen, and for any other value of Z_L, part is reflected and part absorbed, unless Z_L is a pure reactance. Although we have derived this expression for continuous wave trains, it is independent of frequency, and it holds equally well for pulses, bursts of radio frequency, and so on.

Quarter-wave Lines. At a fixed frequency, short pieces of line with a length of one quarter of the wavelength have some interesting properties. When $s = \lambda/4$, the exponent $2\omega s/v$ has the value π, and the phase factor becomes -1. Therefore,

$$\frac{I_+}{I_-} = \frac{Z_L - Z_0}{Z_L + Z_0}$$

If Z_L is a short-circuit, $I_+ = -I_-$; this may be substituted into the equations for V' and I' at $x = 0$ to find the input impedance of the line

$$Z_i = -Z_0\frac{I_+ - I_-}{I_+ + I_-} = \infty$$

If Z_L is an open circuit, $I_+ = I_-$, and $Z_i = 0$. It is seen that the quarter-wave line transforms a short circuit into an open circuit, and vice versa. For different lengths, or different frequencies, the input impedance becomes reactive, since the phase factor is no longer real. Thus, the short-circuited section acts like a parallel resonant circuit, and the open-circuited one like a series resonant circuit. A Q of the order of 10,000 is not difficult to attain, and sections like this form useful equivalents of tuned circuits at the higher frequencies. Because of their ability to make one impedance look like another, short sections are also used to transform a load impedance into another one which matches a source better. However, it must always be remembered that such transformations are strongly dependent on frequency.

PROBLEMS

1) Consider the impedance of the quarter-wave line at frequencies above and below resonance, and justify the analogy with a resonant circuit.
2) Find the input impedance of half-wave lines with short-circuit and open-circuit terminations.

17.3 DELAY LINES

A frequent need in pulse systems is to delay a signal for a short time, which may be several microseconds or only a small fraction of this. An example of this was seen in the half-adder circuit of Fig. 15.28, and many other examples are found in digital computers where pulses must be stored briefly or brought into coincidence. It was also shown in Chapter 10 that useful trigger circuits can be built around these *delay lines*. For very short delays, flexible coaxial cables can be used; since they propagate signals at about two thirds the velocity of light, or 100 meters per μsec, a length of a meter gives a delay of 5 nanoseconds (5×10^{-9} sec). Even this length is not always convenient to incorporate into equipment, and delays of microseconds are clearly not normally practical. We shall now consider ways of getting a much slower velocity, so that microsecond delays can be produced by short lengths of line.

The first method is to make continuous lines with increased values of L_1 and C_1, the inductance and capacitance per unit length, since we have seen that $v^2 = 1/L_1 C_1$. Increase of L_1 is particularly useful, since it increases the characteristic impedance to values that are more nearly compatible with tubes and transistors. The method used is to make the center conductor of a coaxial cable as a tightly wound helix instead of a straight wire; it may also be given a ferromagnetic core, consisting of magnetic particles suspended in plastic. This technique gives impedances of around 1000 ohms and delays in the range of 0.2 μsec per meter. If C_1 is also increased by making the spacing as small as possible, delays of more than 2 μsec per meter are possible.

At higher frequencies these cables begin to fail, because the inductance of the coiled center conductor depends on the reinforcement of the magnetic fields of neighboring turns, and the delay itself causes them to get out of phase. There is also a tendency for the attenuation to become worse. The frequency at which these effects become important depends on the line, but can be below 1 mc for the slower lines.

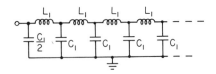

Fig. 17.2   Lumped-parameter delay line.

In computer applications considerable degradation of pulse shape is permissible, since the shape is restored frequently, but for some purposes these defects are very serious.

Another approach is the *lumped-parameter* line shown in Fig. 17.2, consisting of a string of series inductances and shunt capacitors. If the unit of length is a single section, the usual equation for the speed of propagation holds, and this can be set equal to n/T, where n is the number of sections and T the delay time. Then we have

$$T = n\sqrt{L_1 C_1}$$

On the other hand, the line is an n-section low-pass filter; the cutoff frequency for each section is of the order of the resonant frequency, so that $\omega^2 L_1 C_1 = 1$. The rise time is about $1/\omega_c$, and is therefore approximately equal to the delay time of one section. However, it is found that the rise time increases only as the cube root of the number of sections, so that any desired ratio of delay to rise time can be obtained by using enough sections. Since T is proportional to n and T_r to $n^{1/3}$, we can write

$$\frac{T}{T_r} \doteq n^{2/3}$$

Considerable latitude is possible in the characteristic impedance by choice of L_1 and C_1, and values up to 10,000 ohms are readily achieved.

Slightly better performance is possible by arranging adjacent coils to be partially coupled by their magnetic fields; a coupling coefficient of 0.24 is usual. The result is a line with a faster rise time and less overshoot, but the delayed pulse may now be preceded by a small undershoot. This condition is also common with the continuous lines with a coiled center conductor. One of the chief uses of high-fidelity delay lines is in oscilloscopes with a triggered sweep. If the sweep is to be started by the signal pulse, the first part of the pulse will not be visible on the screen, since the sweep takes a definite time to get under way. However, the pulse can be stored briefly in a delay line before it goes to the vertical amplifier and the screen, thus giving the sweep enough time to start; the beginning of the pulse is therefore made visible. The cutoff frequency of the line is made several times higher than the cutoff of the amplifier, so that its distortion of the pulse is negligible by comparison.

REFERENCES

An excellent treatment of delay lines and their principal applications may be found in *Pulse and Digital Circuits* by J. Millman and H. Taub (New York: McGraw–Hill Book Company, Inc., 1956).

APPENDIX

APPENDIX I

Instruments Used in the Electronics Laboratory

A brief description is given here of a few of the most important measuring instruments used in the electronics laboratory.

Oscilloscope. The oscilloscope is based on a special tube known as a *cathode-ray tube*, illustrated in Fig. A1. It has a small circular cathode followed by a series of focusing and accelerating electrodes, which form a thin electron beam; when the beam strikes the fluorescent screen

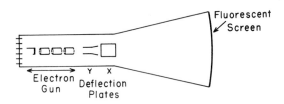

Fig. A1   Sketch of a cathode-ray tube.

at the other end, a small bright spot is produced. The beam can be deflected by two pairs of plates, the X and Y *deflection plates*, if a potential difference exists between the two plates of a pair. The tube is then a very fast plotting device, which gives a rectangular plot of one voltage against another. Ordinary cathode-ray tubes respond well up to a frequency of about 100 mc, and this limit can be extended about a factor of 10 by special design.

The block diagram of a typical oscilloscope is shown in Fig. A2. Usually it is desired to plot a signal against time; the X signal must therefore be a sawtooth wave with a frequency equal to that of the wave to be displayed, or an integral fraction of it. Suitable circuits are shown in Figs. 10.13, 15.9 and 15.10. A synchronizing voltage is usually taken from the Y amplifier to ensure that the sweep frequency is correct. The sweep signal is amplified and a push-pull output generated to drive the deflection plates.

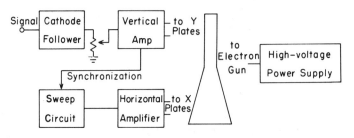

Fig. A2   Block diagram of a cathode-ray oscilloscope.

The Y signal is usually taken to a cathode follower so that a low-resistance gain control can be used without a serious loading of the source. This kind of control is necessary if the high-frequency response is not to be limited by shunt capacitance in combination with its resistance. Frequently a high-impedance compensated voltage divider (Section 2.9) is placed before the cathode follower and used with very large signals. The vertical amplifier, like the horizontal, has a push-pull output. In most oscilloscopes, the high-frequency or transient response is limited by the vertical amplifier; rise times in the range from a few microseconds to a few hundredths of microseconds are found in different instruments.

The number of possible variations on this basic scheme is very large. However, one important variation is necessary for the observation of short pulses with a long time between them, or even single pulses. This type of observation requires the use of a triggered sweep, which sweeps the spot once at a very high speed whenever a pulse arrives. Suitable circuits are discussed in Chapters 10 and 15. Since the sweep cannot start until the pulse is already present, the beginning of the pulse will be missed, unless it is stored in a delay line for a short time after triggering the sweep but before being displayed. An oscillo-scope with these features is sometimes called a *synchroscope*.

Vacuum-tube Voltmeters. Most electronic circuits have too high a resistance to deliver the current required by ordinary measuring instru-ments. Testing of these circuits is therefore usually done with vacuum-tube voltmeters, which incorporate an amplifier and can therefore have a very high input resistance. If the amplifier has sufficient negative feedback, the accuracy is essentially that of the indicating meter itself.

For d-c measurements, a common circuit is the long-tailed-pair amplifier shown in Fig. 12.16, with the meter connected between the plates. The linearity is reasonably good, but the sensitivity depends directly on the transconductance of the tubes, as shown in Section 12.4, and will decrease as the tubes grow older. The zero drift is small because of the balanced nature of the circuit. The accuracy is sufficient for most test work, but may not be good enough for laboratory measurements. For high accuracy, the circuit of Fig. 6.18 (also shown in Fig. A7) would be more suitable; it incorporates a large amount of negative current feedback. With either circuit, the amplifier is designed to deliver no more than about twice the full-scale current of the meter; the latter is therefore fully protected against damage by overloads, however large.

Measurement of a-c voltage is more difficult, and a variety of meters is required for different purposes. The simplest circuit is the peak-reading type shown in Fig. A3(a); a diode half-wave rectifier charges

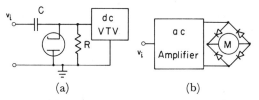

(a)   (b)

Fig. A3   (a) Peak-reading vacuum-tube voltmeter.
(b) Average-reading vacuum-tube voltmeter.

the capacitor C to the peak voltage of the input wave, and this d-c voltage is measured by a d-c vacuum-tube voltmeter. This circuit is so cheap that it is usually incorporated into the general-purpose meters to extend them to a-c measurement. However, it has one major virtue: it can be made accurate up to frequencies of several hundred megacycles by the use of special diodes with short leads and small transit time. The meter is usually calibrated to read the rms voltage on a sine wave. Large errors may exist with other waveforms, since the actual measurement is of the peak voltage.

For frequencies up to about 1 mc, a more satisfactory instrument is the one shown in Fig. A3(b). This has an a-c amplifier, whose gain is usually controlled by negative feedback, followed by a full-wave rectifier without a filter capacitor. The current through the meter therefore depends on the average voltage of the wave after rectification; this is still different from the rms voltage but is much closer to it than the peak voltage is. Because of the amplifier, the sensitivity can be high, and the full-scale reading of the most sensitive scale is typically a few millivolts. More sensitive ranges are easily possible, but are difficult to use because stray voltages this large exist in many circuits.

Meters which actually measure rms voltage are possible, but are in much less common use than the types we have discussed. As long as their characteristics are understood, the latter are suitable for the great majority of laboratory measurements.

Attenuator. A common problem in the laboratory is the accurate measurement of the gain of an amplifier. It is possible to measure the input and output voltages if a suitable vacuum-tube voltmeter is available, but it must be able to measure a very small input with high

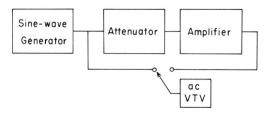

Fig. A4   Use of an attenuator in measuring the gain of an amplifier.

accuracy. A better method is to use an attenuator, as shown in Fig. A4, to reduce a large signal from a generator. When the voltmeter shows equal voltages at the attenuator input and the amplifier output, the gain of the amplifier must be equal to the loss of the attenuator; the meter need not be accurate so long as it is consistent, and does not have to measure very small voltages.

Oscillators and Signal Generators. Many electronic measurements require a source of sine waves of variable frequency and amplitude. It is often convenient to have the amplitude indicated directly, by means of a built-in meter and attenuator; if these are included, the instrument is usually called a *signal generator*. Otherwise, the usual name is *oscillator*, although these usually contain amplifier circuits in addition to the actual oscillator.

For audio frequencies, and usually up to about 1 mc, the oscillator is usually the Wien-bridge type shown in Fig. 14.6. The automatic amplitude stabilization is a great convenience and can be trusted to better than 1 db over most of the frequency range. The oscillator proper is usually followed by a power amplifier to isolate the oscillator from the load.

At radio frequencies, an LC-tuned oscillator is used. A radio-frequency signal generator requires very careful shielding; otherwise the output from the attenuator may be much smaller than the signals which leak through the case, and valid measurements may be impossible. Thus, a high-quality signal generator for these frequencies is much more expensive than a test oscillator, and also more expensive than audio-frequency instruments. Again, the oscillator and the load are usually separated by an amplifier to reduce the interaction.

APPENDIX 2

Suggested Laboratory Experiments

Laboratory work accompanying this course may have several purposes: to give the students familiarity with tubes and transistors; to illustrate the application of these devices to various areas of measurement; and, in many cases, to replace the traditional laboratory in electrical measurements, since in practice such measurements are increasingly made by electronic techniques. Some of the experiments can illustrate topics which must be omitted from the lectures. An effort has been made, in choosing the experiments given here, to keep them as interesting as possible, although many of them must be done for basic orientation, interesting or not. Much of the laboratory derived originally from a paper by Schultz and Wadey,* but many of the experiments have been changed or revised. One feature of their course was the assembly of circuits by the students themselves during the laboratory period. Although this gives students excellent practice and a thorough knowledge of the circuit, it is time consuming, and we have abandoned it. We still use the inverted chassis illustrated in their paper, and attempt to lay out the circuit to resemble the diagram as much as possible, with a ground wire running along the bottom edge and a B⁺ wire along the top. In tracing this circuit for their notes, the students still learn

---

* H. L. Schultz and W. G. Wadey, "A Laboratory Course in Electronics," *American Journal of Physics*, **19**, p. 214, 1951.

something of what it contains. Connection of test equipment and power supplies is greatly speeded up by the use of "banana" sockets and leads with corresponding plugs which include their own sockets, so that any number of leads may be connected to a single terminal. Adapters permit the leads to be terminated in spade lugs or alligator clips for the few applications that are not fitted by the plugs themselves.

The following is a list of the experiments used by the author, with explanations of the less obvious ones. Since the students do not meet any actual electronics for the first month or so of lectures, the first four experiments are used to teach them basic electrical measurements and the use of the oscilloscope.

1. Measurement of Resistance and Impedance. Resistance is measured with an ohmmeter, an impedance bridge, and an accurate Wheatstone bridge, and the results are compared. Capacitance and inductance are measured with the impedance bridge only.

2. Measurement of Frequency and Time. The frequency of a crystal oscillator is measured with a wavemeter (or a grid-dip meter), a heterodyne frequency meter, and if available, a frequency counter. The short time interval is measured by a calibrated oscilloscope, and if possible, by the counter.

3. Measurement of d-c and a-c Voltage. The purpose is to illustrate the various kinds of meter and the accuracy that can be expected from them. The d-c source is a small power supply regulated by two breakdown diodes in cascade to produce a stable voltage of 5 to 6 volts. It is measured directly and through two different "source" resistances to show the effect of loading error. For a-c measurements the meters used are a moving-iron meter, a vacuum-tube instrument of the peak-reading type, and one of the average-reading type. The effects of waveform and frequency are studied.

4. Oscilloscope. Waves and pulses are observed, and the use of the electronic switch is introduced.

5. A-c Vectors. It is demonstrated that a-c voltages add according to the same rules as vectors in a plane. A series R–L–C circuit is excited by an audio oscillator at frequencies below, near, at, and above resonance. The voltages between each pair of terminals are measured by a vacuum-tube a-c millivoltmeter, and the vector diagrams are plotted. Some of the phase differences are checked with an electronic switch and oscilloscope.

6. R-C Filters. The attenuation and phase shift of the lag and lead networks (Figs. 2.17 and 2.19) are measured and compared with theory.

7, 8, 9. Triode, Pentode, Transistor Characteristics. Measurements and plots are made of the characteristics of triodes (low and high μ), pentodes (sharp and remote cutoff), and transistors (grounded-base and grounded-emitter connections). Linear parameters are measured from the graphs. These experiments could be speeded up and made more interesting by producing the plots semi-automatically on an X–Y recorder.

10. Power Supplies and Regulators. Various filters are observed, and their ripple and output resistance are measured. A simple feedback regulator is studied, and the stabilization factor and output resistance are determined. Finally, the small voltage standard (Experiment 3) is examined, and the stabilization factor of each stage is estimated.

11. Amplifier Gain. The gain of a triode stage is measured as a function of load resistance in normal and cathode-follower connections, and the effects of cathode resistance and bypassing are examined.

12. Amplifier Frequency Response. The frequency response of a two-stage amplifier is measured. Negative feedback is applied to the first cathode and the measurements repeated.

13. Power Amplifier. Power output of a tube connected as a triode, and also as a beam tetrode, is measured as a function of load resistance. To measure distortion, the fundamental is eliminated from the output by a twin T; alternatively, the second harmonic can be selected by the filter suggested by Schultz and Wadey.

14. Amplitude Modulation. Modulation is observed in a Class-C plate-modulated oscillator, and detection of the modulated wave is studied. A diode bridge is also used as a modulator.

15. Transistor Amplifiers. Both grounded-emitter and emitter-follower stages are studied by measuring the gain and frequency response. The effects of β cutoff and collector capacitance can be separated by using low and high load resistors with the grounded-emitter amplifier.

16. Phase-shift Control of Thyratrons. The use of a thermistor and thermocouple to measure the temperature of a small oven is studied. Then the thermistor is connected in a phase-shift bridge to control the thyratron current and the temperature of the oven (Fig. A5).

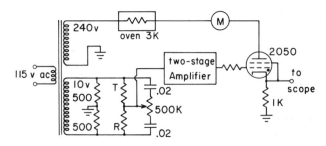

Fig. A5 Thermostat for Experiment 16 using a thyratron
controlled by a thermistor.

17. Pulse Amplifier. A linear pulse amplifier of the Jordan-Bell type is studied, and the gain and the rise time are measured. The circuit of the test-pulse generator used for the measurements is also studied.

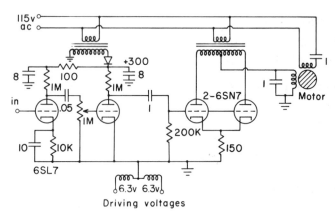

Fig. A6 Servo-amplifier used in Experiment 18.

18. Servomechanism. The amplifier circuit shown in Fig. A6 is adapted from the one used in the Brown recorder, and drives a motor of the same type. Use of 60-cps voltage to excite the slide-wire and the sources to be followed permits the elimination of the chopper. A linear slide-wire is used, driven by a cable from a pulley on the motor shaft. This permits easy observation of the action, and it can be cheaply repaired if the wire is burned out by a wrong connection.

19. Waveform Generation. This experiment, lasting two weeks, studies generation of waveforms by trigger circuits. It is built around a triggered sweep circuit which can deliver a sweep to an oscilloscope and a trigger to an external circuit during the sweep. Study of the operation of this device is the first part of the experiment. The trigger is then used to start a blocking oscillator and a thyratron pulse generator, each with optional delay-line control. The sweep generator and some of the external circuits could well be made with transistors. A transistor scale-of-four with a diode matrix (Fig. 15.29) is studied with the aid of a square-wave oscillator and an oscilloscope.

20. D-c Amplifiers and Analog Computer. This is another two-week experiment. The amplifiers studied are the operational amplifiers

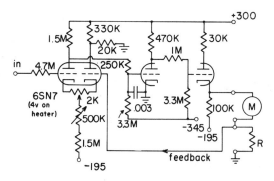

Fig. A7 Vacuum-tube voltmeter with current feedback and low input current.

in the computer, and the vacuum-tube voltmeter shown in Fig. A7, designed to drive a recording milliammeter. Its input current is small enough to permit the study of dielectric absorption in the integrating capacitors, and to demonstrate the superiority of film dielectrics. It was designed to operate from the voltages available in the computer chassis, but could easily be modified to work from other voltages. The computer uses four operational amplifiers, built to the design of Howe and Leite.* Nowadays it would be better to use the plug-in amplifiers that are readily available commercially, and the use of transistor types might be considered. The basic operations of inversion, addition, integration, and differentiation are studied, and the observed gains compared with the calculated values. Then the computer is set up to simulate damped harmonic motion, as in Fig. 15.5. The various solutions are observed on the recorder and the effects of different initial conditions are explored. The damping term can be made negative to give a growing oscillation.

* R. M. Howe and R. J. Leite, *Review of Scientific Instruments*, **24**, p. 901, 1953.

INDEX

INDEX